NEAL KINSEY'S
HANDS-ON
AGRONOMY

Understanding Soil Fertility
& Fertilizer Use

Before we start, please understand this material is not intended to be "the last word on soil fertility." It is only what I understand and use, explained to the best of my ability so others can understand and use it to the best of their ability. I have no secrets. I do not try to keep certain "keys" for myse1f. My biggest job is to put everything I understand into terms which others can use.

The better a client understands this program, the better his or her results. My best clients are those who strive the hardest to learn and apply what the soil tests show to be needed.

— *Neal Kinsey*

NEAL KINSEY'S
HANDS-ON
AGRONOMY

Understanding Soil Fertility
& Fertilizer Use

by Neal Kinsey
& Charles Walters

Acres U.S.A.
Viroqua, Wisconsin

Neal Kinsey's
Hands-On Agronomy

Copyright © 1993, 2013, Acres U.S.A.

Acres U.S.A., Inc.
PO Box 351
Viroqua, Wisconsin 54665 U.S.A.
(512) 892-4400 • fax (512) 892-4448
info@acresusa.com • www.acresusa.com

About the cover photo: This picture of the author, at home in his vegetable garden, was taken in the winter of 1993. The straw was later used for mulching the garden of 3,000 square feet. The farmstead in the background is that of Kinsey's neighbor and first client in the state of Missouri, who began using Kinsey Agricultural Services in 1973. (Photo by Linda M. Kinsey.)

Publisher's Cataloging-in-Publication

Kinsey, Neal & Walters, Charles, 1926-2009
  Neal Kinsey's hands-on agronomy / by Neal Kinsey and Charles Walters.
  xxii, 391 pp., 23 cm, charts, tables.
  Includes bibliographical references and index.
  3rd edition
  ISBN: 978-1-60173-040-4

  1. Agronomy. 2. Soil science. I. Kinsey, Neal & Walters, Charles, 1926-2009 II. Title

  S591.K56 2013   631.4

Dedication

This book is dedicated to individuals who helped provide the support and experience that made it possible. First and foremost, to my wife, Linda, whose support made all this possible; to my good friend, Dale Schurter, an excellent teacher, and the best boss I ever worked for; to the late William A. Albrecht, who provided a solid foundation on which to build; and especially to all the clients who have faithfully practiced the program over the years.

About Soil Fertility & Fertilization Specialist Neal Kinsey

Neal Kinsey has been called a "consultant's consultant." He specializes in only one thing—building and maintaining soil for quality crop production. In addition to consulting on standard crops such as corn, cotton, soybeans, rice, wheat and grain sorghum, and forage crops including alfalfa, pastures, clovers, and even specialty crops such as melons, almonds, avocados, bananas, berries, coffee, citrus, grapes and peaches, Kinsey also helps growers working with turf, landscape plantings, and lawn care.

His biography is contained as a broad outline in this book. In discussing sound agronomy practices, there is neither the time nor the space to tell all here, but the foundational principles are given in as much detail as possible. For instance, it was once standard practice to provide free lawn or garden sampling to any farmer who employed Neal on his total farmable land of 200

acres or more. Though this was begun as a token of apprecia-
tion, it turned out to be a valuable source of knowledge when
the opportunity arrived to begin working on commercial vegetable production, and with large-scale lawn, landscape and nursery stock production, and when golf courses were also added to
his list of clients.

In time, various companies and private consultants began to
call for possible help in growing crops such as winegrapes, potatoes, citrus, sugar cane, tobacco and tomatoes. To cope with the
demand for information, training sessions for clients were
begun. These have now expanded to two- and three-day seminars several times a year.

Foreign work followed, and so coffee and banana production
were added to crop experiences. Popcorn, timber and turf grass
production came along in the early 1980s, followed closely by
rapeseed and ornamentals. Peanut and commercial herb growers signed up. All of these crops helped to demonstrate that supplying the correct fertility to achieve a proper balance worked in
all types of agriculture.

The mail and UPS bring soil samples routinely to Neal Kinsey's service. Thus Canada and the United States have added
sunflowers, flax and mustard seed to the consultation service
agenda. Mexico added several commercial vegetables, fruits and
agave. Various new crops from Asia, including mangoes, spices
and medicinal plants for the commercial market also added to
acreages and experience. Although work with walnuts, almonds
and pecans paced the opening of new frontiers, eco-agriculture
didn't become significant until the late 1980s.

Neal grew up in southeast Missouri and worked on the farm
for his father until he graduated from high school. To pay his
way through college, he worked part-time and summers as a
crop reporter for the USDA's ASCS in Missouri and Illinois. He
obtained his B.S. degree in marketing from Southern Illinois
University at Carbondale. In the fall of 1966, Neal enrolled in a
master's degree program in Food Industry Logistics in Agricultural Economics at University of Missouri, Columbia. Here is

where he first met Dr. William A. Albrecht, who later provided the technical training in soil fertility required by his present profession.

In 1968, Neal and his wife, Linda, moved to Texas. He took a job with a large environmental research project conducted by Ambassador College at Big Sandy. He eventually became assistant to the director. Later, he became business manager, and ultimately agricultural operations manager for the Ambassador College Agriculture Department. While serving in this capacity, he became a certified consultant for Brookside Farms Laboratory of New Knoxville, Ohio. In 1977, Neal established Kinsey Agricultural Services, and now works with growers in all 50 of the United States. He has received soil samples from over 70 other countries, many of which send more samples for analysis annually than several of the individual states here in the U.S.

Table of Contents

Long before man could make a plow or a test tube, nature was creating life, including man, and providing an environment in which all life could live. She used the resources of air, water, sunshine and soil plant food minerals to make life. If she had created only life, these resources would soon have been tied up in all living things. So she created death. This way resources could be recycled and used again and again. There is a basic law which says, *All life forms must return at death what they took from the resources of the earth during their lifetime.*

— Eugene M. Poirot
Our Margin of Life, 1978

Word from the Publisher

MORE THAN THREE DECADES AGO, *Acres U.S.A.* went about the heady business of defining the foundation for modern agriculture. The publication was not even a year old at the time, and making sense to both the organic camp and the conventional "scientific" crowd seemed impossible. They were at each other's throats, and in the eyes of the true believers on both sides, there was no room for compromise. Nevertheless, "we" sallied forth—the second half of the "we" being the late C.J. Fenzau.

Then, as now, scientific commentary based on the chronological record of thought and theory seemed to explode the organic myth, and we figured we'd make a pass at exploding the chemical myth. The experts who perpetuated the so-called scientific theory of chemical fertilizers were seldom required to answer some very honest and sincere questions. The reason seemed obvious as *Acres U.S.A.* got underway.

Unfortunately, some very basic lessons had to intervene; otherwise farmers would not understand the far-ranging implications of what Neal Kinsey has to say in the present volume. One of those lessons has been styled, *Eco-Farm: An Acres U.S.A. Primer. The Albrecht Papers*—four volumes—have also helped answer questions and explain answers. But for our present purpose, a two decade-old entry in *Acres U.S.A.* provides a perfect overview for Neal Kinsey's insightful presentation.

There are few, if any, trained soil nutritionists who are able to understand and present any comprehensive judgment, other than mere lip service, to the standard viewpoints that are important to soil bacteria, earthworms, soil drainage, tilth, structure, and particularly the true function of organic materials in the soil system. After all, organic matter converts, regulates and releases nutrients to soil life which, in turn, makes available biological forms of nutrients to the biological system of the soil from which man has originally evolved. His creation and permission to life are profoundly linked to this biotic beginning.

Nature's way is biological. It is a combination both chemical and organic.

A study of histories of civilizations gives mute evidence that life cannot endure unless nature is allowed to produce nutrients for the *biological systems in the soil* for the plants that nourish therefrom and are then consumed by animals and eventually "man." This is possible only if man, in his ignorance, does not tamper either with "organic" or "chemical" systems.

The chemical industry has accumulated a body of *knowledge* and *financial capacity* to sustain the chemical system. On the other hand, the amateurs of "organic" systems have accumulated amateur knowledge to teach others to be good amateurs. We have few professional producers of food and fiber because, in the absence of adequate compensation and/or profit, they have not been able to *support* or *develop* a responsible body of knowledge that could define the ultimate "biological system of life."

Both chemical and organic systems are essential. Both chemicals and organic materials have an important role in nourishing plant life. Neither is capable of doing a proper, sustained job without an ecologically balanced soil system. It is for this reason, that we become infuriated when our authorities and agricultural leaders expound the merits of one system or another. Neither group is willing to comprehend the full meaning of nature's way of providing biological products for the biological sustenance of all forms of life. This concept was detoured by von Liebig's "Law of the Minimum" in 1848, and has been fully perpetuated by "science," by institutions, by laws, and by commercialization, none of which have to account to nature or give credentials to "life."

When "living life" emerges into an ultimate objective of our nation, only then can we begin to construct the understanding of the ecology of the soil and be able to benefit from its minuteness and wondrous patience. Nature has no limit on time. She is patient and forgiving. She is able to repair herself from the ignoble treatment of man in spite of his tremendous physical capacity for destruction. As we continue to replace nature, we assuredly prevent the development of our mental capacity to learn and fully compliment nature—a requirement expected from us—in *permission for life*. Apparently the growing interest of many farmers in searching for answers reflects the beginning of an intellectual attitude in conflict with both agronomic science and industry. This virgin knowledge is finally emerging as a test and challenge to the introverted and integrated industrial exploiters and absconders of our most precious resource.

It is time to stop the folly of both "chemical" and "organic" competition, and buckle down to the great necessity of compatibility. We must let the cocoon burst into a life cycle that may permit eggs of thought to be created. Nature needs our physical help to save her the time because we, as man, cannot endure such time. If we continue in our ignorance, we have little time left to assure much time in which to do our part.

A soil system for nutrient and energy production is a living system in which bacteria and the many soil organisms must receive nutrition and energy from proteins, carbohydrates and cellulose and lignin—all organic materials in a soil that has a managed supply of both air and water within a balanced chemical environment. This chemical balance involves more than just N, P and K. It requires an equilibrium of pH, calcium, magnesium, sodium, potash, humus and a nutritional balance of sulfur to nitrogen, nitrogen to calcium, calcium to magnesium, magnesium to potash and sodium. Without this balanced equilibrium, neither the organic system nor the N, P and K system has any enduring potential for soil building or plant nutrition. This total equilibrium is even more essential for the vital nourishment of man.

On the other hand, hydroponics is not a living system of plant nutrition. It is a synthesized method of supplying elements for plants growing in an environment protected artificially from the hazards and basic elements of life itself. The time clock and configurations of life are continually influenced by hormone-enzyme systems, by light, temperature, carbon dioxide, photosynthesis, antibiotics and a balanced viable plant sap (globulin-blood) system which requires basic hormones and a specific pH equilibrium in order to biologically produce a healthy plant. This plant must grow nutritionally, ripen and dry. The nutritionally ripe plant is essential for complete animal or human nutrition. Neither the chemical nor the organic systems can assure fully matured or "biologically ripe" food production. By coincidental accident, our agricultural system can produce the desired food quality without the hazards of weather, insects, disease or geographical limitations—and hydroponically, we could be a nation stuffed with partially matured carbon-based compounds that look and feel like food. In reality this so-called food results in partial or complete malnourishment—the predecessor to poor health and eventual metabolic and physiological deterioration.

Perhaps it is unfortunate, but nevertheless essential, that we *must farm soil*. It is only folly that we invite the hazards of hydroponics to sustain a synthetic system of life. Since we must cultivate soil for production of both nutrients and energy as well as fiber, we must begin to feed the soil, not the plant. This is the basic and fundamental change required for progress to begin.

In the past 50 years, many scientists and educators have brought attention to this principle. Industry astutely avoided this philosophy, and farmers honestly accepted the counterview. The farmers now are beginning to express their own experiences, and this is irritating to the authorities. To illustrate, we must regard nitrogen as a source of nutrition and energy for the actinomycete fungi to digest and break down the complex carbons contained in lignin-based organic matter. Some mild and gentle form of nitrogen must be used until our soils can sustain a regular supply of nitrogen. This will furnish a renewable source of carbon dioxide, the by-product of mild-gently formed organic acids needed to release the mineralized nutrients in the soil complex into a form available to plants. This decay process produces humus, which is also essential to the soil and its capacity for total function and performance. It is not practical to handle the tons of organic materials already in position on every farmed acre. Let us learn how to manage both the soil and this organic material and let nature function for us.

Whenever we use N, P and K as a computerized supply of nutrients, or plant food, we eventually violate the natural equilibrium in the soil system. This accounts for the many disappointing production results from one soil type to the next within a field and the unexpected variations from one year to the next. To supply exact pounds of N, P and K per unit of crop production is sheer nonsense.

Farmers, without their own body of knowledge, have been innocently led by this theory, and coached into propagandized obedience. Just ask any fertilizer expert to guarantee results and you will begin to flush out the truth.

Life in the soil sits at the table first, and compost, manures, green manure crops and crop rotations are subject to the same antagonisms. Historically, neither chemicals nor organic systems have produced consistent results unless the equilibrium factors were naturally or properly managed.

It is possible to compare one system against the other in a given soil environment, to show favorable and significant results either in productivity or quality. On the other hand, in a measured quality soil system, a thoroughly managed chemical and organic system will produce consistent results. By chemicals, it is meant that in addition to nitrogen the proper amounts of calcium, magnesium, potash and sodium along with ripe humus. These must be biologically positioned to create a living soil system.

This living soil will release the phosphorus and trace elements at a compatible level for plants to utilize the sunlight energy, water, air and carbon dioxide supply available. The growing period, yield and character will be in direct proportion to the elements and timing of weather from one year to the next.

In seasons of poor crop performance, we always blame the weather. This is cowardly. In good years, we never give adequate credit to the weather. Since weather can be easily criticized, our ignorance continues to endure, and human pride can be maintained in spite of its error. In reality, however, we simply rely on the "crutch" to explain away our ignorance. After all, next year we can try again with the hope that things will be better. There is much we can do through feeding the soil to eliminate the hazards of weather, or at least diminish the effects they might have on crop performance.

We need quality food. More people can be fed with less quantity. The general public, as well as commercial leaders, do not have sufficient background information to make judgments concerning either the effects of various kinds of fertilizer, or the values of organic matter on the living systems with a given soil. A living soil will not require any of the existing soil conservation or crop production practices thought necessary to assure a quantity food supply. Instead, quality foods can be produced, of which less is required for optimum nutrition, not only of man, but in animals and plants as well.

The general public can be swayed by health food promoters, just as they can be "quacked" by the chemical promoter, however respectable their financial and political credentials. Let's not forget that in the beginning farmers were once "promoted" to be aware of the "quacks" selling nitrogen for crop production in states now boasting to be number one. At one time it was disgraceful. By what promotional means did it become respectful?

Our population cannot survive on pre-1930s organic practices alone, but neither is it healthfully surviving through chemicals. Witness the millions of livestock that are carcassed to rendering factories across our land. Then witness the overflowing hospitals treating the symptoms and diseases which could be averted by wholesome and nutritionally ripe foods. Witness the billions spent on fuels and dryers to take water from physiologically immature grain crops, the nutrients of which were not able to fully mature into nature's intended ripeness. Animals and people cannot experience health and ripeness in life from this type of food. Through chemistry, we can too "hopefully" keep trying, but it is futile.

Witness the cost of keeping sick plants alive in the sick soils of our nation, and yet we have the audacity to simply treat this problem with N, P and K aspirin tablets while we close our eyes to the actual causes of these diseases and problems. No, the aspirin treatment is not the answer either, because with ineffective life in these sick soils, nature is not able to supply adequate calcium, humus or water to all regions. Neither can the proper decay of organic materials be accomplished. Organic composting illustrates this weakness of nature—and out of sheer economic impracticality, we cannot compost all of our land. We must learn how to make every acre a compost acre—and this is not done by chemicals or by organics. We must create a unity of both to permit the biological system to work. Herein must lie our fundamental objective.

It may seem odd that "we"—Neal Kinsey and I—chose not to comply with scientific conduct and forgo the use of the personal pronoun "I." For now it is enough to point out that to write in the first person does not offend science. As Phil Callahan put it, this stilted anti-"I" conceit is "inappropriate because it gives to the literature of science a facade behind which its authors appear to be infallible and is the reason why science—which is, or should be, the study of nature, and thus altogether fascinating—is presented to mankind in such a dull guise."

The "I" in *Hands-On Agronomy* is Neal Kinsey, and not this writer and publisher. Kinsey speaks through the experiences he has held in escrow for over two decades, and the other I—Charles Walters, the scribe—handles the mechanical chore of word-smithing, no more, no less.

How well Neal Kinsey complies with that early *Acres U.S.A.* vision will become apparent as readers proceed through Chapter 1 and the chapters that follow. For now it is enough to call for open minds in every camp. Indeed, our "permission for life" demands it.

— Charles Walters
Kansas City, April 1993

Hu-mus / 'hyü-mes, 'yü- / *n* [NL, fr. L., earth] 1 a brown or black complex variable material resulting from decomposition of plant or animal matter under proper environmental and biological conditions 2 composed chiefly of hydrogen and carbon-hydrogen and oxygen with varying percents of nitrogen attached 3 a long chain-like affair with the capacity to bind plant nutrients—phosphate, nitrate, for instance—to itself 4 it can coat itself with some amino acids, certain sugars and many trace minerals 5 a veritable sponge for nutrients 6 it cannot have more than 6% nitrogen on a dry matter basis, 20 to 50% of which is in the amino acid form, and 1 to 10% in the form of amino sugar nitrogen 7 a buffer and a source of nutrients 8 manufactured by microorganisms, including the actinomycetes, yeasts, molds, and clostridium types

1
The Farming Dilemma

NO ONE USED THE TERM killer agriculture or knowledgeable mining when I was a youngster growing up on a farm in southeast Missouri. We raised corn, wheat, cotton, soybeans and a little hay. We also finished a few cattle. Now, a more mature sense of values brings the reality of our farming operation into focus. Sir Albert Howard identified the horns of the modern farming dilemma: partial and imbalanced fertilization, and toxic rescue chemistry.

Neither I nor my father heard or understood that dictum then, then being the 1950s and 1960s. All we knew was that the crops faltered—not occasionally, but year after year. My father had five sons and he concluded, "I hope you won't even think about going into agriculture because it costs too much and I am not going to be able to help you get started. I hope you will go into business and be an accountant or something like that." Accordingly, I went to college with the intention of becoming an accountant. There was a problem with that. I couldn't stand being inside four walls all the time. So I changed my direction while I was at the University of Missouri where I met William A. Albrecht, the legendary professor who contributed so much to what Acres U.S.A. calls eco-agriculture. Albrecht gave the Department of Soils its well-deserved reputation, but by the time I arrived, he had been retired—forcibly, I am told—in the wake of a great grant from a fossil fuel company. In any case, his classroom days were over, for which reason I was able to get more of his ear than might have been possible as classroom fare. He taught a private study course for Brookside Laboratory, and I decided to avail myself of this extra-curricular opportunity. He changed my entire way of thinking.

My family farmed a nice sandy loam farm at first, and then my dad had an opportunity to get a larger farm with some heavy clay soils. We had no irrigation. In fact there were none in the area at the time—That is one of the reasons we finally moved close to the Mississippi River, to what we call heavy clay gumbo soil. We had some sandy ridges, but most of the soil was heavy clay or "gumbo." Farming that territory presented a host of new problems. Our soybeans grew only half-size before foxtail took over. Cotton sometimes grew knee high. When you talked to the old-timers they would recall cotton up to waist high and soybeans that buried a man's shoulders. Yields in either case were great. But when we started to farm the clay soils, foxtail took over, not just our acres, but the general landscape. No one had an answer. I remember a next-door neighbor talking to my dad. "If we could find a way to market this foxtail seed, we could make some money," he said; "a lot more than we could from beans, because I think we grow more bushels of foxtail seeds than we do beans." I believe this was true in some years. Beans that used to make 40 bushels were making 15 bushels because the foxtail was taking over. Nobody had clean beans and then Randox came along from Monsanto, and we thought that was the best thing in the world. It at least kept the foxtail out of the row.

In those days, if you took a standard soil sample, the readout said nothing was needed. It usually came back with a notation that no lime was required, and that fertilizers were superfluous, other than nitrogen and a little starter on cotton and corn. These reports concluded that phosphate and potash were not needed to grow soybeans. For corn, only nitrogen and a maintenance level of P and K became the general recommendation. Some farmers who became clients when I started in the consulting business had grown nothing but soybeans for 20 or 25 years, always on the same soil. On the average, they made 30 to 40 bushels per acre, year after year, always without fertilizers, lime or other inputs. Most of the money was spent on herbicides when killer technology came along.

I wondered aloud, "Why did this happen?" So when a friend at the University of Missouri told me about William A. Albrecht, Ph.D., a contact was made. On the first visit to his office I explained where I lived. At some point during the visit the opportunity came to ask, "Why are our soybeans so short and why is our cotton stunted, because it hasn't always been that way." I related how when farmers cleared out timber in our area and planted soybeans, the first year delivered a yield of about 50 bushels of beans. The next year the yield would drop down in the 40s and the next year it would be 30 bushels or so per acre, which is where it generally stayed. When analyzed for pH, P and K in the soil, the audits showed nothing wrong.

Dr. Albrecht knew soils; he had worked with and understood soils from all over the world—including all the basic soils of the Midwest. And he provided sensible, practical answers to my questions. "Well, now wait a minute. You live over by the Mississippi River and you are in that heavy gumbo soil? That is why your beans didn't get very tall. They got tall in the first place because you had enough available calcium. Now, when you take a regular soil test and send it in, and if you just check pH, phosphate and potassium, you will never find the problems. Actually pH is influenced by a lot more than calcium. Heavy clay soils are high in magnesium, and that is what is keeping your pH high. If you had known to check the various nutrients in the soil and put on the limestone needed to get your calcium levels up, then your beans would have gotten back the yield and reached the size they were in the first place. You are losing out because calcium is what puts all the other nutrients into the plant."

One of my first clients had been our next-door neighbor during my high school years. He had grown soybeans on 750 acres every year for 20 years, plus! He told me he had never made a 40-bushel bean crop. He said he had always averaged 30 to 32 bushels per acre. After the first set of soil tests, he began to do what the Albrecht method taught should be done.

The first year we followed through on the program, this farmer averaged 45 bushels of beans per acre on the entire 750 acres. The second year, the average was 48 bushels of beans. We merely analyzed the soil in detail and found out what was missing, and supplied what was needed in the proper amounts. But herein lies a problem. Most farmers do not trust a soil test. If a soil test is to be trusted, which one and why? This book will endeavor to provide answers for those who are truly searching for a soil testing program that really works.

Today our company has clients in all 50 states, and we have received soil samples from clients in 70+ other countries, many on a regular basis. The fact is, it doesn't make much difference where you live. What makes the difference is whether or not you follow through on the things that don't change. The things that do not change are the laws of science—physics, chemistry and biology. These laws show that you may be able to produce crops without fertilizers, but you can't produce crops without fertility. That is why I look at fertility, evaluate fertility, and then use fertilizers where necessary to achieve it. The more information a farmer gives as to what he expects to accomplish, the better the job we can do for him.

Fertilizers, limestone and other materials can add to the soil's fertility level. But in certain instances, these same materials can actually damage the soil's level of fertility. You can overdo anything. For the last 20 years at least, farmers seem to have stopped looking at what we call the law of the maximum. They are not looking at the basic laws which say that if you overdo one thing, something else has to give.

This is perhaps one reason why some who are concerned for the land refuse to bring in anything from other areas to use as treatments. But even the book of Genesis records how Adam was to dress and to keep the land. He was not just to keep it, but to dress it (supply what was needed) to build it up. As a rule, land left to itself does not get better, it deteriorates. This may occur ever so slowly but it will happen. Our job is to see that it doesn't. Man's job, our job, is to build it up and keep it vibrant and alive.

Needed is a program for fertility that works in all types of situations—on clay or sand, in weather both hot and cold, in a tropical environment. It is possible to work out each situation, as long as we use physics, chemistry and biology.

Therefore, the first principle of soil fertility is *feed the soil* by providing the necessary nutrients in the proper amount. This is not talking about just fertilizing the crop. This is about feeding the soil and letting the soil feed the plant. This means broadcast applications of the nutrients that will build up the levels that are required in the soil. If we want to build up the soil, we must recommend fertilizers that remain as available for plant use as possible. In such situations, any long-term fertilizer should be broadcast. Because if there is such a thing as the Law of Maximum, then you are actually creating some possible problems for yourself if you apply fertilizer to only specific areas just "for growing the crop." Some fertilizers are soil feeders. They build levels of fertility in the soil. These should definitely be broadcast for best results.

Some fertilizers are plant feeders. This means there will be no soil build-up. Response is immediate, after which the fertilizer no longer shows up on the soil test. It is almost impossible for many crops to pick up the plant-feeder types of fertilizers later on in the soil. An extra large dose all at once will not materially change the nutrient profile. On soils that need to be built up these materials are merely an insurance policy for continued expense, year after year. Side-dress fertilization feeds the plant, not the soil. This is one reason I try to get away from a situation that requires side dressing. Always, the real objective is to get to

Lime Your Soils for Better Crops

The science of the soil has done much for our better understanding of how the soil and the plant roots interact to make the crops grow. From better understanding, some principles have resulted for better guidance of our farm practices.

Liming the soil is one of those practices improved through science. We formerly encouraged liming as a struggle against soil acidity. It is now practiced to put calcium into the soil for nutritional service to the crops. It helps them in their synthesis of proteins and other complex compounds of higher food values to man and beast.

Calcium plays its role as a small part of the material of construction. It is recognized more readily in the ash. In animals and man, calcium is recognized easily as bone. In all life it is far more important than merely a part of the final structure. It serves as the tool in many life processes. It is a necessary tool for fashioning the different proteins that only plants can fabricate from the elements. It seems to be associated with the processes by which livestock assemble these plant proteins into choice animal products of great nutritional value. We have long been liming for legumes and we have connected livestock with legumes. But we have been late in recognizing this basic principle of the interaction between the calcium of the soil and the roots of the crops. As a matter of fact, it is the working principle of this food creation assembly line.

Calcium serves, in the growth of plants, to mobilize other essential chemical elements into the plant more speedily. It puts a higher content of the ash elements into the forage. It is always associated with the crops that we say are better feed for young animals. It is associated more with feeds for growth and reproduction than with those for fattening only. It is associated with the soil's microbial processes that build up soil nitrogen. It is also effective in making green manure and other organic matter decay more rapidly and release their fertility for crop production. All life, from the lowly microbe to man himself, is dependent on a good supply of available calcium in the soil.

Liming the soil is one of the contributions to the better nourishment of all that grows on our farms. This soil treatment must, however, be judiciously connected with other treatments. It must not, therefore, be used excessively. If wisely used, this farm practice—as it is now undergirded by the science of the soil—will bring about better understanding and use of the other necessary soil treatments. This better knowledge should conserve not only the body of the soil, but also its fertility or internal strength by which all life must be fed.

— *William A. Albrecht*
The Albrecht Papers, Volume III *(1989)*

the point where fertilizers can be broadcast, with materials being effective at feeding the crop. The bottom line: the exclusive use of side dressing, banding or plant feeding is not best for the farmer in the long run, but it can be a great business for those who just want to sell fertilizer. We make no money from recommended materials sold to the farmer by fertilizer companies. We sell a service. That service is measuring the fertility of the soil and its needs, and recommending what will best serve the crop or crops to be grown there. That is how we earn our living. As long as we give the proper advice, we keep our clients.

To feed the plant, fast-acting, quick-impact, short-range fertility is required. In terms of such a program, the usual procedure is to supply the biggies—nitrogen, phosphate and potash. A consequence of this procedure is to tie up certain of the trace nutrients via the glut.

When trace elements are borderline, a deficiency situation will be the observed result. Yet farmers dance to the tune of N, P and K every day. They create their own yield limiting situations. Still, it must be observed that in terms of micronutrients fast action is often required. But such nutrients should not be introduced into the soil as side dressing. A better system is to feed plants through the leaves using a foliar and treat the soils by broadcasting to build the levels as required. And do this only based on the need, as established by a reliable soil test and/or plant analysis.

A lot of farmers do not believe foliars will work, and certain other professionals have still to tune in on this eco-technology. On the other hand, there are those who recommend only plant testing instead of soil testing. Neither would be the correct approach.

In fact, valid technologies have been used to make foliar feeds and liquid fertilizers since 1951. According to Eco-Farm: An Acres U.S.A. Primer, "These developments went on virtually without the agricultural community knowing anything about them." Sylvan H. Wittwer, under whose leadership Michigan State University conducted investigations on foliar fertilization of plants, correctly summarized: "There is probably no area of agricultural crop production of more current interest, and more contradictory data, claims and opinions, or where the farmer in practice has moved so far ahead of scientific research." Even today, the average land grant college often does not have a single scientist who has the working knowledge necessary for using liquid fertilizers in crop production. There will be those who object to this statement, citing Hanway's Iowa State University research, which came some 12 years after Wittwer's, but this hardly qualified because it failed as a result of using the wrong type of ingredients.

Credentialed and uncredentialed outsiders standing in the wings knew that Hanway's foliar N, P and K efforts would fail because the compound being used did not answer plant requirements, would burn crops, and because it would cost too much. It involved the application of gross amounts of nitrogen, phosphorus and potassium to soybeans in three applications, using amounts required by the holy writ of soil fertilization.

Working with nursery crops, flowers for market, strawberries, apples, pears, and cherries, agronomists started answering growth cycle requirements with seaweed extracts many years ago, all with successes that were spectacular, erratic, and rejected. There were things that could be done with the leaf that proved next to impossible when working with complex soils.

In the early 1950s, Wittwer was working under arrangements with the Division of Biology and Medicine, Atomic Energy Commission. Experiments entailed the use of radioactive isotopes in assessing the efficiency of foliar applied nutrients compared to soil applications of those same nutrients. It was found that the efficiency of the foliar fertilizers was from 100 to 900% greater than the dry-applied fertilizer materials.

Trees, grasses and field crops all respond to the foliar assist. Even so, foliar nutrition is the second part of fertility management. Use a reliable plant test to feed the plant and a reliable soil test to feed the soil, and generally you will come closer to the correct solutions.

The first principle is feed the soil and let the soil feed the plant. If, in the meantime, there is something missing, it must be supplied in the most economical way. Many nutrients obey the "law of the little bit." The plant will take most of what it needs from the soil in any case. It is the last bit that puts support over the top when there is a deficiency. The second principle is concerned with the nutrient balance we are required to achieve. In other words, the fertility level we are working to achieve for each soil is the foundation required for plant growth. Our objective is the right amount of everything. Once we achieve the proper nutrient load, then we have the foundation to begin achieving proper fertility support for plant growth. Whatever the crop in the production sequence—corn, soybeans, rice or wheat—these generally can be grown in the same soils without too much trouble. Rice production can work with a little less calcium. Soybeans, on the other hand, can use a little more calcium. Clover, alfalfa, sugar beets, sugar cane, vegetables, citrus groves, pasture grasses, trees, and flowers or turf grass, all will grow best in the very same soil. That soil is the one which contains all of the necessary nutrients we know to test for in the proper relationship to every one of the other nutrients. A soil that grows the very best corn will also grow the very best alfalfa. Should we analyze a soil and discover a nutrient content proper to production of the above named crops, and the crop is timber, it will be top quality timber. If the crop is grapes, it will be top quality grapes.

There are some elements that barley can endure, which other crops can't, one being extra high sodium. Barley does not have to have high sodium, but it can live with it. A pine tree can live in an extremely acid soil. But the pine tree that lives in extremely acid soil doesn't produce the best wood. That record is reserved for the pine tree grown in the same soil that will produce the most excellent stand of corn or alfalfa. Much the same is true of barley. Top quality barley relies on the common denominators that underwrite quality corn.

I have never seen a soil, not one, that didn't confirm and conform to the design unlocked by analysis. I have rarely seen a soil that required me to say, "I honestly can't tell you anything that you should do with soil fertility to improve your crop."

Most soils when tested show there are many things that should be done. But the general principle holds: top quality blueberries grow on the same soil as the very best corn. Yet once you get even one of the nutrients out of balance, a whole new set of factors becomes inserted into the equation.

Some basic proofs have been provided by the man I mentioned in the opening paragraphs of this book, Dr. William A.

Albrecht (especially see *Soil Fertility & Animal Health: The Albrecht Papers, Vol. II*). Dr. Albrecht retired in 1959. I received a certificate as an agronomist from him via his work from the Brookside Farms Laboratory Association, Inc. in 1973. He passed away a year later. Albrecht received his doctorate from the University of Illinois. He originally intended to be a medical doctor, but his studies convinced him he could do more to help people's health by concentrating on the soils that feed them. While studying plant pathology, plant physiology and soils, he concluded that soils are more a cause, whereas doctors treat effects. He taught soils at the University of Missouri. He also helped the Midwest develop inoculates for legumes. In the process he started looking for answers to why crops didn't respond properly. A lot of the information that he used came from Germany and Holland. In particular, there was a Dr. Oscar Loew in Germany who put forth the idea that excess magnesium was a poison to the calcium in the nucleus of the plant cell. Equally important was the Albrecht revelation that a nutrient balance was the foundation for achieving proper fertility.

If our company consults with a farmer within a 100-mile radius of the office, we only accept soil samples taken once they attend a course that shows the importance of properly taking samples. There is a reason for this. Most farmers are not serious enough when it comes to pulling soil samples because they really have not learned their true value. One sample per field is generally not sufficient to fairly evaluate how to fertilize properly. Therefore, we contract with a farmer on an acreage basis, then go in and map the farm and pull the samples. It costs him the same amount of money whether there are many or just a few samples. Generally, we will pull far more soil samples and will probably pull ten times more probes of soil than the farmer would account for. Once we contract with the farmer and do the sampling, the farmer can never be blamed if something appears to be wrong in the sampling method. It is always our fault. Now I can sit down with the farmer with the utmost confidence in the soil analysis. The next thing we suggest is, "Don't tell us about all your soils, but if you have one soil that is extra good, maybe one small spot in the field that we may not be able to find, tell us where it is. We will pull a sample there for you." The objective is to compare the highest producing soil to the rest.

The closer you can build other fields or areas with different nutrient content to the levels of the soil that does the best, the closer you can bring those other soils to doing the same thing.

A farmer from Kansas called one day. He said, "I have an 80-acre field and one end of it never makes good grain sorghum, but the other end always does. We spend more than we make on the bad end. I would like to send you a sample and have you tell me what is wrong with it."

Then I suggested, "I would like you to take a sample out of the poor end and take a sample out of the good end, and send them both, but don't label them in any manner that would show what is good and what is bad. You code them so that you know which one is good and which one is marginal or bad. From the soil analysis, I ought to be able to tell you which is which over the phone."

Farmers have even pulled samples and said that one was good and one was bad on purpose. They knew the "good one" was the bad one and the "bad one" was the good one. They just did this to see if it would really throw us off. If you have a spot that always does the best it will be the closest to right. There are some exceptions. If you grow wheat, some exceptionally good wheat land will not necessarily grow the best corn because certain nutrients that are needed to yield top corn may still not be present. There are things that make wheat do well, but they do not really affect corn as much. In southeast Missouri, the soils that are highest in manganese—many soils there barely have enough—will do well with wheat, and the wheat can really be a little short of the ideal calcium level. This one particular area can grow good wheat, but can't grow good soybeans on some of the same soils. The reason farmers can't grow good soybeans is that calcium is short. Wheat, being a shallow feeder type of crop—though it is true that the roots can go deep—doesn't have to have

Hands-On Agronomy

Weeds—Guardians of the Soil

The German farmer did not consider many of our common weeds harmful in themselves. According to him, the harm came from the farmer's failure to control the weeds which were growing in his fields. The German had a most efficient, simple method of handling barnyard manure. The manure pile was under continuous construction, and as the manure came from the barn or corral or roadway, it was stacked with layers of manure or litter alternating with layers of weeds. By this method of manure-pile building, the farmer explained, the amount of the final fertilizer was markedly increased through the addition of the food-filled weeds; and fire-fanging of the manure was prevented because the weed layers permitted proper aeration.

I examined one pile of this fertilizer that had already gone through the processing. The stack on the outside looked like any typical manure pile now and then seen in American barnlots. Inside, the pile resembled true compost somewhat, but was really just mellow, well-rotted manure of a superior quality. I have since wondered if this German farmer could not have been employing a fertilizer-making process handed down from the Romans. The Catholic monks in Europe a few centuries back were known to have employed in their very efficient agriculture some of the teachings of Cato, who had lots to say on this subject.

—*Joseph A. Cocannouer*
Weeds, Guardians of the Soil *(1950)*

the same relationship with nutrients that soybeans do. But if you look at a soil that grows the best soybeans, and all the nutrients are in the right proportions, it will also grow the best wheat and the best corn too. Sometimes you have one thing that affects a crop more than another. If you have extra calcium in a soil, well, naturally the legumes are going to do better because they can take advantage of what the extra calcium provides. Weeds that like extra calcium will do better, too.

Two brothers in North Dakota who had been certified organic for years once contacted us. The problem was, bindweed was taking over their farm. They told this one fellow—who was a client of mine—that they were just going to have to go out of organics and lose their certification. Their fertility program was manure, and that is all they used. They didn't have enough manure to put it on every field every year, but they had tremendous quantities of manure for their farm. Having never been on their farm or met the fellows to this day, our connection was the telephone. The first question was, "Do you have some fields that are really bad and then some other fields that aren't so bad?"

They responded, "We have one field that is 90% taken over by bindweed and we have another field that is probably only 10% gone." There was time to take samples from the fields. Leaves from the bindweed were sampled. Two different labs were used. One lab was used to do soils, and a second lab analyzed tissues. The lab receiving the tissue never saw the soil samples, and the lab that got the soil never saw the tissue samples. But both were tests we understood and recommended. Now if the soil analysis shows a farmer needs boron on his corn, and he fails to supply the boron, and he will take a leaf analysis, it will show up immediately, provided the tissue analysis properly gives every limiting factor. In short, use the tissue to balance out.

In the case of the bindweed, the soil and the weeds were analyzed. The results were as expected. They revealed that too much manure had been used, and the potassium levels had gotten extremely high. Bindweed loves low calcium, high potassium soils. This weed has the ability to forage for its needed calcium. Bindweed showed no deficiency of calcium. Other crops, however, exhibited a shortage of calcium.

Bindweed releases an exudate into the soil. This plant's acid dissolves enough calcium to supply its own needs. Bindweed also loves potassium, and with extremely high potassium and low availability of calcium in a soil, bindweed thrives. The remedy was easily discerned. So I recommended liming to correct the calcium level. In turn, the calcium would help to control the excessive potassium. As a consequence, the bindweed couldn't thrive anymore.

Top-producing soils have a specific nutrient relationship, but so do poorly producing soils. A soil sample, properly done, will tell you where you ought to be, and the closer you can get to the prescribed numbers, the better the soil system will produce.

When I started out as a consultant in 1973, I think it cost $1.50 to do a soil test through the university extension service in southeast Missouri. I charged by the acre, and if you had a large enough farm it cost $1.50 an acre. Dr. Albrecht sent a letter to me when he sent my certificate to verify completion of his soil fertility study course. He wrote, "Neal, you really aren't an agronomist. You have just shown that you have the ability to go out and become an agronomist. An agronomist is the fellow who goes out in the field and does it. When you get out there and actually are working with the farmers and solving their problems, that is what will make you an agronomist." He also said, "You are not going to get any of the good soils because when you charge that kind of money the guy that doesn't have any problems doesn't want to spend the money. The fellow who is going to spend the money is the one who has the problem. He may not tell you it is a problem, but it is."

Three good friends were my first clients. I got their farms on a consulting basis because they were pushing me to hurry up and get done, and basically they didn't have big problems. They just wanted to find out what to do and they were sort of following along as I was learning what to do.

Another client signed up a 210-acre farm to sample. He farmed 1,500 acres, but he picked out this one 210-acre irrigated farm. He said the reason he was calling me was that his brother-in-law had good results with our program. After I did the soil testing and came back from the area, before it was ever sent in to be analyzed, he looked at the map and was amazed. He exclaimed, "You have sampled that farm and every problem area that's in there, you have it drawn on this map within 100 feet." I always strive to draw everything we sample to scale. Then he admitted, "I hired a specialist who came down here from Ohio, and I paid him $8.00 an acre to help me grow corn. I lost money. Then I didn't learn my lesson, and I hired another expert from here in Missouri. I paid him $10.00 an acre and I lost even more money. I really wouldn't have you come except I know what you have done for my brother-in-law. This is my worst farm. In the very best year on this 210-acre farm, put to grade, furrow irrigated, I have made 23 bushels of soybeans. There have been years when I didn't make a ten-bushel crop."

He followed through that year and did what was called for on the tests. The next year he called and said, "I want you to do that 210 acres again, but it is not my worst farm anymore. I have another 160 acres, and now it is my worst farm." Eventually he put in all 1,500 acres, a step at a time. In the beginning, I really didn't realize how much of an advantage it was to be able to work with problems. But as a result of being exposed to problem after problem after problem, you finally learn that as long as you follow the chemistry, the physics and the biology, you are going to solve the problems if they are rooted in fertility.

Dr. Albrecht once explained, "I used to think, if I could have any soil I wanted, it would be pure humus." He literally buttressed his soil fertility program with the isolation of humus from the soil. He extracted enough humus to run a soil sample on the humus, and he did this time after time. He reasoned that the most fertile productive soils must resemble the makeup of humus. Albrecht evaluated humus and, sure enough, that is what he found. What the most fertile soils have in terms of nutrient balance is also what the humus has in terms of nutrient balance.

This is not to suggest that we can take a clay soil and turn it into humus. I am merely suggesting that the closer we can match up our soil to the components of humus, the more productive it becomes. Soil will always be clay if it's clay. You can never make humus out of clay by taking clay and correcting the fertility load. There is a difference between clay and humus. Humus has been alive at one time and clay has never been alive.

What is humus? It is the completely decomposed remains of plants and animals. If you take an average of what remains after the complete decomposition of living organisms, plants, animals, whatever, doesn't it seem likely you would get back to the same thing? It seems logical to me that we could determine the average nutrient makeup of living organisms by looking at the soil, and we could also determine the average makeup of the soil by looking at the makeup of living organisms. Back in the middle 1970s, a consultant in California asked me to come out and work with some citrus and nut growers, as well as cotton people. He said, "I want to introduce you to a good friend of mine. He is a medical doctor and I want you to do a soil sample on his garden. He has one part of the garden that does wonderfully well and the other part has problems growing anything." He insisted on paying for all this because the physician had helped him solve a daughter's extremely serious health problem.

The medical doctor lived as much as possible out of his own garden. His wife was a nutritionist. The two were allergy specialists. When he was around age 55 he expanded his practice and started working more with nutrition to solve health problems. I took samples from the poor and the good garden soil. About a month or two later, I went back to California to deliver the results. He asked me over "this afternoon" because he had only about 30 minutes since he and his wife had to attend an important meeting. After explaining that the calcium level in the soil ought to be 68% saturation, he said, "That's the same thing you and I need in our bodies to have the right calcium balance." When I told him what the magnesium should be, he said that was what he and I needed, and the same thing with potassium. He had 1,500 patients and they paid him to tell them what to do so that they would not get sick. His patients were movie stars

Remember That You Are Dust

We should frequently meditate on the words of Ash Wednesday: "Man, remember that you are dust and that you will return to dust." This is not merely a religious and philosophical doctrine but a great scientific truth which should be engraved above the entrance to every Faculty of Medicine throughout the world. We might then better remember that our cells are made up of mineral elements which are to be found at any given moment in the soil of Normandy, Yorkshire or Australia; and if these "dusts" have been wrongly assembled in plant, animal or human cells the results will be the imperfect functioning of the latter. . . .

In 1897, for the first time, Gabriel Bertrand of the Academie d'Agriculture [in France], succeeded in showing that a "dust" of the soil, that is to say a mineral element in trace form, was essential to the functioning of living cells. All observations have since confirmed this discovery. An attempt will be made . . . to show how "dusts" of the soil are "assembled, bolted and screwed" to form the cells of our body and allow them to function. The special aim will be to demonstrate how illness can be due to an upset in the balance of this "assembly."

—André Voisin
Soil, Grass & Cancer *(1959)*

and athletes and politicians from all over the world. They came twice a year for checkups and so forth, and he would tell them what to do.

That man was 70 years old when we met, and he came to the office six days a week at six o'clock in the morning, and he didn't leave until six o'clock at night. He said, "I can see very clearly what you are telling me. If we could straighten out the soil so that we have the right nutrient relationships that would translate to the plant." It does. Dr. Albrecht showed that with feeding tests with animals. "That means a lot of the problems we are having to deal with as doctors should be solved by agriculture. This would leave time to concentrate on things like recovering from accidents, birth defects, and the degenerative diseases."

If we analyze humus, which comes from all living organisms, that humus and the most productive soil analyze to be the same. What makes us the healthiest is exactly what we should have inside us as far as mineral content is concerned.

What did Dr. Albrecht find when he analyzed humus? He found the same thing as that little old pie chart in the textbook. Every soil textbook shows the ideal soil as 45% minerals, 5% humus, and 50% pore space of which half is occupied by air and the other half by water. What he found when he analyzed humus was the same mineral, air, and water relationships as are found in the most fertile, productive soils. The only problem with that pie chart is that if you don't already have it, the texts do not tell how to get it. In your mind's eye, italicize this sentence—the basic makeup of the plant and animal kingdom as it decomposes and becomes humus matches the nutrient makeup of the most productive soils. That is one of the reasons why we say that the nutrient balance we use is the basic foundation of soil fertility. The closer you get to what the soils should have, the more problems you solve.

Clay won't ever become humus even though we provide the exact amount of each nutrient to achieve top fertility. The same basic nutrient relationships are there though. The same proportion of calcium, the same proportion of magnesium, the same proportion of potassium—and if you think about it, it does make sense.

Whether it is a farm situation with corn and alfalfa, or whether it is a case of lawns and trees, the laws of physics, chemistry and biology make sense. We may be dealing with potted plants in southern California. It may be a greenhouse, or palm trees in the Caribbean. No matter what kind of plant you are talking about, the same laws of science apply. These laws are our common denominator. As long as we use these laws, we can work with someone all the way on the other side of the world. As long as we have our road map, which is our soil analysis, the program is clear. The laws that affect soil fertility do not change for Missouri, for the east or west, or for some other country. Those laws are just as certain as the sun and the rain.

I do a lot of work in northeast Arkansas as well as southeast Missouri. We are located just 60 miles from the Arkansas border. I can cross the Mississippi River and enter Illinois. But when you go to Arkansas, you don't cross a river. You drive until you find a marker. It reads, "Arkansas Line". There is a gravel road, and here's a field on the one side, and there is a field next to it on the other side. The farmer in Arkansas is told, "This only works for Arkansas soils," and the farmer in Missouri is told, "This only works for Missouri soils." Yet there is just a gravel road separating them. People farming on separate sides of the road are told to use different advice from different people. Cross the Mississippi River and go into Tennessee. What the researchers in Arkansas say about growing cotton with foliar nitrogen supposedly does not apply in Tennessee.

The point is as long as you stick to the basic laws of chemistry, physics and biology, you can work with soils anywhere. Those laws will work when the weather is frigid. We might have to use a four-wheel drive vehicle with a drill and auger bit to sample the soil, but those laws will work. The same nutrients have to get into those plants, wherever they grow. The laws of nature work on banana plants just as well as on spruce or evergreens. There are some government plantations down in the Dominican Republic where I've done fertility work for bananas, coffee, milo and cotton. Whether up in the mountains where they grow coffee, or down on the plain where they grow bananas, the principles are still the same. I have also worked in deserts. The principles work just as well in desert soils as they do in soils with a tropical setting and a lot of rainfall.

Everything I use answers a formula. Nitrogen recommendations answer a formula, but nitrogen is one thing you can count on least because of the volatile nature of nitrogen in the soil. You can check it today and get a big rain, and suddenly part of it is gone. That is one of the reasons a normal soil test does not include nitrogen from any source but humus.

You have to work around each situation, but in terms of measuring fertility, the lessons are the same and in place. When you get the numbers right, and the plant is suited to the environment, expected improvements will follow.

I began working with a client in British Columbia who had production problems. He said the operation "came out in the red every year we've ever done any work on our soils." He grows carrots and all kinds of vegetables. He tried to grow enough to take care of his own needs and still sell produce into the market. He worked on my program for one year and reported back at the end of the year. "This year is the first time we have ever made money."

We continued to receive samples each year from that property until a big flood washed the soil away and the client retired. The program works and will work. It works across the board for the basic crops. It works for vegetables and for fruit and nut trees as well.

A client in Germany owned 4,000 acres of timber. He was growing blue spruce for the commercial market. Customers would come in and buy a block at a time at a certain height. He had some blocks of trees on which they could never get the proper height. He had other blocks of trees that grew beautifully. His forester wondered how anybody could come from the United States and tell him what to do for blue spruce trees in Germany. I suggested the forester take samples out of those lots, following our set of sampling instructions. The forester pulled the samples according to instructions and sent them over. The samples were analyzed and taken back to Germany. The owner and the forester sat down with me to go over them. They had sent 14 samples and they were going to choose one area where they would follow through on a fertility program. The forester couldn't speak English and I couldn't speak German. With an interpreter it took almost a half day to communicate. At the end of the half day, the forester said something to the owner in German and the owner smiled and said, "My forester said that he would like to do 14 tests instead of one test because he said you put everything in order from the best to the worst."

All I can do is follow the numbers. This was heavy, black, muck soil right on the then East-West German border, which, in fact, split the farm in two when the Iron Curtain was established.

There were two or three professors over there who felt that they could solve the acid rain problem in the German forests by correcting the calcium level, and I believe that it could be done. The only problem is some are trying to correct the situation with gypsum (calcium sulfate) instead of high-calcium lime. Just remember this, in order for gypsum to work properly you must already have a reasonable calcium level in the soil. If the calcium saturation is too low in the soil, it is a mistake to apply gypsum. But the correct liming program works on trees and it also works very well on turf grass.

A turf grass farmer not too far from Little Rock, Arkansas, had one of the most balanced soils that I have ever seen, albeit not because of me. It was there when I came. He takes all the grass clippings and dumps them over on the edge. If anyone picked up those grass clippings and composted them, he or she would have one of the most balanced composts possible. I mentioned this, and the fellow just said, "We sell sod, we don't sell grass clippings."

Most sod farms are not well-off because they keep on taking the sod away. But on this farm, one end is terrific. At the other end of the farm, grub worms are eating up the profits. It shows in the soil analyses.

Chemically speaking, if you analyze the soils and rocks in an area, they will have the same makeup. Southern Illinois has several high-calcium limestone mines. Around those mines, the soil will generally be high in calcium until you get down into the river where the water has eroded the soil away. I have a client in southern Illinois whose corn wasn't doing well. He was raising good corn at first, and then he said his yields kept going down. He had a calcium limestone mine right in the middle of his farm. His calcium had gotten too high, and he had neglected magnesium. Every time he needed lime he put on limestone from the available quarry. He corrected the pH, but he forgot the limitations that walk hand in hand with pH. The magnesium dropped accordingly. The nearest dolomitic limestone mine was 130 or so miles away. He had to send a truck out from his place. Neighbors called him crazy. The very next year his corn harvest came right back to where it was before.

Geologically speaking, the soils and rocks in the same area will have the same makeup. If there is calcium in the rocks, there will be calcium in the soil. If there is plenty of magnesium in the rocks, there will be plenty of magnesium in the soil. This is an important point to remember. If the soil has not been moved in or out by erosion, rocks and soils in a given area remain blood brothers. There are soils in the Chandler, Arizona area, just south of Phoenix, that are very high in potassium. Still, area farmers think they have sodium toxicity problems.

I worked with one farm near Chandler where the operator used a moldboard plow and a crawler caterpillar to break the soil, turning it over 22 inches deep every year. If you have good porosity in the soil, sodium and chloride are two of the first things to leave. An open soil with plenty of calcium and plenty of water will not permit sodium to accumulate. This farmer thought he had sodium because his pH was high. His problem was potassium and magnesium, and his potassium was so high it was tying up his trace elements and hurting his crops. His sodium levels were not the problem, they were not high at all, let alone in excess.

The Land

Henry George, United States economist and land reformer (1839-1897) discovered that the value of land is measured by the number of people who passed the front gate each day. If one came by, your place might be worth $1,000; if 100 came by, it could be $100,000. Even your gold mine might be worthless if no one could possibly travel past your land.

"So," he said, "the people give you the value of the land, and the people may take it away. Blessed are the people."

"Also," he said, "landowners are only custodians. They are the users of the land. If they use it well, they may keep it. If they use it poorly, the people should take it back again, and let a good custodian have it."

The feudal kings, using a similar theory, granted fiefs of land to chosen feudal lords. The people who lived there were also given to the lords, as serfs. But again, there was a string attached. The lord was only a custodian. He could retain the land and the serfs only as long as he cared for them as well. If he abused the land or failed to feed the serfs and give them social security, the king could reclaim the fief and give it to a better lord.

God, as the partner of feudal kings, approved these transactions.

Do not smile. Feudalism worked as well in relation to its original ideals as democracy works in relation to our Bill of Rights. Remember, in the ancient ceremony of knighting the feudal lord, a lowly serf hit him across the face with a glove, to remind him all over again that he must serve the whole community, caring for the land and feeding the people, or lose it all.

> Are we so proud? Who cares for our land? Who cares for our people? Who intervenes when bad farmers pollute the land and hurt the communities? The farmer's eye should fatten the cattle. His dreams should sow the crops. His mind should fertilize the soil. His love should attend the harvest. Where have America's farmers gone? Will they ever return?
>
> —*Lee Fryer & Dick Simmons*
> Earth Foods *(1972)*

You can start across Arizona and go into southern California. Some of those farmers in the mountains say they have a sodium problem. They are not down in the Imperial Valley where the creeks and rivers meander across the landscape. Their problem isn't sodium at all. It is potassium. But they never get a detailed analysis that enables them to discern this fact. On the other hand, in the Red River Valley in North Dakota, farmers have extremely heavy soils that hold a heavy payload of potassium. Because they don't audit the ability of the soil to hold potassium, they simply look at how many pounds are there. The heavier the soil, the more ability that soil has to hold fertilizer, and the more ability it has, the more it takes to saturate the soil with the proper amounts of nutrients. Some testing facilities tell those farmers that they have so much potassium that they do not need any.

The first time I went into the area, I discovered that many of those soils needed potassium. At a meeting I was telling the farmers to put on potassium and one guy spoke up and said, "Well, you know, the university tells me that I don't need any potassium. Yet I can tell exactly where I use it on my crops."

It is good to have luxury amounts of potassium, but it is not good to have excessive amounts. Excessive potassium ties up boron, which is what builds the grain, and it crowds out the manganese, which causes the grain to be set in the first place.

What I am looking for in terms of a soil program is getting the right amounts in the right place at the right time. If you have too much or too little of any nutrient, it is going to hurt you. The rocks and soils in a given area tend to have the same nutrient content, and certainly scientists tell us that our soil comes from decomposed rock. Consider this, for rock to become fertile soil, it would have to break down from rock to gravel to sand to silt and finally down to very fine clay—to the finest clay particle possible. You actually don't get any nutrient holding capacity from sand. Sand doesn't hold any fertilizer. The only two things that hold fertilizer in soils are the clay colloid—the very smallest particle of clay—and the humus, the very smallest particle of organic manner. You have to measure how much of each there is in order to know how much fertilizer that soil needs.

Admittedly, soil is made up of sand, silt and clay, even though clay basically holds the nutrients. Still, the soil makeup is the amount of sand, silt and clay. We call the mix soil texture. Soil texture is important in two ways. Soil texture defines the amount of sand, silt and clay as it affects water holding capacity. A fine sand has the ability to hold about an inch and a half of water. A silt loam could hold two inches of water, and a silty clay loam might retain even three inches of water before the rest is lost to run-off. A silty clay loam can hold twice as much water as a fine sand. In other words, if you get two inches of rain, silty clay loam—dry to start with—could absorb the whole load. That fine sand would never hold the water. Fine sands also hold the least amount of fertilizer and heavy clays hold the most. There is one difference, and that is if the water isn't there, you'd better be able to supply it from somewhere. You can take a fine sand that has the proper nutrient relationships, and get enough water into it, and take a silty clay loam that has the same nutrient relationships, and you can grow just as much corn on that fine sand as you can on that silty clay as long as you have enough moisture. If you have the same amount of fertility, the difference is the water. I have clients on fine sands that will raise 190 to 200 bushels of corn and then go right on to their heavier soils without the proper nutrient relationships where they will raise 175 bushels of corn, all on the same farm. Yet some would tell all those willing to listen that heavy soils always out-produce sands.

There is another advantage to sands. Problems can be corrected faster. If sandy soils are out of balance, it takes less money and you can get a faster response in terms of production than you can with a heavy soil. On the other hand, once you get those heavy soils corrected, you can make all kinds of mistakes, and the nutrient load will last for a much longer time. Sand keeps calling for help. It does not have the nutrient holding ability of clay. Speaking of the soil texture components, only the clay particles hold nutrients in a sandy soil. It isn't the pounds of fertilizer that produce the crop. The pounds of fertilizer merely tell how to get the proper nutrient balance in the soil.

An-i-on / ´an-,i-en / *n* [Gk, neut. of *anion*, prp. of *anienai* to go up, fr. *ana* + *tienai* to go] 1 the ion in an electrolyzed solution that migrates to the anode 2 a negatively charged ion 3 an acid forming element 4 opposite of a cation

Cat-i-on / ´kat-,i-en / n [Gk kation, neut. of kation, prp. of *katienai* to go down, fr. *kata- cata-* + *tienai* to go] 1 positively charged base elements, either alkali metals or alkaline earths 2 migrate to the cathode in an electrolyzing solution 3 the opposite of an anion

2

Cation-Anion Connection

NEW WORDS NOW COMMAND ENTRY into the farmer's vocabulary—cation, anion, exchange capacity, base saturation—also some new nuances attend the use of a soil audit that must be mastered. But all have to do with the clay of the soil and the electricity of nutrition, and how nutrients, or the lack thereof, govern everything from crop production to weed control. This outline will be expanded in this chapter.

In buying a farm, some people seem to prefer space and location to prime land. Land in the Missouri Ozarks—often seemingly quite useless for crop production—sells for more than prime land in the Little Dixie area of northern Missouri. There are some yellow, clay soils in the Ozarks of Missouri. I went there to sample a farm on one special occasion. This fellow wanted to develop his farm, but the soils were extremely poor. They grew scrub oak, not much more. As we were pulling the samples, I discerned a nice yellow clay soil, thinking this was great because it could be built up easily. When the analysis came back, it was immediately evident that the soil had no more ability to hold fertilizer than a sand dune in Florida. It was a yellow clay, but if it had ever been broken down into a fine colloidal soil, that portion had been lost. The finer particles of humus and clay which hold the plant nutrients in a soil were gone, leaving only a coarse yellow clay with very limited nutrient-holding capacity.

A soil colloid is a particle of clay that has been broken down to the point that it can't be broken down further. Such a clay particle and humus carry a negative charge, much like the negative post on a storage battery. Fertilizers must have a positive charge to be held to the soil colloid. Calcium and magnesium from lime compounds have this positive charge. So does sodium. Hydrogen, as a gas, also has a positive charge. Negative sites on a clay particle will attract and hold positives, according to our scientific conceptualizations. The more clay colloids in the soil, the more negatives there are to attract positively charged elements, much like a magnet. Positively charged elements are called cations. Negatively charged elements such as nitrogen, phosphorous and sulfur are called anions. Negative ions do not hold to the clay colloid. The bottom line is that clay has a negative charge and the element being held on that clay has a positive charge. Most of the chemical reactivity of soils is governed by clay colloids. These colloids are extremely small, and can't be seen with the naked eye.

It should be pointed out that some laboratories do not actually measure the amount of clay in a soil. Some operators put it between their thumb and two fingers and rub it around as if to say, "Well, that feels like so much clay," and so they put that number down. If you start getting good, round numbers on a soil test, you can just about say, "Well, they are just estimating the exchange capacity." That is a standard practice in Europe. It is a standard practice for a lot of soil testing classes. Obviously, if you cannot see the colloid with the naked eye, how are you going to determine how much of it there is unless you involve sophisticated instrumentation? Colloids are plate-like in structure. These plates lie upon one another, very flat, forming the clay soil.

Colloids come from clay and organic matter. In other words, there is a humus colloid and a clay colloid. Both have negative charges. They are very small, much like dust or talcum powder—only smaller and finer in makeup. These smallest pieces of clay—along with humus—attract and hold nutrients, but they are also easy to lose. If you could collect the dust that wind moves across a field and analyze it, you would find that it has the highest fertility of any part of the field. The most fertile part of the soil always leaves first, via either water or wind erosion. The longer erosion continues, the worse the soil gets.

When we pull soil samples, a lot of farmers think we overdo it. Take a flat field. Basically, if you can find out which way it drains, sample the low end and the high end. The biggest area we recommend being put in a sample the first time is around 20 acres. The low end will almost always have the highest nutrient content because the lion's share of nutrients is held on the clay particles, which are that light colloidal dust. On upland soils, whatever way the water drains, the fertility goes that way, too. Soils can be built up. They can also be torn down. In the area where I live, soils that are considered the worst soils—the ones that nobody really wants, the ones that are sold for poor horse pasture—were considered the most fertile soils in southeast Missouri when my grandmother was a child. Growers farmed it and farmed it and let it erode away. They would raise wheat year after year and burn the stubble, then plant something else for a second crop. Nobody really wants to try to raise crops on it nowadays. Much of this land is now blown sand.

The first thing to do for your land is to correctly measure the amount of clay and humus the soil has in it. Nothing less than a detailed analysis will answer the questions. The procedure to rely on is atomic absorption. Technicians use a flame and actually measure the atoms, and how much the atoms will absorb in terms of color.

This test shows a different amount of light for each nutrient. That measurement has a name—*cation exchange capacity,* or CEC. As mentioned earlier, cations are nutrients with a positive charge. *Exchange capacity* is merely a measure of capacity of the soil to exchange nutrients. Whether the CEC is large or small, it affects the soil's capacity to hold nutrients such as calcium, magnesium and ammonia nitrogen, and it also affects the quantity of a nutrient needed to change its relative level in the soil. A lighter soil will hold less of everything. Consequently, it doesn't take as much fertilizer to get the right nutrient balance for total saturation. But that nutrient load can be lost or quickly taken up by cropping it. If you have an exchange capacity of, say, 5, that is like a sandy soil for certain. It is not going to hold very much fertilizer. Another soil may have an exchange capacity of 10. It will hold twice as many pounds of nutrients as the soil with a CEC of 5.

The term *cation exchange capacity* is not used on our soil tests. The nomenclature *total exchange capacity* fits much better. "Cation exchange capacity" means that the laboratory is measuring a certain part of the cation content. It may be measuring all, and it may not. We use the word total on the form to assure the client that we are measuring *all* the cations that could have a major effect on the soil analysis.

A number of soil tests do not report the sodium content in the soil. If you get a soil test that doesn't measure sodium content, it does not measure the *total exchange capacity,* and therefore the exchange capacity will be expressed differently. The exchange capacity is not something you measure and then fill with nutrients. It is developed because the soil can hold a certain amount of calcium, magnesium, potassium and sodium. Each of these nutrients must be measured, or a valid answer will not be provided.

There is also a category called *other bases* shown on our soil test. It covers cations not usually singled out in terms of how many pounds are available in small amounts. Thus, use of the term *TEC,* or total exchange capacity, instead of CEC. The TEC shows the measured amount of "holding power" of the clay and humus in a soil.

Cation Exchange Capacity

The first order of business for the soil colloid . . . is to hold nutrients—nutrients that can be traded off as the roots of a plant demand them. Thus the first index from the laboratory—the energy of the clay and the humus.

Almost all laboratories report cation exchange capacity, and they do this in terms of milliequivalents, or ME. If it helps, you can think of an electrician measuring in terms of volts and amperes, or a physicist measuring magnetic energy in terms of ergs and joules. The soil laboratory has its own lexicon. It expresses colloidal energy in terms of milliequivalents of a total exchange capacity, since soil colloids—composed of clay and organic matter—are negatively charged particles. Negative attracts positive. Cation nutrients are attracted and held on the soil colloids. Since anions are not attracted by the negative soil colloids, they remain free to move in the soil solution or water.

ME represents the amount of colloidal energy needed to absorb and hold to the soil's colloid in the top seven inches of one acre of soil 400 pounds of calcium, or 240 pounds of magnesium, or 780 pounds of potassium, or simply 20 pounds of exchangeable hydrogen.

—*Charles Walters & C.J. Fenzau*
Eco-Farm: An Acres U.S.A. Primer *(1979)*

Let me illustrate the point. Potassium has a single + beside it, meaning a single positive charge. So do sodium and hydrogen. But calcium and magnesium exhibit a double plus charge, thus a ++. The latter are strong-arm elements. They have the capacity to push single-plus elements aside.

Hydrogen is at the bottom of the pecking order. Then come sodium, potassium, calcium, magnesium. The positively charged nutrients obtained from the use of lime and manures and fertilizers are called cations. Their positive charge is attracted to the colloid because it has a negative charge.

As mentioned, the clay colloid has a plate-like structure. This plate may be hexagonal, square, chunky or blocky, but it basically maintains a plate shape of some type. All of the cations are attracted accordingly. For every plus charge there is a negative, or minus charge.

That is great as long as we have enough open negatives for the single plus-charged elements like potassium, but when we start saturating a soil to achieve pH 7, not enough room will remain for weaker cations, and therefore additional nutrients with a single positive charge will not be easily positioned on the soil colloid. This is likely part of the reason why potassium will not be built up in clay soils when the pH is above 6.5.

Adsorbs is a term that needs to be added to every farming vocabulary, with special emphasis on the "ad." It means *held on the surface*, in this case on the surface of *the clay particle*. When a plant root releases its acids, an exchange between hydrogen and a cation nutrient takes place.

Sand has a low exchange capacity because it contains smaller amounts of clay and humus and holds less nutrients than other soil. Gumbo, on the other hand, has a high exchange capacity. A Florida sand used to grow leather leaf fern probably has a 3 or 4 exchange capacity. Some heavy clay soils have a 40 to 50 exchange capacity, or ten times more ability to hold nutrients. If you started out with nothing in either soil, it would take ten times more fertilizer to balance the high exchange capacity soil compared to the low capacity soil. That is why we have to measure the soil and mark the nutrient equilibrium, or lack thereof. High TEC soils therefore hold much larger amounts of fertilizer and moisture because they contain higher amounts of clay and humus.

In a Mississippi survey, 82% of all farmers questioned said that they thought soil tests should be taken on farms to determine how much fertilizer should be used. Only 28% of the sur-

Hands-On Agronomy

veyed farmers actually used soil tests. Many farmers it seems, do not really believe in using soil tests.

Until this book was first published, virtually all of my clients came to me by referral. Since most farmers and growers do not really trust soil tests, I cannot properly convince anyone of the value of soil testing in an hour or even in a day. If you start reading all the literature on soil tests, it might seem appropriate to ask, "Why should they?" At a meeting in Illinois, the head of the state Extension Service and I served on the same panel. One of the farmers asked if it was possible to use a soil test to determine the fertility of a soil. The head of Illinois Extension said, "No. You only use a soil test to determine roughly how much fertilizer to put on to feed the plant." When my turn came I explained, "I tell every farmer that from the analysis I do, I can sit down with him—not knowing what his soils have produced previously—and rate the samples from the best to the worst."

Farmers give various reasons why they do not trust soil tests. One fellow, in his early sixties, said he hadn't used soil tests for years, but in a sense he had. He said way back when the AAA program was in effect, and the government paid for the limestone, he had some very good pasture and some very poor pasture. He went out and took soil samples and he said, "You know what? I noticed the poor pastures needed two tons of lime and the good pastures also needed two tons of lime. One day I was digging post holes and got down to some old yellow clay, and I thought, "I wonder if I had soil like that how much it would need." The next time I sent in some soil samples, I reported that the yellow clay was from one of my pastures. It came back needing two tons of lime just like the rest of them. I decided, why should I walk all over these fields and take these soil samples to get the government to pay for the lime. From then on, I just kept a bucket of soil in my barn. When I thought I needed to put on lime, I put some of that soil in the sample bag and sent it in. They would tell me I needed two tons of lime."

I recall another farmer. His fertilizer dealer called me. He said, "We have a major problem in this area." This guy had overlimed his fields. He took a soil sample one year and sent it in to the university. They told him to put on two tons of limestone. He took a sample the next year and sent it in to the university. He didn't tell them that he had put lime on the year before. He thought that they ought to be able to pick that up, which is not the case. The recommendation came back, two tons of lime. He got so much lime on his fields he tied up the other nutrients, and his yields dropped. The fertilizer dealer said he took a soil sample from another client's land and split it up into three parts. He did this because he said, "Always, if a sample comes from the northwest part of the county it needs three tons of lime. If it comes from the northeast part of the county, it needs two tons of lime. If it comes from the south part of the county, it only needs one and a half tons of lime." He just wondered if it really made any difference. So he split up this one soil sample and reported that it came from each of the three areas. Each of the three came back with the lime recommendations as "needed" in the three different areas.

Several years ago, I went to see a possible client in Oklahoma. We walked over his ranch for a good half day, and he asked a lot of questions. He was a psychiatrist with a "ranch", actually. When we got back to his ranch house, he looked me straight in the eye and said, "Neal, you don't really believe that they run every one of those soil analyses like you are leading me to think? You don't really think they are meticulous about putting all those numbers down accurately, and that the report really reflects what is there?"

I said, "It is not a matter of believing it, I am certain of it."

He said, "Well, you will never convince me. I don't believe it." He then related the following story.

"When I was getting my doctorate in California, I got a job working for the university running the soil tests. At the beginning I was really meticulous. I would run those tests and did all the numbers just right. It would then go into the agronomist and he would make the recommendations, and I really didn't know what was going on. One time I told the agronomist that

Hands-On Agronomy

Reciprocal Relationship
of Soil, Plant and Animal

What is soil? Soil is basically fragmented rock ground down by the action of streams, by erosion from rain, by wind, by the mechanical breakdown from animal life, by the chemical action of growing elements within it, by the expansion and contraction of freezing and thawing, by the action of energy from the sun, by the trituration of rock by glaciers, by growing vegetation, by the action of bacteria and molds, by the acids and bases that are created by growing organisms, by the minute root systems that help to break it down, such as the micro-rhizomes that find their way into the smallest crevices of rocks to cleave them by the force of growing and dissolve the exposed surfaces by the chemical elements which they contain.

Good soil is teeming with fungi, bacteria, protozoa, earthworms, beetles, crustacea and larvae of insects, as well as reptiles, and even small animals. The root systems of our crops and their productivity are actually altered as the population within the soil changes. Man alters these by the addition of organic and inorganic elements, by governing the moisture, varying the temperature, and controlling radiant energy.

What does man remove from the soil? Man removes plants and animals and their products. He removes much of the plants, the animals and the excrements without returning them. These are considered of organic nature. Of what do they consist? Primarily they are proteins, fats, carbohydrates, minerals, and water. Plants and animals are produced from a living soil. Their return to the soil constitutes the completion of the ecological cycle. They are basically made from inorganic rock, the water of the ocean, the gas of the air, and the energy of the sun.

Some students of ecology argue that only the proper combination of the mineral elements need concern us, for water is obtainable, air is all about us, and radiant energy can even be produced artificially. Others hold staunchly to the theory that it is the return of organic elements to the soil that is all important to the production of the most beneficial crops for man's use. They further believe that true plant and animal health comes only with a large return to the soil of the organic wastes, manure, garbage, carcasses of animals, and the plants themselves that have been broken down into humus by the action of bacteria, molds, and the earthworms.

Though hydroponic solutions of water, inorganic elements, air and radiant energy, produce plants, they ask, "What is the effect of consuming such plants as food on the optimum development of animal life, not only for the present, but for the generations of future animals?

There are those who feel that there is the middle ground where soil not only needs the mineral element, but that activators from organic material returned to the soil enhance plant growth, either through making the mineral elements more readily available or also by actually being incorporated into the new plants. They recognize that the leaf is a great chemical factory for transforming water, mineral, organic materials from the soil, gasses from the air, and radiant energy from the sun into the nutrients for growth and reproduction of root, stem, flower, leaf, and seed.

The ecological cycle has always been variable. The plant and animal population, including man, has been physically modified as natural forces have altered environment. The simple factor of rainfall is continually changing. The rainfall may be gentle, evenly stretched over the so-called rainy season, or it may fall all at once in the space of a few hours leaving catastrophe to animal, plant, and soil. When rain comes as a deluge, the total precipitation for the year may be high, but because of the short space of time involved, the summation of the effects may be similar to those found in years of serious drought. There are years of cyclonic winds, sometimes accompanied by driving rains in a given area, altering the ecological pattern. In other years, not only may the rainfall vary but variable humidity may be experienced; or a dust storm may be tragic to one area where the soil surface is eroded, yet may be a blessing to another where the soil is deposited.

The effect of weather on the living elements in the basic soil of a given region may alter its water retention and fertility. In turn the pattern of vegetation may be completely changed, the wildlife pattern redistributed. The large animals may migrate. The lesser may die off in large numbers and those remaining become scrawny. It may be years before the former environmental factors return, if ever.

Man has been pointed to as the perpetrator of the greatest disasters to fertility and potential agricultural resources by ignoring the relation to each other of forests, soils, and the animals that dwell in them.

Marco Polo recounts the abundance of forests and animal life of China, but by modern times these have largely disappeared. Lack of conservation practices in the water sheds of the Tigris and Euphrates destroyed the fertility of the valleys and their civilization. In the desert areas of North Africa where shifting sands have swallowed the fertile fields of past civilizations, the adventurer finds the olive press and other evidence of human habitation in a vast sea of waste, again credited to the misunderstanding of total ecology by the men of that day.

Similarly, extensive areas of our own country have been transformed as the ecological pattern of soil, plant, animal, and human life have been altered.

Students of bionomics find today that the primordial life cycle from the soil to the plant, through the animal and back to the soil is frequently disrupted. Man fails to return to the soil much of his crops, his animals and excrements, thus breaking the natural cycle of life. So, in striving to maintain his economy, man must artificially return to the soil that which he removes.

—Francis M. Pottenger, Jr., M.D.
Missouri Agricultural Experiment Station's
Research Bulletin 765

I would like to take a look at the soil tests. I went in there and pulled out the soil tests and the recommendations. I noticed that if the farmer reported that he could grow 150 bushels of corn, the analysis didn't make any difference. If it was 150 bushels of corn, the amount of fertilizer was the same every time. He just took out of the textbook what it said for 150 bushel of corn." It didn't make any difference where the phosphate was or the potassium. He said, *We will feed the plant and we don't worry about the soil.*

The Oklahoma client concluded, "I thought to myself, 'Why do I need to worry about running soil analyses if they are not even going to be used." He said this incident came up in the springtime. Finals were coming and soils were pouring in. He knew basically what was going to happen from one area to another, and if anybody ever checked up on him, he knew they wouldn't do anything. He concluded, "According to the area, I just started writing down numbers. There were so many, I couldn't catch up and keep up with my studies. You know, it didn't change the fertilizer recommendations a bit."

Right in the area where we lived, there was a fellow who graduated from Purdue University. He wanted to have a soil test made. It didn't have anything to do with Purdue at the beginning, but in the end it did. Anyway, he wanted to have his soils tested, but he also went out and pulled samples and sent them to the University of Missouri. The soil test results came back from the University of Missouri. It revealed that the pH was something like 5.0 to 5.6. The results came back from our lab. The pH was around 6.5. He said, "Everywhere I look, I am a point to a point and a half lower on the university tests compared to the tests that you people do. How do I know which one is right?" So he sent samples to Purdue. When those levels agreed closely with our lab tests, he was satisfied.

University of Missouri uses salt pH tests. The tests we use are water pH tests. There is an important difference. The salt pH test will generally read a point to a point and a half lower, maybe sometimes a half point lower. Herbicide instructions call for a pH of such and such, but that is not for a salt pH test. It is for a water pH readout. So if your pH shows a 5.5 on a salt pH test and I show 6.5 on a water pH test, it could affect the herbicide program. If you are going to use herbicides, it is important to know which is which. In farm periodicals, they almost always fail to tell you which one is being used.

There are several different ways to run trace element tests. There are different extracting solutions. Even if the same extracting solution is used, and the same shaker from the same company to shake the solution is employed, if one laboratory shakes it fifteen minutes and another shakes it thirty minutes, the

The Importance of Calcium for Large Yields

To talk intelligently about soil fertility and crop yields, we must understand about soil and plant colloids and base exchange phenomena. Nutrient ions necessary for plant growth must be in solution so that they can be absorbed into the roots. Soil and plant colloids help to store these nutrients in the soil and in the plant. They make possible the base exchange phenomena, which make it possible to apply large quantities of lime and fertilizer to a soil, which can then hold it in readiness for the plant when it needs it.

When we apply limestone and mix it with the soil, we have a mixture which is only partially ready to support a good crop. Not until the calcium and magnesium in the limestone have disintegrated and become part of the colloidal complex in the soil through base exchange reactions does the growing crop benefit from the calcium and magnesium in the limestone. If limestone is applied to the soil and the ground remains dry, the limestone remains ineffective. If the limestone is too coarse, it may not be effective very rapidly.

—*V.A. Tiedjens*
More Food from Soil Science (*1965*)

results are going to be different. A higher concentration will result for the one that was succussed longer.

The laboratory that I use feels that you get a more accurate reading if you shake it longer. They don't cut down the time of shaking in order to get more samples processed. The question is, how do we get the most accurate readings, the ones most helpful to the farmer and the fertilizer dealer? The laboratory I use buys

Hands-On Agronomy

the more expensive extracts because it wants to do the best job. There's a lab close to where I live that runs three times more samples in an eight hour shift than the lab I use could run with three shifts a day. They supposedly measure all the same things. They just cut down on all the time involved.

I have clients who have been with me since the mid-1970s. I have seen a soil look great one year, and the next the bottom falls out. There seems to be no explanation. It doesn't fall out on every field. It's not the rain. It just happens. I don't know what the scientific explanation is. If I don't catch it, and there are crops that really benefit from calcium, the yield will suffer. Calcium is the one thing that I notice most of all, but there will be other nutrients—phosphates, for instance.

I met one farmer, now retired—still one of the most interested clients I have ever had—who decided to use our testing services. It was late in the spring when the samples went in. It got dry early that spring. He said, "Look, we need to start to work, and this field is the driest, and we can go ahead and get it ready for cotton. Would you use this test from this other lab and tell me what to do? I know you can't tell me that you know exactly what to do, but at least that is better than what I would otherwise do." That particular lab simply said he needed to apply two tons of limestone. Although Dr. Albrecht always cautioned, "Don't do it," we sat down and used the formulas. We went through and calculated out how much limestone was needed. According to the formulas from the numbers on his lab test, he needed high magnesium limestone. Magnesium deficiency is basically not a problem in most soils, but some of the lighter soils do need it if they have never had it. His had never had it. When our sample came back, it turned out that he didn't need high magnesium lime. He should have used high calcium lime. I did him a disservice. I can't use somebody else's numbers and know the right thing to do. I have to use the soil test I understand, and not one from another lab.

Now, why should anybody believe that my service is better than somebody else's? For one thing, I try to find out what is the next limiting factor, and then try to review the principles of physics and chemistry in order to answer the questions. I know that all of these things have an effect—sand, insects, disease, variety, drainage, placement, weeds—but increasing the soil's fertility does more to take care of problems with yield than anything else. It also helps to moderate some of these other factors.

The answers contained in what I call *The Albrecht System* are based on over 40 years of practical experience in the field. Not my 40 years, but 40 years that this system has been applied before I ever started.

A California company hired me to consult on 100 acres of lemons because they had problems with the trees. While I was on the job, the farmer said, "We have 35 acres of winegrapes and we would like you to do our grapes, as well." I told him that I had never worked with winegrapes before, but I could call and talk to a fellow who had worked with winegrapes on this program for a number of years. This was in the mid-1970s. The consultant told me, "You just go ahead and have them do the same thing they would do if they were growing a good crop of corn. That is the first step. After they have followed the recommendations, have them increase the potassium level as high as you can up to 7.5% saturation of the soil." Later on, we were at a conference together, and he told me how he had learned to work with grapes. "We treated those soils as if we were going to grow corn, and then raised the potassium levels. I learned that in France. I went to the managers of various vineyards and asked to take a soil sample from the very best area each had, and told them I would send each a copy of the test results at no charge. In every case it came back just the way Dr. Albrecht said it should be, except the potassium was on the high side." If we have no idea of how to grow a particular crop, there is always that first time, then we contact a consultant who uses the same soil tests and fertility program and has already worked with that crop.

There was 75,000 acres of rice in southeast Missouri in the mid-1970s. I met with a rice producer and sat down to tell him what to do. It was almost exactly opposite to what all the literature says should be done to raise rice. The literature at that time stated, "Don't put on lime if you are going to grow rice." The reason they give is that it may create a zinc problem or an iron problem. That is what happened to a lot of central Arkansas farmers when they started growing rice. They had borderline iron and zinc problems, and when they put on the calcium they tied up those elements, and it had been assumed that this happens everywhere. In the southeast Missouri area, certain farms have excellent zinc levels and tremendous iron levels, and under such circumstances you can put on all the required lime you need without tying up too much of either.

There were two brothers who grew some of the very best rice in our area. This is right at the northern edge of rice growing soils, and at that time a 140 bushel rice crop was almost unheard of, yet one of their fields consistently produced 140 bushels per acre. They also had other fields that didn't deliver a good crop. All I did was sit down and show them the differences. I started having rice growers put lime on their rice acres. As soon as the soil's calcium levels were corrected they started receiving premiums at the mill because of the crop's milling quality. Several reported a 50 cent premium per bushel.

A good soil test is dependent on a good soil sample. Sampling instructions are more than mandatory. They are bible text. I always insist on a composite sample from each area. And do not put more than 20 acres in a sample. On a twenty-acre field that is level, where the farmer says there is no difference, I will take 20 probes of soil and put it into one sample. The first time over, take one probe of soil for every acre. If it is a larger farm with 160 acre fields, I may—if it is level—fudge a bit and take one for every one and a half acres. Then I put those together, but no more than 20 probes, or 20 acres, to make one composite sample. If a farmer has an area he is concerned about, and it is big enough to fertilize separately, it should be sampled separately. Composite samples must be well mixed. If 20 probes are taken, a half-gallon or a gallon-sized zip-lock bag should be used to contain the soil. The probe with soil can be placed right in the bag. A hit with a large screwdriver will normally cause the soil to fall into the bag. Probes should go six to seven inches deep in any soil if it is being worked two inches deep or more. If the soil will not be worked at all, only take a four inch sample.

Avoid unusual areas for a soil sample. Don't sample where old bales of hay were split open for feeding. Don't sample in an eroded area. Stay away from old house sites. If a house burned down on an acre, stay away from that spot. The zinc content there usually will be four or five times higher than surrounding soil.

For soil sampling, divide the fields into areas. Draw a map that shows where the samples came from. Use proper sampling tools. You can take a sample with a trowel or a spade. First of all, be sure you get all the rust off by running it into the ground a few times. Just remember, you want to have uniform sized cores of soil. What I use is an old, low-priced T-probe with a cut-away side. That cut-away side is extremely beneficial because, when I pull the probe up, I can immediately start looking at that soil and see its profile. If I have a soil that is extremely hard, I put a pull pin through the top and use a three pound lead weighted polyurethane mallet to drive the probe into the soil.

Always number and record the samples. One big problem that occurs when people send in samples for analysis is that they don't pay enough attention to sample identification. Sometimes samples arrive that carry the exact same numbers or identification letters on them. On the other hand, I have farmers who send the worksheet that lists samples by number, what crop is going to be grown, what the crop was last year, what the yield was, and I always have some who will write, "My fertilizer dealer has these fertilizers available, and if I can, I would like to use them." I will not make that recommendation if there is something else that is better, without stating so.

If I know what a farmer is trying to accomplish, I can do a much better job for him. At least if I know what crop was there last year and what is to be grown this year that is a tremendous help. And in the case of tree crops, the age of the trees or the year

The Soil Audit

A soil audit requires a map.

Areas obviously labeled differently require special probes. Several rules rate consideration in effecting proper sampling.

1. After making a soil map, divide fields according to soil types and conditions, past fertilizer treatments, and take samples from each area large enough to permit separate management. Composite samples should not include more than 20 acres under most circumstances.

2. Avoid sampling unusual areas or spots such as old fence lines, dead furrows, eroded spots, fertilizer spill spots, field depressions. These areas will not be representative of the whole field. Such areas should be sampled separately if tests are desired.

3. Individual samples can be taken with a clean spade, a sampling tube (soil probe) or an auger. A soil probe will provide the most accurate composite since it tubes a uniform core of soil the full depth of the aerated topsoil. If a spade is used, be sure the sample is uniform in profile to represent the soil from the surface to the

depth being sampled. The proper depth should include the major feeder root zone for the crop being grown (the top 6 to 7 inches for most crops and soils). Subsoil samples and other special samples desired should be taken according to special needs.

4. Collect an adequate number of individual samples of uniform depth to represent each area and mix them thoroughly in a clean pail to make a composite sample for testing (or send the entire sample for testing).

5. Record sample locations on a map to help you or your consultant interpret the tests and make proper recommendations.

6. Package and label samples correctly to avoid breakage and mix-ups. Include adequate information such as name, field number, sample identity, depth of sample, date, crops being grown, etc., to insure complete and reliable results.

Field #1 Composite Sample A

> This diagram illustrates the points being made. One composite soil sample usually covers a five to ten acre area. Note how 12 probes were made in the section designated as 1-A. Certain obvious conditions made this area distinct. The soil seemed consistent. Its history required it to be treated as a unit—on and on. It is well to build a history of each field the way real estate companies build an abstract of real property.
>
> —*Charles Walters & C.J. Fenzau*
> Eco-Farm: An Acres U.S.A. Primer *(1979)*

planted is needed. When only general information is given, only general recommendations should be expected. The more specific the information for each soil tested, the more specific the recommendations can be.

If you pull your own samples, pack them tightly in a box, especially if you are going to send them via U.S. mail. Make sure they cannot move around to avoid spilling and unwanted mixing.

A number of people have asked me what I considered to be an ideal soil. I would respond, "There is no need for me to talk about an ideal soil because everybody has to work with what they have." But for a meeting a few years ago, I put together on paper my ideal soil. The exchange capacity would be 12. Remember, 12 is not the ideal exchange, but if I had to choose, it is a good level. An exchange of 12 would mean quite a bit of clay, a good nutrient holding capacity. Also, if there is a problem with a big deficiency, a farmer would not have to spend so much money to correct it. The pH would be 6.3. When everything is right in a soil, the pH is going to be between 6 and 6.5.

Fungi in the soil like more of an acid-type condition, so the further soil pH gets below 6, the more the fungi will operate. On the other hand, bacteria like a high pH, so the higher the pH gets, the more bacteria will function as a force. When the pH is between 6 and 6.5, the numbers denote an environment in which the bacteria can do well, and so can the fungi.

I believe the soil I have included here is one I would choose for good quality and yield. Others would do just as well though, if we work to balance what we have.

The humus content for this ideal soil would be at 5.1%. This would provide approximately 100 pounds of nitrogen release from organic matter over a growing season. Humus can actually hold nitrogen, sulfur and another important anion, boron, in a form that is available for growing plants. Clay will not hold any of these very well. Each of these elements will be discussed in greater detail in later chapters of this book.

To determine a soil's productive potential, start by determining the total exchange capacity. That is the first thing we need to know. Then, after we know the capacity of the soil to hold plant nutrients, there is another portion of the test that goes hand-in-hand—the base saturation percent. The reason it comes second is because you can never establish the base saturations unless you know the exchange capacity. Understanding base saturation teaches us that in each soil there is a specific percentage of nutrients that grows crops best, and that it is not the soil that receives the most pounds per acre that always delivers the best crop.

The longer a farmer works with this program, the more this will become plain. Anatomically, you use the pounds to get the percentages, and percentages tell how a soil is going to perform. Yield and quality are determined by the percentages, not the pounds. Thus our bottom line: base saturation percentage tells us what the soil is composed of in terms of cations—calcium, magnesium, potassium and sodium. It also tells us that the availability of these nutrients to plants generally increases with their percent saturation.

Magnesium and manganese are exceptions. A higher percent saturation of magnesium in a soil does not necessarily mean that this nutrient is more available. It is possible to get to the point where the percent of magnesium—as it goes up—actually makes less magnesium available to the plant. Here is the optimum percentage base saturation of cations generally for most soils. The cation calcium should be 60 to 70% of the saturation of the soil. In other words, 60% of the minerals attached to the colloids should be calcium. That is on a light, sandy soil. On a heavy clay soil, 70% would be optimum. The correct number for magnesium should be between 10 and 20%. On a heavy clay soil, it would be better at 10%. The ideal is for calcium and magnesium to total 80%. In a high clay soil, 70 + 10 = 80, and in a light sand, 60 + 20 = 80. Very light sands below 4.0 TEC have to have even more magnesium in order to spoon-feed the plant. Heavy clays do not need that higher magnesium percentage. In fact, it is a detriment.

There is another side to this story. The nutrient side is perhaps not the most important side. The other side is the effect that calcium-magnesium have on the physics of the soil. A heavy clay soil needs to have more calcium. A light, sandy soil needs to have more magnesium because magnesium tightens the soil and pulls it together. The higher the magnesium content in a clay soil, the stickier it will be when wet, and the harder it will be when it is dry. Sodium can cause hardness but magnesium is basically what gives stickiness to a soil. On the other hand, the higher the calcium, the looser it becomes even to a point—if you overlime your soil—you can actually account for so much space in a soil that needed moisture gets away. Increasing magnesium increases the amount of water held by that soil because magnesium attracts and holds extra water. The lighter the soil, the more important it is not to overlime and not to get too much calcium into that soil from whatever source.

Potassium should be at 3 to 5%. On grapes, cotton or woody-type plants, a better number would be around 7.0% to 7.5%. When you are at 7.5% potassium, the load will cut down on the available hydrogen in that soil. In short, there are tradeoffs. A soil with a deficiency is also a soil with too much of something else. We have to realize that if we build the potassium up to 7.5%, and we have 10% magnesium and 70% calcium, something else has to leave to make room. This will be the weakest link in the chain, namely hydrogen if the pH is below 7.0. Hydrogen should be between 10 and 15% of saturation. Hydrogen in this pH range gives a bit more acidity to the soil so that it will increase the availability of phosphate, potassium and other nutrients. These nutrients tend to tie up. With hydrogen, some acidity can be provided so the plants can better utilize them.

The other bases are 2 to 4%. We concentrate on these in the trace minerals tabulation rather than as a base saturation percentage. They are needed in minute amounts. No one I know has concentrated on them long enough to say, "We need this percentage of manganese, or this percentage of iron," and so forth.

The above inventory of figures (the base saturation percentages), then, tell a farmer how productive his soil is. If you have a heavy clay soil with 70% calcium and 10% magnesium, and the rest of the numbers fall in place, and you have a second soil with, say, 60% calcium and 20% magnesium, the 70 + 10 soil is going to outproduce the other one every time. If it is a heavy clay, the 70 + 10 equation has more of what contributes to the ideal situation for a clay soil—more calcium to keep it loose and less magnesium to hold it together, because clay soils are naturally tight. They have too little pore space. The problem in a clay soil is generally too much water occupying the available pore space. In a sandy soil, the problem is generally too much air. In soils with a TEC of less than 5.0, the 60% calcium and 20% magnesium saturations would be better. Thus we increase the magnesium in the sand in order to get the pore space out, and pull the particles together, and increase the calcium in a heavy clay to push the particles apart, causing them to aggregate in clumps in that soil.

True soil balance means determining and adding the proper amount of each nutrient. Fertility is the balance between elements. Not only is each element necessary individually, but a balance of all soil elements is necessary collectively. Every element works on every other one in an interdependent way. Adding too much of any nutrient means complexing some other nutrient needed for proper plant nutrition. Justus von Liebig is the fellow who gets credit for the concept of using N, P and K, meaning nitrogen, phosphate and potassium. He determined that there was a Law of the Minimum. He said that if you don't at least have this minimum, then your crop is going to suffer. That applies not just to N, P and K, but to all the other nutrients as well.

André Voisin, a member of de l'Academie d'Agriculture de France, distilled his years of research into the Law of the Maximum. This law states that if you put on too much of a given nutrient, it is going to tie up something else that is needed. He found that if you put on too much potassium, it ties up boron. If you put on too much phosphorus, it ties up zinc and possibly copper. If you put on too much nitrogen, it ties up copper and sometimes some of the other elements, even zinc. If you put on too much calcium, it could tie up all the other nutrients, depending on their level of availability.

Thus our lessons fall into place. When the pH is 7 or higher, the exchange of hydrogen will be zero. As you come down the scale from a pH 7, then hydrogen begins to increase in direct proportion (as long as a water pH test is used to measure the phenomenon). If pH goes from 7 to 6.9, exchangeable hydrogen will go up by 1.5%. If pH goes from 7 to 6.8, exchangeable hydrogen will go up by 3%. For every 0.1 that pH is dropped, exchangeable hydrogen from pH 7.0 downward will go up by 1.5% until you reach pH 6.0.

When micronutrients are present in the soil in adequate amounts, and the soil has the right base saturation percentages, then they are most available, but not necessarily in adequate amounts. At the right percentages of calcium and magnesium—if the micronutrients are in that soil—these are going to be present in their most available form. Still, there are a tremendous number of soils that can be balanced in terms of all major nutrients, and be missing micronutrients in bare minimum amounts. They are in the deficient category even after we have done everything we can to balance the soil. It is not correct to say *balance the soil,* and micronutrients will take care of themselves. Some soils simply do not contain adequate minimum amounts of micronutrients. But if they are already there and tied up by excesses, they will be released as the excesses are brought under control.

Cal-ci-um / 'kal-se-em / *n, often attrib* [NL, fr. L. *calc-, calx* lime] 1 a silver white bivalent metallic element of the alkaline earth group occurring only in combination 2 chemical symbol:

$$\boxed{\begin{array}{c} 20 \\ \textbf{Ca} \\ 40.08 \end{array}}$$

3 a plant nutrient that should occupy between 60 and 70% of the positions on the soil colloid in terms of the exchange capacity 4 at the proper saturation, improves soil texture, makes phosphorus and micronutrients more available, and improves the environment for microorganisms 5 helps plants form better root systems, stems and leaves for efficient use of sunlight energy, water, carbon dioxide, nitrogen and mineral nutrients 6 most important fertilizer element 7 essential for building normal bones and teeth, important in blood coagulation, and lactation; enables heart, nerves and muscles to function; regulates permeability of tissue cells

3
A Hands-On Approach

SOILS ARE PUT TOGETHER IN PLATES. Some soils are colloid or sub-angular. They have a prism shape or one best described as long triangular. In any case, it all boils down to plates, one sitting atop the other. The ideal soil in terms of a textbook example is 45% minerals, 5% humus, and 50% pore space, of which half is occupied by water and the other half by air. The question poses itself: how do we get the minerals to be 45 to 47%, and specifically how do we get the correct amount of air and water into soil if it does not already have it? The answer is less complicated than the question. In fact, when you get the mineral balance in its correct equilibrium, you will have achieved the right mix of air and water in the soil.

The chemistry of the minerals also affects the physical structure of a soil. Therefore, the only way to deal with the textbook mandate is to first correct the minerals. If the mineral component is imbalanced, it is never possible to achieve and correctly maintain the right amount of air and water. The mineral component, in turn, depends on base saturation percentages and the soil's humus level. This complex determines how much air and water space a soil will permit. When a soil audit reveals a correct mineral balance and at least a minimal humus content, any air and water problem will be minimized.

Obviously, poor soil structure means too little space in the soil. Heavy equipment compacts the soil by restricting the amount of space between soil particles. Either air or water has to give way. To construct the proper environment for plant roots and soil microorganisms, minerals in the right amount in effect govern the physical structure. Good soil structure which has 25% air, 25% water and 50% minerals and humus, in essence is based on mineral building blocks.

There are several ways to influence soil structure favorably. One of those ways is to use manures, composts, mulches, biological stimulants, or anything that encourages microbial activity in a soil and/or supplies their needs for survival. Deep tillage—rippers, plows, chisels—all can create a temporary effect by breaking up hardpan and plowpan barriers, but this physical approach should not be seriously considered as a long-term solution without first correcting key nutrient levels. A third way is to use deep-rooted plants such as sweet clover or alfalfa. It is also possible to use a soil conditioner as described in chapter 4. And finally, soil structure can be influenced by proper fertilization of the soil, namely supplying nutrients in the right amount as determined by soil tests.

Our objective is to remove compaction so that roots can not only grow in the topsoil, but also penetrate subsoil layers as deep as required to pick up water and any available nutrients. In a non-productive soil, roots simply cannot get through any of several barriers. The best ripper in the world will not cause hardpans to melt away unless a correct mineral balance has been constructed first. A proper mineral balance, therefore, is the precursor to lasting success, whatever the hands-on approach.

The Organic School

A controversy of much interest is the attack on commercial or chemical fertilizer by the proponents of organic fertilizers. "Fertilizer kills the earthworms, it sours the soil, it burns out humus," the organic school keeps repeating. Such statements have mighty little to back them up. The USDA Beltsville Experiment Station reports, "Earthworms thrive and do a better job of soil building on well-fertilized land—more benefit is obtained from fertilizer when earthworms are present."

There is some question, however, whether our researchers are ever going to be able to set up comparative tests. There is the problem of the difference in rate in which the fertilizer elements become available from chemical fertilizer and organic fertilizer. The nitrogen and phosphorus may be released very slowly from the compost. This will result in differences in the growth and maturity of the plants at any particular time. The vitamin content may as a consequence be different whether the plants are harvested the same day or at the same stage of maturity on different days. Comparisons of this kind, therefore, become useless to the scientific investigator.

Yet we all know that we need vast quantities of organic material in the soil. Organic material is the crux of the whole soil building program. Ample supply gives us a soil in which roots can find food. It means a favorable environment for the molds, fungi, bacteria and earthworms. All these play an important, if poorly understood, role in connection with our own health.

As Roger Bray of the University of Illinois has put it:

For an ideal soil, humus would be a big key. Also, humus is
the big key to water holding capacity as well as fertilizer holding
capacity in terms of the amount that is in the soil. But to help
illustrate the value of humus, the soil's capacity for water retention is proportionally relative to the humus content. Soils with
relatively high amounts of humate material show better resistance to droughts and produce better yields where rainfall or
irrigation may be lacking. A soil with a good humus content, say
4 to 5%, can hold more than double the amount of moisture the
1.5 to 2% humus soil can hold. We live with a 0.5 to 1.5 inch
rainfall reservoir in our area because most of our soils are below
2.5% humus. Below 2.5% humus, nutrient elements leach out
because it is easier to lose nutrients from a soil with low humus.
Also, microbiologists point out that a soil with 2.5% or less
humus keeps microbes on a starvation diet.

Most people think they would like to have high humus in the
soil, but Albrecht's work in this area revealed that even humus
cannot completely annihilate all the problems. With soils that
are high in humus always expect copper deficiency problems.
Peat and muck-type soils generally mean production problems
because of copper deficiency.

The term *humus* is not used on most soil audits, but there is
the designation, *organic matter percent. Humus* and *organic matter* are often used interchangeably. Humus is made up of decom-

posed residues which have been completely broken down in the soil by microorganisms. The *organic matter* or *humus* terms notwithstanding, when talking about a long-term reservoir for nitrogen, phosphorous, sulfur, boron and zinc, I am not talking about undecomposed residues. This is referring to the humus (that is, completely decomposed organic residues)—without it, the reservoir function wouldn't happen.

Why does humus hold nitrogen, phosphorus, sulfur and boron while clay does not? Because humus is "stronger" than clay. If you could take a handful of clay in one hand and a handful of humus in the other hand, and measure the nutrients, humus has three times the nutrient holding ability of the clay.

Organic matter contributes to soil productivity in many ways. It improves the physical structure of the soil. It increases water infiltration. It improves tilth, decreases erosion, and supplies plant nutrients.

Now let's compare the beneficial properties of soil humus.

It releases needed nutrients to the plant. It releases the nutrients slowly out of the humus over a growing season, cafeteria style. We can speed that up or we can slow it down. The speed up is geared to overuse of nitrogen, basically.

Humus improves the physical properties of soil. It helps hold water better. It certainly adds to the tilth and friability of soil.

Next, it aids in micronutrient nutrition of plants through chelation reactions. It encourages microorganisms in the soil because it serves as a good source of food for microbes.

Humus aids in solubilization of plant nutrients from insoluble minerals. This means that it helps break down fertilizers that are on-scene in the wrong form and tied up or complexed.

True humus has high absorption or exchange capacity for plant nutrient elements. That is one of the reasons humus has three times the nutrient holding ability of clay. It can grab and hold the nutrients right on the outside, *adsorb* them, if you will. Albrecht made a classical study of the holding capacity of humus. He and his associates isolated humus and subjected it to the strongest acids in order to knock loose the nitrogen. Nothing worked. But a sufficient amount of the exudates from plant roots did the job. Plant roots could unhinge the nitrogen easily. Microbes and plant roots can, we can't!

Humus increases a soil's buffering capacity. Farmers who have a high humus content in the soil can make more mistakes without paying for them immediately. Maybe the grandchildren or great-grandchildren will pick up the costs, but for the moment humus permits mistakes. I have clients in northeast Iowa who have 7 and 7.5% organic matter in their soils. Some soils around Ames have 5% organic matter. The buffering capacity of such soils is tremendous. The term *buffer capacity* requires explanation. Excessive nitrogen applied to a light sandy soil will ruin that soil system rapidly. The same application can be made to high humus soil and it still might last for years. *Buffer* means that you can make a lot more mistakes without seeing ill effects immediately. Buffer capacity is also an index for water holding capacity. The farmer who has to work with small amounts of water gets into trouble faster if he does not have the needed buffering capacity.

The dark color of humus favors heat absorption and permits early spring planting. A dark color also permits the soil to dry out faster for more timely field entry.

Also, certain components in humus may exert plant growth-promoting effects.

Humus supports a greater and more varied microbial population favorable to biological control, but it also favors a microbiological contribution to fertility.

Humus reduces toxicity of certain substances, both natural and man-made. To illustrate the point, let's look at zinc excess and copper excess in Florida citrus groves. These are the old groves that have levels capable of "killing" 50 year old grapefruit trees. Often they have double that level in soils still used to grow trees. Over the years they have also supplied the other nutrients as indicated by balance. The real stock answer to combat toxicity has been to increase the organic matter in the soil. Florida growers do not like the term *manure*. Many of them refer to spreading "used cow and chicken feed" as simply spreading *organic*.

Humus increases the soil's water holding capacity. Humus can be built by increasing the efficiency of microbial decomposition of plant residues. And it can be destroyed by working soils that are too wet.

I had a client, now retired, with the prime goal of building up the humus content of his soils. He grew only legumes. He used materials to stimulate microbial activity. Everything possible was done to encourage microbes, even following proper tillage practices. He farmed heavy gumbo soils. One year—after he had been working on this program for three or four years—conditions stayed wet and wet and wet. The very day he could get a disc from one side of the field to the other without it balling up too much, he started working the soil. In his case, I pulled soil samples in the late summer. Accordingly, I pulled the samples in late August. This farmer started out on a 210-acre farm that had 2 to 2.5% humus content. In a matter of three or four years, he built his level up to 4%, with some acres a little above that figure. It looked good for a couple of years. Now suddenly he was back to 2.5% humus again. Then, as I started looking at the soils, the humus percentages kept climbing until finally about half the acreage still had 4%, as it had before. Finally the picture emerged. I called the client and asked whether he started to work the fields beginning with the one that was driest first. He said, "Yes," and then I named another field and he said, "Yes," he'd worked that one next. Then I named another field. I could name the fields and the sequence in which he worked them. The first one lost humus back to the starting point. By the time I got to the ones in the middle, it became evident that it didn't rain after he started working those fields until he got the entire farm planted. By the time he got half the fields worked, all the land had dried out to the point where he wasn't working his soils any wetter than he had before. Where he worked the soils wet, on the field that was the driest, yet still so wet it should not have been worked, he lost all the humus he had built up in three or four years.

A lot of the old timers still say, "If you work a clay soil wet, it will take a year to get it straightened out." The why and wherefore is not difficult to understand. Working wet soils annihilates air and water spaces. Removal of the air space destroys the environment that microbes need. Without air, the aerobes cannot break down residues in the proper way.

There is a set way to achieve this transformation if humus is to be built. Basically, you need a carbon to nitrogen ratio of 10.4 to 1 in order to build humus. The finished product should be above 10 to 1. Most corn, soybean and crop stover computes to 60+ parts carbon to 1 part nitrogen. If there is not enough air to permit microbes to increase and multiply, the quality and quantity of humus simply evaporates. Unfortunately, there are years in which a 2,000 or 3,000 acre farmer may have to work some fields wet, or he is not going to get his crops planted. But in agriculture, proper tillage practices—as well as proper nutrient balance—is required if top results are to be achieved.

Withal, farming does not lend itself to single factor analysis. Growers who worship at the altar of pH need to understand that good pH does not guarantee a balanced soil. Many Illinois farmers I know say they want a pH 7 on the Albrecht system. The reason is that a pH 7 on the water pH test Albrecht used gives an assurance that the calcium level is at or near the correct level for them, though magnesium is still too high. There are some exceptions where sodium is also a problem. If you take some cornbelt soils of Illinois, at pH 7, no calcium deficiency will show. It just so happens that the closer the Illinois farmer aligns his operation to pH 7, the better his crops. But farmers relying on a salt pH test must know that this higher reading translates closer to pH 6. Some growers say they don't want pH 7 or even pH 6, but pH 6.5. No matter what the pH readings are supposed to be, does a good pH assure a balanced soil?

The answer is "No." The soil pH is influenced by four major cations. Calcium influences pH, as do magnesium, potassium and sodium. Extremely high sodium will cause an extremely high pH. Potassium can also influence pH even more than calcium and magnesium.

Hands-On Agronomy

As the boxed material on page 70 clearly points out, magnesium, pound for pound, can raise pH up to 1.67 times as high as calcium. A soil high in magnesium and low in calcium can test above 6.5 and still contain an entirely inadequate amount of calcium to properly grow alfalfa. Of prime importance are calcium and sodium—sodium, because it must be buffered or removed, calcium, because most of the time it has to be supplied. It is an Albrecht axiom that once all the nutrients required are supplied, the pH will be right.

Many farmers have seen the information given on pH from The Fertilizer Institute. It depicts *desirable* pH ranges for some few crops, the term *desirable* being somewhat incorrect. It really should be *tolerable*. Blueberries are shown to tolerate a pH between 5 and 6, but the best blueberries grow in the 6 to 6.5 pH range, provided all the required nutrients are present in the proper amount, and the water pH test is used, as measured by the Albrecht model of testing.

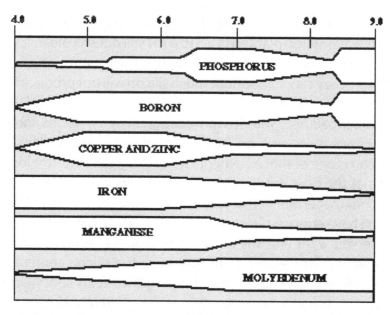

Soil pH affects nutrient availability.

Back in 1979, I was hired to go to Pennsylvania to see two brothers who were operating a pick-your-own truck farm and nursery and greenhouse. They asked me to evaluate their soils, using the soil tests, starting with the best to the worst soils. The very best soil was right in line. One of the brothers said, "How would that soil do growing blueberries?" I said, "Well, I have never worked with blueberries, but my experience suggests that blueberries ought to do better on this soil than on any other soil you have in spite of the fact experts will tell you that you have too much calcium, and that blueberries do not like calcium."

He said he wanted to show me something. So he pulled out a soil sample from a major state university and a letter that said, don't plant blueberries on this soil because the calcium is too high and they will die. He said, "Now what do you say?"

I repeated the same thing I had already told him.

The farmer went on to explain, "By the time we pulled our samples and got them back, the blueberry plants had arrived and we decided to plant them on the very spot I asked you about. They turned out to be the best blueberries in the area, certainly the best blueberries we had ever grown. Not only were they the most productive, they were also the largest and sweetest."

A watermelon planted in a 5 to 6 pH soil doesn't mean it will grow well, regardless of whether agricultural institutions say it will. A heavy clay soil without much silicon will not produce the best watermelon crop. On the other hand, a heavy clay soil that has been balanced will often produce great watermelons, some-times not. It depends on the amount of silicon in that clay soil. Silicon is one of those elements we call *way out*. Watermelon is one of the best nutritional sources of silicon. It concentrates silicon. That is one of the reasons it does so well in sand. If you don't have enough silicon in a clay soil, you can have all the balance you want and still not get the crop tonnage. There is a problem with this. We do not measure the silicon content of soils. When someone asks me if he can grow an excellent yield of watermelons in a clay soil, my answer is, "If you balance it out and there is enough silicon."

Hands-On Agronomy

Silica*

It is a proven fact that silica plays an important fertilizing role in the plant kingdom. Tests have shown an improvement in cultivation following the addition of silicates. Silica also functions as a vital element in protecting plants against mold penetration, and it has been found to influence the use of other ingredients useful to plant metabolism. A rich supply of natural organic silicates can be found in *Equisetum arvense*, the source of vegetal silica.

Better known as horsetail, spring horsetail, or scouring rush, this perennial grows wild in all temperature zones of our planet. It belongs to a small group of plants known as pteridophyta, which is distinguished as nonflowering and non-seed-bearing. Horsetail thrives on clay-like sandy soils. It occurs mainly in marsh lands but can be found in woods and forests, moist fields, meadows and along the sandy shores of creeks and streamlets. Some varieties have adapted to other environments, living along roadside and stony ground. Horsetail has such an awe-inspiring history that a short trip into the distant past is fitting.

Silica deficiency may exist if your diet consists of too many refined foods. Silica is abundant in the shell of brown rice, in leafy greens and bell peppers. When food is processed, silica is unfortunately removed. Fiber is usually the first to be cut or washed away, and along with the fiber, the silica. Stripped

14
Si
28.0855

Silicon

*silica = silicon dioxide, SiO_2

cereals and other processed foods have decreased silica supplies. This massive loss of natural silica has been paralleled by an increase in degenerative diseases.

—*Klaus Kaufmann,* Silica *(1990)*

Unfortunately, silicon is something we do not know how to measure properly. Sand basically contains more silica than does clay.

The very best alfalfas do not have to be in soils above pH 6.5, although pH on the high side will create an environment that alfalfa can stand, more so than the other way. The alfalfa crop thrives on soils favoring bacteria. Bacteria work best in the top few inches of soil. Withal, microbial life can cover over some of the problems that are created otherwise. A good environment for microbial life often depends on manures or humates or biological stimulants to supply many of the things we do not know how to measure.

Crops and plant species each have a story to tell, if we have the wit to learn. Take the rhododendron, for instance. The rhododendron and azalea both have a reputation for requiring acid soils. Yet, the very best rhododendron and azaleas do not grow on acid soil. But they do grow on a well-balanced soil. It is true they can endure acid soils and still grow, albeit not with the same quality. If one nutrient is out of kilter, the rhododendron will have trouble. A rhododendron can stand a low pH soil and high magnesium. It can *endure* low calcium and high magnesium.

The sensitive nature of balance can be illustrated with reference to one of my clients in Nevada, where boron is often a problem. Boron above 2 ppm is excessive, yet he encountered boron at 20 ppm. There are plants that will grow with boron at above 20 ppm, but not golf course grass, which is what my client wanted. There is a multiplier in dealing with soil pH that is best expressed in logarithmic terms. If you have pH 7, it is neutral. If you have pH 6, it is ten times more acid. Going down to pH 5, acidity is one hundred times greater.

Plant removal of basic cations such as calcium and magnesium on an annual basis hardly has any effect on pH because so few pounds are removed in relation to the amount in the soil. A 150-bushel corn crop takes roughly 28 pounds of calcium and 28 pounds of magnesium. The lightest, sandiest soil often will have 800 to 1,000 pounds of calcium in it. It would take years and years for crop removal of these nutrients to cause acidity. The chief culprit is leaching or tying up of basic cations by rainfall or irrigation water. Materials in irrigation water, especially nitrates and bicarbonates, can tie up available calcium and thus can affect the uptake of other plant nutrients. But these are not the only considerations to be made on the subject of depleting soil calcium. We have to consider nitrogen fixation by bacteria on legume roots. If nitrogen is not securely held as water moves through, it takes some of that nitrogen and carries it away. Ammonia may take sodium, but will otherwise cause calcium to leach away, and so will any type of nitrogen that converts and moves as nitric acid through that soil. By the time nitrogen has traveled through the soil, it has been changed chemically to nitrate. Nitrogen takes either sodium or calcium as a passenger on its trip to the sea. However, as it leaches from the soil, nitrogen will not reduce the magnesium held on the soil colloid.

Bacterial conversion of nitrogen compounds in the soil—whether from manure or compost, from commercial nitrogen, whatever—is the key to lowering soil pH. As the nitrate nitrogen moves through the soil, much of it converts to nitric acid, which then leaches available soil calcium. That is why overuse of nitrogen reduces calcium, especially when soils have not been balanced to the proper saturations of nutrients and maintained in that particular soil.

In short, imbalance can create other imbalances. The weakest link in the chain is going to affect the yield. In many soils the weak link is not nitrogen, phosphate, potash, not even calcium. I have had clients whose soil tests show they do not need calcium. They used at least as much phosphate and potash, and

The Secret Life of pH Management

The pH of a soil is affected and influenced by four elements: calcium, magnesium, potash and sodium. How much of each is present in a soil must be known before an appropriate lime and fertilizer program can be designed.

Magnesium, pound for pound, can raise the pH up to 1.67 times as high as calcium. A soil high in magnesium and low in calcium can test above 6.5, but will be entirely inadequate for the growth of alfalfa or the growth of legume bacteria, and above all for maintenance of an environment necessary to decay organic crop residues into humus.

It is more essential to manage the factors that construct the soil pH as determined by present soil tests than it is to be concerned with the calculated amounts of nitrogen, potassium & phosphorus. Why?

• The conversion and availability of mineral elements are related to and regulated by the system of decay in the soil. The proper decay processes are initiated and determined by usually full levels of calcium and reasonable levels of magnesium.

• A balanced equilibrium of calcium and magnesium creates a soil environment for bacteria and fungus activity for the proper decay of organic residues into CO_2, carbonic acid and a host of many weak and mild organic acids, all necessary to convert and release mineral elements in the soil system.

• An imbalanced equilibrium of calcium and magnesium permits organic residues to decay into alcohol, a sterilant to bacteria; and into formaldehyde, a preservative of cell tissue. The symptoms of this improper decay system can be observed when previous year's stalks are plowed back up just as shiny and fresh as they were when turned down.

• Under these circumstances larger and increasing amounts of nitrogen and fertilizer minerals will be required just to maintain normal crop yields. The soil system is not complementary to release the minerals or the other soil essentials for optimum growth.

• And remember also that large applications of nitrogen consume larger amounts of calcium as well as "burn-up" crop residues and humus. You can get increased yields for a few years from this stored-up wealth of humus, but eventually you will have to account for this withdrawal.

• Without an active organic matter system in the soil you cannot grow any crop at all, no matter how much nitrogen, potassium and phosphorus you add. The soil is a living, complex system that not only holds the 12 necessary minerals needed for plant life, but also is the factory that produces carbon dioxide, digests lignin into humus, provides nutrition and energy for desirable bacterial and soil animal life, and is the container for both water and air. Can you germinate and grow a plant in subsoil material without humus action present?

• In the absence of a system of organic matter management and calcium it will soon be essential to consider buying dry-ice (as a source of CO_2) and propane gas (as a source of additional carbon). Both are sad excuses for our ignorance and mismanagement of calcium and magnesium and at the same time a dear price to be paid for our continued disregard of this important and vital soil equilibrium.

• A soil program with managed levels of calcium and magnesium will allow the nature of the soil to function complementarily to the process of life and in many cases actually diminish or even eliminate the causes of many problems we can't explain or do much about ourselves. Some of these benefits and affects are:

1. More efficient photosynthesis.

2. Maximum use of heat-degree days—a natural time clock of the life systems of plants.

3. Create and maintain root and stem capacities for optimum use of sunlight energy and thermal efficiency by the leaves of the plant.

4. Thereby the plants can use water, CO_2, nitrogen and mineral nutrients with greater efficiency.

5. A healthy and normal functioning plant can maintain an adequate hormone and enzyme system so vital to resistance to insect and disease hazards.

6. A balanced soil equilibrium will regulate and manage the quality and availability of all mineral elements needed by growing plants.

7. Excesses of minerals during the early growth stages often plug up the vessels of the stem and are the frequent cause of early death. A dead plant system cannot mature or ripen itself.

8. An excess of magnesium as well as nitrogen in the soil initiates the processes which prevent the crop from growing dry and nutritionally ripe which is a major goal of every farmer.

9. Carbon dioxide availability is more important to high-yield potentials than nitrogen or any mineral element. The supply in the atmosphere could sustain life for not much more than 30 days, and depends on the soil decay system to replenish its supply. Without the

beneficial effects of calcium in the soil system and its effect on soil structure and tilth, the processes are retarded and inefficient.

10. Clay soils high in magnesium and low in calcium cement together tightly, are subject to compaction and clodding, crust over easily and prevent the insoak of water and the recovery of capillary water during the dry periods of the season.

11. Soils in such poor tilth and structure increase the effects of the many weather hazards that annually impair normal plant growth. With a managed calcium-magnesium equilibrium we would not have to lean on the many poor excuses of weather we use every year to explain away our ignorance and personal mistakes. We cannot do much about the weather, but we can use the experiences of our mistakes to create a more integrated soil management system that would tend to diminish or even eliminate the many variable hazards of the weather.

—*C.J. Fenzau*
"The Management of Calcium for a Wholesome Soil and Crop System," Acres U.S.A., *November 1971*

invariably they were using too much nitrogen. But sulfur and micronutrients were limiting the yield. Four different clients in southeast Missouri raised their corn yield in three years by 30 to 40 bushels per acre when they started using sulfur and micronutrients. That's the only change they made. When the soil test showed certain fertilizers they could cut back on to save money, they spent it on micronutrients. Yet micronutrients only make a difference when everything else has been corrected. If there is a magnesium excess, loading on micronutrients will not help. Magnesium deficiency is also a limiting factor. So are deficiencies of calcium, nitrogen, phosphate, sulfate and potassium.

I began working with some 75 farmers in eastern Iowa. If you took the calcium/magnesium relationship in their soils—and they would provide how many bushels of corn they grew over the last four or five years—I could closely calculate how many pounds of nitrogen they used. Actually, I prefer that they tell me how much nitrogen they use. Then use that to compute the average corn yield. However, if something is way out of line, this computation isn't possible. Iowa cornbelt soils generally are in tolerable shape to start with. Yet almost all have a calcium shortage, too much magnesium, not enough sulfur and not enough boron.

In any long-range program, calcium comes first. This is not to say that calcium takes precedence over N, P, K & S for growing this year's crop. Primary elements always come first where needed for growing the immediate crop. But for the efficiency of overall nutrient uptake, calcium has to be in that soil in adequate amounts. Its status has to be determined via laboratory test because calcium deficiency seldom shows up visually in the field. Secondary effects—such as high soil acidity—usually limit growth first. High soil acidity makes it possible to experience manganese, aluminum and iron toxicity. Academically, the reason calcium deficiency seldom comes up is that usually there are hundreds and even thousands of pounds in the soil, and it is not likely that more than 50-100 pounds will be used by most crops in any one year. This goes back to the concept of feeding the plant instead of feeding the soil. And again it is a very costly mistake.

FREQUENCY OF LIMING
DEPENDS ON:

- Soil texture.
- Nitrogen fertilization rates.
- Calcium and magnesium crop removal.
- Amount of lime applied.
- Soil pH range desired.

Hands-On Agronomy

Calcium is essential. If not enough is available, it means that there won't be the right amount of air and water, and there won't be the efficiency needed to get other nutrients into the plant. In saying that 60 to 70% saturation of calcium is required, I am not talking about the whole soil. The saturation referred to here is actually in the clay colloid and soil water. At 60 to 70% calcium around the plant root hairs, microbes do well, and the exchange of elements also works well. In the absence of calcium, more potassium ions are required around root hairs to get the same amount of that nutrient into the plant. It also takes more nitrogen around those same root hairs to affect uptake into the plant. As the calcium concentration is increased, so is efficiency in getting other nutrients into the root. This means less nitrogen to do the same job, and less phosphorous and less potassium. Conversely, the lower the calcium in the soil, the more nitrogen etc., is required to get the same crop yield.

Every other nutrient has to ride over the back of calcium to get into the plant. Calcium puts the starch into the leaf. Calcium activates several enzyme systems. It increases yield by reducing soil acidity. Its use as a fertility agent increases calcium availability. Moreover, calcium improves microbial activity. I always look at calcium first for long-term nutrient efficiency because calcium helps increase the uptake of every other fertilizer nutrient.

ADVANTAGES
FROM LIMING ACID SOILS:

- Lowers toxic levels of aluminum and manganese.
- Increases some microbial activity-decomposition.
- Overcomes the potential for calcium or magnesium deficiencies.
- Increases symbiotic nitrogen fixation in legumes.
- Increases availability of phosphorus and molybdenum.

Common sources of calcium are calcitic limestone, which has 31.7% calcium, and dolomitic limestone which has magnesium as well! 215 to 225 pounds of magnesium and 425 to 450 pounds of calcium per ton will usually be the analysis for the top dolomitic limestone.

Gypsum is a source of calcium, but it should be used only when there is a need for calcium and the calcium saturation is above 60% in that soil. Marl rock rates consideration in some areas. On the east coast they use a material called aragonite, literally marine deposits ground up in the islands. It is high in calcium. There is also hydrated lime and burnt lime which should be used with caution.

Basically, when lime is mentioned, unless otherwise specified it will be referring to calcium or dolomitic limestone, and gypsum. Hydrated lime or burnt lime may be useful in large amounts if the soil is barren. Frequency of liming depends on soil texture and nitrogen fertilization rates because nitrogen drives out calcium. Nitrogen may drive out some sodium, but overall, it will take out calcium. Frequency of liming is hardly influenced by the removal of calcium by the crop, but the frequency of liming does depend heavily on the amount applied. Frequency of liming also depends on the soil pH range desired. But you will recall that when the nutrients are right, the pH will be right.

There are some advantages to liming acid soils. The process lowers toxic levels of aluminum and manganese. It also governs iron release. However, in certain soils too much can lower the level of iron and cause iron chlorosis. In addition, lime increases microbial activity, manages decomposition and overcomes the potential for calcium or magnesium deficiencies. Lime helps increase symbiotic nitrogen fixation in legumes and it increases availability of phosphorus.

To determine availability, we must analyze limestone for its calcium and magnesium content, and the fineness of grind. Nutrient and particle size analysis is necessary, particularly the latter, because the finer the particles, the more available the calcium. For what is termed agricultural limestone, on an eight-mesh screen 100% goes through. But only 90% may go through a 20-mesh screen, and 60% through a 60-mesh screen. Yet to be precise, we need one more screen size. I tell farmers that if 60% will go through a 100-mesh screen, there is no need to worry. The grind will be fine enough to receive full benefit of the calcium and magnesium that lime contains.

For limestone of that fineness applied in the fall, a third of the calcium will become available the first year, another third the second year, and another third the third year provided there is enough moisture. This suggests full utilization on irrigated acres. Without enough moisture, it may take four years to see the full effect, rather than three. Lime reacts in one to three years when the particle size allows at least 60% to pass through a 100-mesh screen. What passes through an eight-mesh screen, provides only about 10% breakdown over the same three years. From a 20-mesh screen size, there is a little over 40% breakdown, and from a 60-mesh screen size, about 75% breakdown. But if 60 to 100% of it goes through a 100-mesh screen, this means nearly 100% availability over three years.

Basically, limestone is calcium carbonate or a mixture of calcium carbonate and magnesium carbonate. Most areas require calcium carbonate. Other areas, especially sands, may require a calcium-magnesium carbonate or dolomitic limestone. Water treatment plants that take their water from the river use calcium carbonate for filtration. Often they just dispose of it afterwards. Power generating plants that burn high sulfur coal also use calcium carbonate. The by-product from either one is often useful for crop acres. Sugar beet refineries use calcium carbonate to filter beet juices, the calcium becoming a waste product. If the analysis shows to be adequate, it works fine as a liming material. We have successfully used all of these sources in one area or another to supply calcium.

Calcium carbonate pH can run as high as pH 8.2 to 8.4. The small amount used in relation to the soil mass will not create an adverse effect, however. Calcium actually controls or reduces a part of the soil magnesium, and magnesium causes pH to be higher than calcium. Some few short range pH problems can result, but basically limestone application to answer a calcium requirement and to buffer excessive magnesium will generally result—within three years—in the pH going down, not up.

Molybdenum will remain available at a pH close to 7 because of the effects pH has on that element. For the most part, pH 6.5 will keep phosphorous available. A pH 7 or below—all the way down to 5—will keep boron available if there is any in the soil. As the increase toward pH 6 comes into view, the amount of copper and zinc available is decreased. At pH 6.5 the caution flag goes up for each of the above named nutrients.

Iron availability starts to decrease between pH 6 and 7, meaning trouble if there is barely enough iron. As the calcium is raised, the iron level decreases. Manganese, on the other hand, gets to about 6.5 before it starts to decrease. Therefore soil pH does affect nutrient availability. This is one of the reasons that a number of crops thrive at low pH levels. Blueberries thrive at low pH levels because this acidity means plenty of iron and manganese. Alfalfa thrives at a high pH because it tends to receive plenty of phosphorous and molybdenum in the higher ranges. But alfalfa has a problem without boron. At pH 7, boron availability starts to drop off, and most soils don't have enough boron to begin with.

All things considered, calcium carbonate should provide a 100% neutralizing value. But using the Albrecht system we rarely look at *neutralizing value*. We look at how to add calcium. Dolomitic lime, calcitic lime, finely ground oyster shells, burned oyster shells, basic slag, gypsum—all those products have calcium in them. Gypsum, meaning calcium sulfate, does not neutralize the soil. The pH will not initially be adjusted by gypsum because the sulfur and calcium content offset each other.

You should determine the advantages of liming and how much lime should be used by measuring the amount of clay and humus in the soil. The Albrecht system uses the CEC to determine limestone needs. Such is not determined on the basis of pH. Even at a classical pH of 6.5 to 7.0, it is still possible to need calcium, and if that calcium is not supplied, crops are going to suffer needlessly.

I had a client near Fallbrook, California, with pH 8.2. He still needed calcium, and put the calcium on his soil, a ton of gypsum and a ton of calcitic lime. He was growing for Sunkist, and they had told him at last report that he had the best fruit of any grower in the valley. His pH went from 8.2 to 8.4, after applying the lime he needed. This caused no problem because his other nutrient levels were adequate. I never look at pH to determine when to lime or what kind of lime to use. Just look at the deficiencies in the soil as determined by the soil test results. The pH will adjust to the proper level when all nutrients are corrected. Liming materials must be evaluated according to the calcium-magnesium content and according to the fineness of grind. The limestone test I mentioned earlier is not expensive, only about $25 per sample.

In order to evaluate liming materials, I use a formula developed in the 1950s. Even though few consultants use it, it is an excellent tool for evaluating the calcium and magnesium availability from limestone, etc.

Breakdown of limestone depends on the fineness of grind. An extremely fine grind will move into soil quickly. On legumes such as soybeans and edible beans, the ease of solving a calcium deficiency can be proven with a simple observation plot. Beans can be planted and allowed to grow 12 inches tall. Calcium, as shown to be required by a soil analysis, applied on top of the soil to 12-inch-high soybeans without being worked in will permit a timely test. Although the following would be difficult to detect by using only a soil test, a calcium increase will show up in the leaves promptly. After liming it will be necessary to wait until it rains an inch, or to irrigate. Then a leaf analysis should be taken on each following day. By the third day, a leaf analysis will reveal the presence of the added calcium in the leaf. It isn't necessary to apply calcium in the fall in order to get it into a legume.

Why is it possible to have hundreds of pounds of calcium in the soil and still show a calcium deficiency in the leaf until we get to 60% base saturation? Perhaps it has to do with what has been taught in the classroom for years. To achieve maximum uptake of nutrients by a plant, the calcium saturation in the soil solution around the root hairs must be at least 60%. Has this ability for calcium uptake somehow eluded the research done in terms of soybean production after all? Not so elusive is the fact that tissue analysis reveals that it takes application of an inch or so of water and three days, after which more calcium is there.

But be careful with calcium levels. The day you get calcium up to 85% base saturation, 90% of the available iron will generally be complexed, locked up as in a vault. With base saturation below 80%, greater nutrient availability is the measured result. Calcium can tie up magnesium, potassium, boron, zinc, and copper. It does this because it affects pH. All pH swings tie up various nutrients. Calcium increases nitrogen availability as it saturates the negative sites on the soil colloid. Soils that have 80% calcium saturation allow a farmer to paint the field green with easy nitrogen uptake. But this high calcium content helps construct a weak stalk, the mechanism being the application of too much nitrogen and easy nitrogen access into the plant. This can tie up the copper that is so necessary to stalk strength.

Any time there is a shortage of potassium, manganese or copper, a weak stalk will be the observed result. High potassium ties up manganese. High nitrogen ties up copper. High calcium ties up potassium. Each and all can cause a weak stalk, but calcium is the culprit if everything else is available in adequate amounts, and a high calcium level prevails. It does not take a great flush of nitrogen to get an excellent yield. My approach to high calcium is simple in the extreme. I start backing calcium down until everything else is there in equilibrium. High calcium doesn't have to be a detriment, but it almost always is because it is allowed to tie up other nutrients the plant requires.

There is another rule. The higher the calcium, the easier it is for moisture to leave the soil. This fact annihilates the old saw that you can't get too much calcium. In fact, you can get too much calcium. I consulted on a corporate farm owned by two families. They had 2,300 acres, and they were told that they couldn't put on too much lime. They applied six tons to the acre because the location was southern Illinois and there was lots of acidity in that part

When the Soil Has Been Overlimed

When a soil is overlimed, more than 80% of the capacity of this soil is saturated with calcium and magnesium. pH of this soil is higher than 7.0 and the farmer says that his soil is alkaline or sweet. According to the location, the climate, and other conditions that cannot be controlled by the farmer, the soil may be naturally alkaline not only because of the excess of calcium and magnesium in it, but also because of the accumulation of sodium and potassium in the same. Southern salty soils are usually very alkaline with pH 8.0 to 9.0.

The irrigation in a dry climate or in a dry summer makes the upper layer of any kind of soil more alkaline because the evaporating water drains the soluble salts upward into the upper layer of the soil. Where special cultures are raised, such as blueberries, a seemingly normal soil is to be made more acid once in a while, i.e., the calcium and magnesium base saturation has to be brought down to 50% and pH to 5.0, or even lower than that.

How to reduce the alkalinity of the soil is quite a frequent question. To correct an acid soil, namely, to increase the pH of a soil is definitely an easier and cheaper task than to correct alkaline soil or reduce the pH of the same.

To make a soil more acid we have to wash out or to neutralize chemically some substances in the soil that make it alkaline. This is a very complicated chemical process in which not only the substances that we apply and those that we want to wash out or to neutralize are involved, but almost all the plant food elements and the whole chemical and physical complex of the soil take part.

Therefore, when the project of reducing the alkalinity of a particular soil is under way, a close chemical control is a must in order to avoid undesirable side reactions.

There are several methods to reduce high alkalinity in soil.

1. *The application of mineral acids,* an example is sulfuric acid. Such an acid will turn the alkaline substances into neutral and water soluble ones. The alkaline substances that exist outside the colloidal system of the soil, will turn into sulfates, namely, into neutral salts and will be washed out if there is sufficient water. The application of strong acids, however, is not very popular because of practical inconveniences with diluting the same and with getting the liquid into the soil. This material may be used on small areas and in special cases only.

2. *The application of acid salts,* namely, salts that have been composed by combining strong acids with weak bases; such salts are: iron, aluminum or manganese sulfates. The strong bases in the soil push out the weak bases in the acid salt and occupy their places; thus, the strong bases turn the acid salts into neutral salts. By this procedure the strong active element from the soil is pushed out of the action, and, consequently, the alkalinity of the soil is decreased.

—Rudolf Ozolins
private papers, Acres U. S.A. collection

of the state. They had one field that couldn't be treated because there was a ditch there. They piled the lime on one side of the ditch. They couldn't get over to the other side until spring. In spring, naturally, they didn't get it spread. I came on-scene another year later in the fall to analyze their soils. Where the limestone was piled, you couldn't tell it was intended to be applied to the

Hands-On Agronomy

other little field. When I saw the results I knew why they had hired me. All of that soil was 81, 82, 84, 85% calcium. Magnesium was tied up, potassium was tied up except for that one little field behind that woods, which was right on the money. Actually none of those acres needed limestone. They told me that soybeans were their best crop, and they were taking yields of 45 to 50 bushels of soybeans per acre before that fatal limestone application. Within two years after applying the limestone described earlier, they were down to 30 bushels of beans per acre. The reason yield dropped was they had tied up magnesium and potassium. Once this was understood, work was started to get that calcium out, and the farm returned to superior yields.

It all depends on the numbers. Some people in the northeast say that they need 80% of saturation for calcium, not 68%. Every lab has to have a model soil to calibrate machines, and that model soil is not something that is decreed by the government. It is something that each lab determines. Each day the lab calibrates its machines according to a soil model. If they run a lot of samples that morning, they will do it again at noon. Depending on the number of samples, they may do it three or four times a day.

Every lab has a different numbering system. Some 80s are like our 68s. Two brothers up on the Ohio-Michigan border heard that I worked with people who had used too much lime in their soils. One of them said, "Our Dad was convinced that we needed to get our soils up to 80% calcium like one of his friends had done. Our soybean yields have declined by one-third or more." The brothers realized what they had done. It was a mistake. They thought 80% calcium on the neighbor's soil test was the same as 80 on theirs. It was not. Their recommended 68% was actually equal to the neighbor's 80% because of the difference in testing and reporting the calcium content. It took about four years to get their fields straightened out. When you start looking at the numbers and percentages on two different soil tests, don't take figures from one and try to use them on the other or apply them to your operation because it won't work out correctly.

Mag-ne-si-um / mag-ˡnē-zē-em, -zhem / *n* [NL, fr. *magnesia*] 1 a silver-white light malleable ductile metallic element 2 chemical symbol:

12
Mg
24.305

3 occurs abundantly in nature as an alkaline earth 4 used in many industrial processes, including photography, pyrotechnics 5 MgO used in fertilizers, cements, insulation 6 in medicine, the magnesia is an antacid and mild laxative 7 in soils, magnesium has 1.666 times as much exchange capacity as an equal amount of calcium 8 high magnesium and low calcium permits organic residue to decay into alcohol, a sterilant to bacteria 9 it should occupy between 10 and 20% of the soil's exchange capacity 10 in the human body, it is essential for nerve and muscle activity and in bone structure, aids in growth promotion

Hands-On Agronomy

4

Calcium, Magnesium & Tillage

CALCIUM AND MAGNESIUM GO HAND IN HAND. Magnesium is a constituent of chlorophyll. In fact, chlorophyll and photosynthesis rely on its presence and availability. Magnesium aids in phosphate metabolism. And it activates several enzyme systems.

For the moment, we are required to understand the functions of magnesium in a crop, but we also must comprehend the functions of magnesium in a soil.

Magnesium, in conjunction with calcium, is the key to air and water in the soil. Magnesium helps hold the soil together and tightens it up. Too much of this wonder element hardens the soil when it is dry, and makes a clay soil sticky when it is wet. In my area, the soil we call gumbo becomes so sticky it builds up to three or four inches on the sole of your boot before you can kick it off. This boot test suggests 30% base saturation, perhaps more. Ideally, that number needs to be 12, meaning that 30% is 2.5 times as much magnesium in that soil as ought to be there. It seems necessary to deal with soils that are excessive in magnesium more than any other problem. In addition to the influence of magnesium on soil structure, there is also the nitrogen connection which will be discussed further in chapter 5. Magnesium has more of an influence on soil pH than calcium. If I could hold enough calcium in one hand to raise the pH by one point, and I took the same amount of magnesium in the second hand, the last would raise pH by 1.67. It is therefore a 1.67 to 1 relationship. Any time you have too much magnesium in a soil, the pH is going to be extra high. If I can get magnesium out or complex it with sulfur, I will have a far greater effect on dropping pH than if I take calcium out. Magnesium in undisturbed soil will be a carbon copy readout of rocks in an area. Deficiencies occur most often in coarse textured, acid soils. Soil extremely high in calcium can actually tie up the magnesium to the point that we get a magnesium deficiency in the plant but excessive magnesium still exists in the soil.

Magnesium occurs as a cation with a ++ charge. This provides a stronger attachment than sodium or potassium which

Magnesium deficiency causes whitish strips along the veins and often a purplish color on the underside of the lower leaves.

have only a single + charge. When it attaches to a colloid, there are not very many ways to get magnesium off. Calcium can tie it up, but when magnesium is excessive (the Ca and Mg % is over 80%), calcium will not sufficiently reduce it except when calcium over-saturation occurs. Magnesium should only be considered as excessive in a soil when the percent saturation combined with that of calcium is in excess of 80%.

Too much magnesium in a soil prevents the plant from getting enough magnesium. If the magnesium level in the soil is extremely high, a leaf tissue analysis on corn and many other crops, including grasses, grapes and berries, will generally reveal a magnesium deficiency. That is one reason I always caution farmers to use a tissue analysis for short-range evaluation, and use a soil analysis for long-range analysis. Let's recap. Using our tests, target figures are 60 to 70% calcium, 10 to 20% magnesium. With an exchange capacity of 8.67 or less, the target begins to rise from 12% magnesium. The lower the exchange, the higher the percent of target magnesium up to 20%. An exchange capacity of 9.0 or higher, means the ideal magnesium level should be no more than 12% and no less than 10%. The magnesium problem is easiest to illustrate on corn. Less than 10% saturation of magnesium will cost at least ten bushels of corn per acre. (This yield loss in corn is not a unique occurrence, less than 10% magnesium affects virtually all types of crops adversely in terms of yield.) Magnesium above 15% saturation on soil with a CEC that is 7 or higher will

---

SOME ASPECTS OF MAGNESIUM IN THE SOILS:

- It is contained in minerals such as biotite, dolomite and chlorite.
- Deficiencies occur most often in coarse-textured, acid soils.
- It occurs as a cation (Mg^{++}).

cost ten bushels of corn per acre because the plant simply won't get enough.

Most state universities are never bashful in telling farmers to pour on nitrogen. At one land grant university test farm with 40% magnesium and 45% calcium base saturation, they order up 240 pounds of nitrogen to grow a 175-bushel corn crop, which it does. They do not explain that on soils with a TEC of 8.70 or higher, once you get above 20% base saturation in terms of magnesium, the cost of the error will be at least 15 bushels of corn per acre. If magnesium can be reduced from 20% down to the high teens—the reduction is going to make another five bushels of corn per acre. Below 15, the reduction will deliver another ten bushels of corn per acre. If base saturation falls below 10% magnesium, it will also cost the farmer 10 bushels of corn, and below 7½ % up to 30 bushels of corn per acre. To compute nitrogen for corn, the old rule of thumb is that it takes 1.5 pounds nitrogen to produce a bushel of corn. Depending on magnesium levels, it doesn't happen that way. The first order of business is to see whether magnesium is above 10 and below 15. If we have 68% calcium, 12% magnesium, plenty of phosphorus, and adequate potassium with adequate sulfur and trace elements, it only takes one pound of nitrogen to produce a bushel of corn on such fertile soil. At magnesium base saturation 13 or 14, it takes 1.25 pounds of nitrogen to produce a bushel of corn. Above 15, it takes 1.3 pounds of nitrogen. At 18 and 19 base saturation magnesium, it figures out about 1.4 or 1.45, and above 20 it takes 1.5 pounds of nitrogen to produce a bushel of corn. Just remember that it requires a different approach to magnesium on soils below 8.70 TEC.

This is not to suggest the purchase of that much commercial nitrogen. But it does take into account nitrogen released from that which is contained in the soil humus. After you compute in the above, then the rest must be supplied. In a corn-soybean rotation, compute three-fourths of a pound of nitrogen per bushel of beans. As a practical matter, this will be a safe assumption. On the average, soybeans do not provide a pound of residual nitrogen per bushel

Hands-On Agronomy

Calcium and Magnesium

Calcium and magnesium are considered as elements of secondary importance in the industry and market of the commercial fertilizers, but the truth is that for the soil and for the plants calcium and magnesium are primary in importance both quantitatively and also for their bio-chemical significance.

A deeper look into every living body, including the human being, discovers the fact that nothing can live without calcium and magnesium. The skeletons of human beings and those of all fully developed animals are built of tri-calcium phosphate. The immense world of microbes and all the bio-chemical processes require certain amounts of calcium and magnesium. There may not be a green plant without the action of magnesium, for magnesium controls the development and the bio-chemistry of the chlorophyll molecule; subsequently, there is no photosynthesis, namely, no food for other forms of life without the work of magnesium. Every agricultural product contains certain amounts of calcium and magnesium, and logically a fertile and productive soil must contain calcium and magnesium—in fact, it holds very large amounts of both of these two elements. It is necessary to have 1,000 to 36,000 pounds of the so-called exchange calcium and 200 to 3,000 pounds of the exchange magnesium per acre to satisfy the colloidal adsorption capacities of the different soils.

It has been proved that calcium is the most important element among all the plant food elements. Therefore, before any kind of fertilization project is worked out upon soil, it must be seen that the percent of calcium and magnesium base saturation as a part of the

> total exchange capacity of the particular soil has been established, as for instance, 65% for calcium; 15% for magnesium for the common kinds of the cultivated plants. And it is as important to eliminate the deficiencies of these two elements as it is to avoid the excesses of the same in the soil.
>
> —*Rudolf Ozolins*
> *private papers, Acres U.S.A. collection*

of beans. On the average, beans put in escrow approximately three-quarters pound of nitrogen per bushel of beans for the next crop in the rotation. In a poor growing season, it can be as little as a half pound of nitrogen per bushel of beans. DuPont researched soybeans for years. One of their studies revealed that, in an average year, soybeans only take 50% of their nitrogen requirement from the air, and under adverse conditions as little as 25% of the nitrogen is taken from the air. Textbooks say that legumes take 70% of their nitrogen from the air; even so, they still have 30% that has to be picked up from the soil under excellent growing conditions. The point here is magnesium, not nitrogen. The higher the magnesium above 15% base saturation, the more problems in terms of corn and grass type crops such as wheat, oats, barley—but it is worse than that for legumes. The problem with legumes such as soybeans, alfalfa, clover, etc., shows up when you drop below 10% base saturation of Mg. But when you get to 12% you already have too much magnesium to get optimum production out of alfalfa and other legumes. If you are growing soybeans or alfalfa and you have 18% magnesium and everything else is right, it doesn't work like corn. With corn we pull magnesium from 18 down to 15, and we use less nitrogen and get a yield increase. If you start pulling alfalfa land down, you won't get any increase at all if you go from 18 to 14. Nor if you go from 14 to 13. You won't get an increase until you get down to less than 12% base saturation of magnesium.

Hands-On Agronomy

A client in Illinois was growing red clover for seed. In his area farmers considered two bushels of red clover seed per acre an excellent yield. The year his magnesium dropped down below 12%, he doubled his red clover seed production to four bushels per acre. His soybean yields increased by ten bushels an acre over a three or four year period. He found some old alfalfa seed. He really didn't know how good it was. He just happened to find it in one of his storage sheds, and he seeded it in his wheat that February. It came up as a solid stand and he kept that stand for about three years. I asked him, "Did it run out faster?" He said, "No, it was messing up my rotation so I finally just worked it in." Ohio research has revealed that certain legume yields start to decrease once you pass 11.75% base saturation magnesium. The study was undertaken to disprove the validity of using cation exchange capacity for making fertilizer recommendations. The outcome failed to substantiate the looked-for results.

Any cation, whether it is calcium, magnesium, potassium or sodium, can in sufficient amounts tie up any other cation. In extremely low TEC soils high potassium can easily tie up magnesium. This is especially the case in sandy soils. In high clay type soils, it is just the opposite. Magnesium gets so high that it starts tying up potassium. As the percentage of magnesium drops, the pounds of available potassium actually go up. If we take that ideal soil, 68% calcium and 12% magnesium, and use a product with pure calcium in it, and take it from 68 or 69%

SOME FUNCTIONS OF MAGNESIUM IN CROP GROWTH ARE:

- A mineral constituent of chlorophyll.
- Actively involved in photosynthesis.
- Aids in phosphate metabolism.
- Activates several enzyme systems.

base saturation, but put no magnesium on it to counteract the treatment, the application will drive magnesium down 1%. Every time the percent of calcium is increased by 1%, the magnesium goes down by 1% also. The exception is a magnesium source that also has calcium, such as dolomitic limestone.

Remember, the numbers say calcium and magnesium should total 80%. When calcium and magnesium together total more than 80%, and calcium goes to 68%, the result will still be too much magnesium. Also keep in mind that if adding calcium or if an excess of calcium saturation exists due to natural conditions which result in decreasing magnesium to less than 10%, even if the total is 90+% when calcium and magnesium are added together, that soil lacks sufficient magnesium to raise the next crop. Where magnesium is less than 10% all crops suffer. What difference could that make? For one thing it means less yield from the crop. However, it makes a big difference on the other side too. If you have 80% calcium in your soils and 5% magnesium, this means too much magnesium in that soil because the two added together total 85. The high calcium percentage is affecting the magnesium rendering it unavailable as a plant nutrient. If you bring that calcium from 80% down to 70%, magnesium will jump from 5% up to 15%. This means we have to drive out some of the magnesium before we see the proper effect. You must bring the calcium down and raise the magnesium up in order to feed the plant. Otherwise we have to buy magnesium. It can be applied as a foliar feed application, as enough soil applied material to feed the next crop or use enough sulfur to acidify it and kick it loose. On the other hand, even though a soil shows 5% magnesium and 90% calcium, the physical effect is a heavy, tight soil because the magnesium is still there working on the physical structure. But it is not available in a sufficient amount for the plant to use. At times a farmer will say, "Well, you tell me that magnesium keeps the soil tight, and I only have 6 or 8% magnesium in this soil and it is still hard and tight." If you have 6 or 8% magnesium and an 80 to 90% calcium level, the calcium is masking the true picture. If you brought calcium down to 68 from 90 base saturation and you had 5% magnesium, this means we have brought the calcium down 22 points. Such a reaction will now add 22 points to the magnesium value. If we get the calcium down to 68, the magnesium then will be 27. When calcium is driven out of the soil by too much nitrogen, magnesium remains unless calcium is maintained above at least 60% base saturation and sulfur is used to remove the magnesium. Every time you put too much nitrogen on soils that are above a total of 80% calcium-magnesium, the process takes calcium down, allows magnesium to go up, and the magnesium is never going to be neutralized or taken out unless sufficient calcium and sulfur are used to complex the magnesium. If you own land or farm it for someone else, you should remember this point for the benefit of that land, because most consultants and fieldmen never learn it well enough to use it in their soil fertility recommendations.

Influence of Calcium on Magnesium

Numerous observations lead to the following conclusions:

1. Besides their own physiological functions, the magnesium salts exercise poisoning effects on all plants, including the higher algae and higher species.

2. This poisoning effect by magnesium rests mainly on the displacement of calcium from its important place in the cell nucleus.

3. The poisoning effects by magnesium are wholly prevented by the presence of ample amounts of calcium salts.

4. A distinct excess of calcium salts lowers the function of the magnesium which manifests itself in reduced plant production.

5. The nuclear substance of the lower algae and fungi is calcium-free.

From the very beginning it was very clear that with respect to the calcium factor in practice we are dealing with mainly pronounced differences in calcium and magnesium contents of the soil. If the magnesium exceeds the calcium, which is prominent in the sub-tropical and tropical regions (deserts excluded), then the calcium fertilization shows itself more important. But should the calcium content be noticeably higher than the magnesium, accordingly the latter as application may well be tested. It may be a question of needing a magnesium sulfate fertilizing which in yield production surpassed all other magnesium fertilizers. According to our researches in Tokyo, there are 4.8 parts crystallized magnesium sulfate as capable for work as 100 parts pulverized magnesite for barley culture. But when magnesium sulfate is applied as top-dressing, one part is sufficient. At the research station of North Carolina it was observed that calcium-rich soil with 0.4% magnesium showed symptoms of magnesium deficiency by tobacco. But an application of 20 to 30 pounds magnesium sulfate per acre could remove the symptoms of magnesium deficiency. Often it is convenient to combine the magnesium with the potassium fertilization. The potassium-magnesium-sulfate has established itself brightly in this case.

—*Oscar Loew*
"Die Ernahrung der Pflanze" (1931)
private papers, Acres U.S.A. collection

An excess of any one of the four major cations—calcium, magnesium, potassium or sodium—makes that major element "the weakest link in the chain." It is not bound heavily on the soil colloid. So, when we put sulfur on a high calcium soil, it is going to work by reducing principally calcium. If we put sulfur on a high magnesium soil, it will reduce the magnesium, provided there is already sufficient calcium present. Or it will work in the same way with potassium or sodium. After calcium, magnesium, potassium and sodium are under control, sulfur will start pulling down needed levels of all the cations. Therefore it is extremely important to discontinue large doses of sulfur once there are no excesses to control. From that time only apply the amount of sulfur needed to grow the next crop and maintain the levels of other nutrients in the excellent range.

Free lime is not considered by atomic absorption tests. North and South Dakota, Kansas and several other states have areas with calcareous soils. Some of these soils are extremely deficient in plant available calcium, but agronomists there do not take special notice because of free lime. In effect, we only take notice of calcium when it is in the form a plant can use. Consequently, we are merely measuring what is available for the plant to use during a growing season. If it is there in an unavailable form, we do not need to know about it until it is released for plant use. People who measure free lime say they need no calcium because they have all this free lime, yet it is mostly in the wrong form. It is not in the form that the plant can use. Once we get it into that form, it will show up on the soil test.

When both are deficient, we have to buy calcium and magnesium. On a soil just under 80% saturation of calcium and magnesium combined, where calcium is deficient, if you correct calcium to 70%, low magnesium can be the result. Below 10% means a magnesium deficiency. You can always tell the correction factor by adding the percentage of calcium and magnesium together because they have a direct effect on each other. If the combined total is above 80%, you always use only calcium. If the total is less than 80%, then calcium and magnesium are generally required in order to get the correct amount. It is absolutely mandatory to have the right calcium-magnesium percentages in order to have the right amount of air and water in the soil. One method that is used to reduce the magnesium level in soils is to use gypsum or even sulfur. But that only works when there is sufficient calcium to maintain adequate porosity in that soil which then allows the magnesium to leach through. Without 60% calcium or higher (which can be an even higher required percentage on tests from other labs – and thus this number is not always sufficient to work properly when using another lab's test results) gypsum or sulfur alone is not sufficient to solve the problem.

An actual example with extremely high magnesium and yet with calcium that is too deficient for gypsum or sulfur to work properly may help demonstrate where too much soil fertility advice on this type of problem goes wrong. Let's say we have 53.07% calcium saturation and 40.38% magnesium saturation. One element we can consider using to get magnesium out of the soil is sulfur. But there is another key to moving magnesium out of the soil with sulfur. Magnesium will never leave a soil, even if you pour on the sulfur or sulfates until calcium saturation is above 60%. One reason for this is that 60% or higher calcium makes the soil porous enough to permit the movement of other cations such as magnesium, or sodium, with the water. Without water movement through the soil, sulfur simply accumulates. As a consequence, before we would even try to take magnesium out of this typical sample, we would correct the calcium to at least 60% of the soil's base saturation. Enough lime to bring calcium up to 68% means an increase of 15%. But our objective is to bring magnesium down below 12%. To do so requires applying enough calcium to reach 72%, which in my mind is better than allowing magnesium to stay above 12%. The calcium reaction will generally require three years because the calcium in lime breaks down at about one third per year unless an extremely fine grind material is utilized.

When magnesium is needed, the lowest priced source—in a calcium/magnesium compound—is dolomitic limestone. Magnesium oxide is not generally a good source of magnesium because it breaks down so slowly. Magnesium sulfate is expensive but works well. When potassium and magnesium and sulfur are required, Sul-Po-Mag or K-Mag (potassium-magnesium-sulfate) might be sufficient, that is if only small amounts of magnesium are needed. Dolomitic lime or potassium-magnesium-sulfate are the two I would normally recommend because of both economics and effectiveness at increasing magnesium levels in the soil. Other materials are either not very effective or are more expensive. It might be possible to pulverize magnesium oxide and build it back into a prill, to make the magnesium available. The U.S. market does not favor the seeker in this case.

Remember, if you apply calcium to a soil when potassium is in excess, this will have a big effect on reducing the potassium. But if you have a normal potassium level (3% to 5%) and you apply only a ton of calcium lime, generally it will have little effect on the potassium. Application of calcium controls magnesium, and the magnesium increase ties up the potassium and a magnesium or calcium decrease releases potassium back out. This is a trade off situation. Trouble usually arrives when we overuse calcium or overuse magnesium. Too much of either ties up the potassium.

To correct compaction, you need to begin by getting the calcium levels to at least 60% saturation. That means the right chemistry and the right tillage. It may not be necessary to get calcium to 60% if a soil conditioner is to be used. Parenthetically, some clients have done amazing things with soil conditioners. But how do we get soil to respond in terms of soil chemistry at 60% base saturation of calcium? For breaking up a hardpan, tillage alone may not work. Tillage and fertilization go hand in hand, but for a tillage program to work properly, you have to have a reasonable balance in terms of the fertility, especially calcium, magnesium and sodium.

After the soil has been limed properly, then some type of a ripper or deep tillage tool—a sub-soiler or even a chisel plow to penetrate through any hardpan or plowsole—would be recommended according to the need.

The first order of business, of course, is to establish whether a hardpan in fact exists. The instrument of choice is a soil compaction tester. It has a gauge that measures up to 300 pounds per square inch pressure. The one I use is made by Dickey John at a cost of between $175 to $200, perhaps more by now. In a field situation, we see how deep we can go before we hit 300 pounds per square inch pressure. That is where roots will stop growing. The drier the soil, the easier it is to hit the 300 pound barrier. Never probe a very dry soil to find the resistance to root growth. It is best to test in a soil that is relatively moist.

A simple soil probe test is often of merit. Push the probe down, right in the crop row. Then just lay it down flat on the ground with the cut away part of the soil tube towards the top. Start with your thumb and press directly down on the core of soil. Move from the top of the core downward until you feel resistance. If you meet resistance within a half inch, it will be safe to say the magnesium level is in the 20s and maybe in the 30s. If resistance is reached at 2.5 inches, then the magnesium level will be below 20%, but above 15%. If you get down to four or five inches, it is likely going to be below 12%, and at least getting close to the desired 68% calcium and 12% magnesium. The right balance will be indexed when you have a good, crumbly, aerated soil for at least four or five inches.

I visited a farm in Red Oak, Iowa and at the time they didn't know anything about soil balancing, but their corn always did well on one 40-acre field. I took a soil probe into the field. Testing as described here, I could go all the way to the handle. That farmer had 68/12 on calcium/magnesium when the sample results were reported. Reportedly people around there said that if you claimed to raise any more than 150-bushel corn, you were a liar. Yet, that field produced 172-bushel corn on the whole field. There was no irrigation, just dry land, and it wasn't a heavy soil. It was an upland soil. There aren't very many soils of any type generally found to be like that.

Most of the time you will hit strong resistance before you get past a 12 inch depth. Once you know where it is, the next thing to determine is how much of a compacted layer you have. It can be as much as an inch or more thick. Generally, a ripper pulled at a 12 to 14 inch depth, will break through a hardpan formed due to equipment and implements used to work the topsoil. But before you even think of using a ripper, certain rules should be followed. Let's say the hardpan is evident, and it is found at eleven inches, at which depth one inch of hard soil exists. That defines the critical area at the 12 inch depth. The objective is to just barely penetrate the 12th inch. If you rip 18 inches deep, the procedure determines the depth to which the soil will pack the next time. In other words, the shallower the soil can be worked to be rid of a hardpan, the more successful will be coping with any future hardpan.

Again, the first order of business is to correct calcium saturation. We have to deal with this in our area because of the demands made by modern agriculture. Often farmers bring in big earth moving machines. They level soils for the purpose of planting rice. They raise rice for two years and then raise soybeans for a year or two, then back to rice. They flatten the terrain out, flood the rice, or furrow irrigate the beans or the grain sorghum in the rotation. I have sampled soils during August for in-depth analysis because the farmer wanted to lime or grow a crop that fall. Some of those soils were packed to the point that it took a three pound lead-weighted mallet and 75 blows to get the probe 6 $^3/_4$ inches deep. These data represent tremendous compaction problems that must be dealt with. The first thing, always, is to lime the soil if the calcium level is not at least 60% when rippers start working the soil, too much magnesium and the lack of adequate calcium will make it runny and sticky, and over the course of a few good rains the soil will slurry right back together once it becomes wet enough. The Soil Conservation Service says on Sharky clay soils—which are the type soils we have to deal with along the Mississippi River—it does no good to rip those soils because of the propensity to slurry together again. Needless to say, there are arguments between farmers. One will say he has ripped the soil and it didn't run back together. Another will say he ripped, and it closed up like slurry cement. The determining factor, again, is the calcium level. At 60% calcium or higher, the ripped soil won't run back together. The only problem with most growers is that they look at pH rather than calcium. So one farmer will have plenty of calcium, the other won't.

From my vantage point, it is necessary to determine where the compaction layer is. The next rule is to go over the field only one time when the soil is dry. Pull your equipment, tillage tool, ripper, whatever, at least four and a half miles per hour. For most soils, you should only do this one time in the fall. If you go over it twice, you put so much air space between the soil particles that sometimes it won't settle back again. Too much air space and you will lose part of your moisture next spring. One client had a 60-acre wheat field along the Missouri River. He wanted to rip it because it was compacted, but it never dried out. It was always wet because of the water table. His

Hands-On Agronomy

solution was unique. In January or February he set his alarm at midnight. That was the time when it got cold enough to freeze. He then would start ripping until the tractor started to spin in the morning.

His grandfather once made 50 bushels of wheat on that field years ago, but most of the time—because wheat doesn't like wet feet—20 or 30 bushels of wheat became the norm. The year he ripped the frozen soil, water wasn't a problem, and he made 64 bushels of wheat per acre.

Break through the deepest compaction layer. Work to the depth it takes, generally 12 to 14 inches. The required depth can be determined with a soil probe or a soil compaction gauge, or even with a crowbar. Use narrow shanks set wide apart. If you don't have a ripper and you don't have extremely tough soil, and a chisel plow with narrow shanks is available, set those narrow shanks at 30 to 40 inch centers. If you have them on 12 inch centers, take off two, leave one, take off two, etc. Let's say you determine you need to go 14 inches deep and you can only get to 13 inches. Slow down or take off shanks, but don't go over it again. Next year it should be easier to go deeper.

After ripping for about three years, it should be possible to stop for two or three years, unless something is being done to compact the soil again. It is absolutely mandatory to keep the compaction layer broken up by minimizing traffic over a field. Travel over the same tracks if possible. Generally, it is not a good idea to break up the subsoil in the spring because too much air space is permitted in the soil.

We have what is called a ripper-hipper in our area (sometimes a hip and ridger). It can rip right under the row in order to get the cotton root to go straight down. It will rip and hip right on top of the old row, and make a bed on that row on which to plant. I tell the farmer to rip right under the row if possible. In terms of corn production, a ripper between the rows, especially in the area of wheel tracks—is an excellent procedure to get more air back into the soil the last trip over, when the corn is not too tall.

I had one client who failed to follow instructions. He forgot the rule only go as deep as you can pull. I told him to take off shanks until he could pull at the proper depth, but he failed to do that. He kept all of his shanks on, and he put the ripper down as deep as it could go. The next time I was up at his place he said he was upset because he put that ripper on his tractor and burned out his tractor motor. Obviously, a fair measure of sometimes uncommon good sense must be utilized at all times.

I had another client who had the biggest Massey Ferguson the market had to offer. He had about nine shanks on the back of it, and he was running 15 inches deep to get his hardpan broken up. He hit a stump and pulled the whole back end out.

A tillage tool that requires both understanding and tender loving care is the disc. In my book it rates special attention for use on lighter type soils. If you have a finishing disc and the cutting side of the blade is shiny all the way up to the axle, that is fine. But if you have a shiny blade all the way up the other side as deep as it is cutting, you are just packing your soil back. The disc blade on the cutting side should be shiny, but on the outside it should only be shiny for about the first inch or two. If you have light sand, it is easy to determine whether a disc packs or not. Some areas we sample are very sandy. An inch of rain might fall at night. By noon the next day, all the water is gone. Often the farmer has it in mind that if the disc doesn't ball up, then that soil is not too wet. They assume light soils are not subject to compaction. Actually, compaction can be caused not just by the tracks of the tractor, but also by the farm equipment. Most discs do pack back. To deal with this propensity, we try to keep root and water avenues to the subsoil open by using a sub-soiler. We try to keep our humus levels up. In terms of management, there are some things a farmer can do. Sometimes the farmer who does what we would say is all wrong is the person who will come out ahead in the short run. One specific situation is farming under *wet conditions*. Sometimes the farmer who plants under wet conditions will have a soft enough place to get the roots through. Once roots break through that wet, softened, normally

Hands-On Agronomy

dry and hard compaction layer, the plant will start building its root system below because it can feed down there. I am not suggesting that this is the way to do it. But I am saying that sometimes the farmer who works his soil wet is going to have a crop that looks better than the farmer who plants under dry conditions. The key is getting those roots through the obstructing barrier. Nutrients and the water must move down, water being a prime concern. If the water can penetrate, so will roots.

I have clients who raise rice. They often get into their rice field with big equipment, and they disc the rice stubble in while the water is still standing on the field. They do not get compaction when they do that. As long as water is standing on the field, this traffic won't compact. But when equipment rolls across the spots that are muddy, that is when the farmer gets stuck and starts compaction with a vengeance. When all that space is filled with water, buoyancy will hold up the equipment. When the soil starts drying out and mud becomes evident, that is when water leaves the air spaces, and that is when smearing can cause a problem. Again, I am not suggesting that soils should be worked this way. Admittedly, I used to think that rice farmers were going to tear their soils to pieces, but they didn't.

Some of my clients farm in Germany using large equipment, too. In one area, the money crop is sugar beets. They will bring the moldboard plow into play, and they don't wait until it is dry. They work the soil wet. If necessary, they plant it wet. And if necessary, they harvest it wet. They do everything wet if they have to. Because of this they buy machines that will "out-pull anything." Because of the sheer size of many operations, harvest often runs into wet conditions, with much resultant packing. Wet conditions contribute mightily to the creation of hardpan in a soil. If the crop is planted and roots get past the compaction level before the soil dries out and gets hard, the plant will feed. In such a year, the farmer who works his soil wet may come out ahead.

A lot of growers believe that freezing and thawing take care of hardpan. Dr. Al Trouse has gone as far north as Minnesota and into Canada. He will testify that freezing and thawing will not take care of hardpan. One researcher at Rutgers raised 120 bushels of soybeans to the acre on a test plot. He dug out the soybeans to determine the journey of the root system. I have seen pictures of them. The mass looked like a woman's hair, only the soybean root ran six feet deep. He said, "If you want to grow top yields, you have got to get those roots down. If you don't get those feeder roots down, you simply don't get the yields."

Another side of the picture can be developed and printed with a soil conditioner. Many clients use soil conditioners but it may take three and four times before a breakthrough of the compaction barrier takes place. The heavier the soil, the more likely it tends to be that way. The reason is—and this is going contrary to what a lot of people say with soil conditioners—that often it is not possible to use enough conditioner economically to do it. A case report should illustrate the point. I have seen conditioners used in lawn and landscape work in California, Texas and the Midwest. I had one client in California who reported soil as hard as concrete. His thumb could get only as deep as his thumbnail, and it was hard from there on. They have extreme amounts of sodium and chloride in many western soils, including this area. Until removed, it remains impossible to do anything. In this case, they put on an ounce per 1,000 square feet once a month for three months. This computes to roughly one gallon per acre, which is not a recommended practice. After that treatment, it was possible to take a finger and run it all the way down in an adobe type soil.

In a landscape situation, this is possible, but problems can develop when the soil becomes too loose. I have some clients who tell me that they never get a soil opened up using a soil conditioner as recommended, sometimes until the third or fourth year. That is why I suggest sub-soiling first. If a soil conditioner will do the job, use that—but if the soil conditioner falls short, then consider a deep tillage implement, if conditions will permit.

Farm talk is often quite elusive. I can relate a personal experience, one prompted by a soil conditioner discussion. At one time I responded to the question with, "I don't have clients who use soil conditioners. I have never heard about how they work." A farmer told me, "You ought to give them a try because they work pretty well." I went to one of my very best clients, a fertilizer dealer with five farms, and asked if he had heard of or used soil conditioners. He stopped and took a deep breath. "Well, I never told you, but I've used soil conditioners for a number of years." He would rip where the soil was hard, but he used soil conditioners to keep pore space open. He said, "You know that 160 acres with that low swag in it down there at the Weeks Farm?" I said yes because I sampled it every year. He said, "Well, about three years before you started working with it, we put a soil conditioner on that soil. Previously crops did not grow in that swag, because water always stood there. Ever since using the soil conditioner it has grown a crop there every year. I never tell anybody that I use a soil conditioner because a lot of people don't think it works, and I sell fertilizer to a lot of those guys."

I tell everybody about soil conditioners because I don't sell them. I will give you alternatives. You can use the mineral balance, the ripper or the soil conditioner whichever will work best for your situation. I became convinced by an old friend by the name of Jake Weeks (No connection to the farm mentioned in the previous paragraph). Jake sold chemicals for years. A new company took over when he was in his 60s, and they fired him. He couldn't get a comparable job anywhere. He found out about soil conditioners. He talked to some of the farmers he had known for years. He asked them to try the soil conditioner. One of the farmers put the soil conditioner on a heavy black soil. He put on four ounces to the acre and marked it with a flag. Six weeks and two inches of rain later, he got the farmer to bring out his backhoe. They dug a trench right across the place where they had applied the product. From down in the trench it was not possible to see where the flag was. One fellow got into the trench with a knife. He started pulling the knife along the side of the trench about 36 inches down. When he got to where the flag was, he couldn't pull it past that point.

The fellow on the backhoe was a Doubting Thomas. He started to pull across the treated soil with that same knife. When he got to where that flag was, he literally shook trying to pull that knife through untreated soil but he could not do it. In a month and a half, the effects were to be seen three and a half to four feet deep.

I cannot look at a soil or a soil report and tell whether a soil conditioner will work the first time or the second time or the third time. One farmer once told me, "Use it at the four ounce rate until you know it works, and then cut back to the two ounce rate." Apply in a spring, fall, spring sequence. The heavier the soils, the more this observation holds. A good soil conditioner can be expected to increase permeability to water movement, decrease bulk density and enhance water holding capacity. Used on a lawn, roots go deeper, water stays longer and grass remains greener.

I have mentioned Dr. Al Trouse. He once visited the Herman Warsaw farm, at the time very well known for record yielding corn. He dug a trench to see if there was compaction layers. The findings depend on the definition of a compaction layer. When Trouse dug a trench, he took along a brush and a trowel. He could pick out the wheel tracks, the press wheel tracks of the planter, and he could pick out where the chisel plow shank ran. He could also identify when a moldboard plow was used and where a disc passed over. He could identify every one of those places as found in the trenches.

I once attended a seminar in Indianapolis where he spoke on root development and compaction. He said, "Now in the morning at nine o'clock—if you will be out here in this corn field—I will have a trench dug." At 6:00 a.m. the next morning he and two assistants dug a trench. He took us into the cornfield, showed us the trench, and said, "Now this is unusual. The corn roots in this field go deeper than is normal. What I am going to tell you is that this is the first year they have ever grown corn here. In fact, from looking at the soil, I would estimate that it was in pasture until two years ago." The owner wasn't there so who was to verify it? While we were standing there, this pickup truck pulled up and two guys got out and walked over to us. One of them said, "I thought I better come over here and see what is going on in my field."

Al Trouse, as if it were a normal, everyday occurrence, said, "I'm sorry to cause you a problem, but I didn't know whom to ask and I needed to dig a trench. I hope you don't mind. I'll fill it up when I'm done but while you are here, I'd like to ask you a couple of questions. Could you tell us the history of this field?" The farmer said, "Well, until two years ago, it was in pasture. Last year I grew soybeans on it and this year is the first year it has been in corn." Trouse asked about tillage practices. He had already shown us the moldboard plow layer and pointed out where the chisel plow and the disc had been used. The farmer proceeded right down the line to tell us what Trouse had already related.

The point is that there is no soil worked with heavy equipment without some compaction problems.

Ni-tro-gen / 'nī-tre-jen / *n, often attrib* [French *nitrogène*, fr. *nitr* + -*gène* -gen] 1 colorless, tasteless, odorless gaseous element that constitutes 78% of the atmosphere by volume, stacking up 75 million pounds over every acre of land 2 chemical symbol:

$$
\boxed{\begin{array}{c} 7 \\ \mathbf{N} \\ 14.0067 \end{array}}
$$

3 focal element in the nitrogen cycle by which nitrogen passes through successive stations in air, soil and organisms to achieve fixation 4 a governing factor in the decay of carbonaceous materials   5 amino nitrogen takes up 6% of compounds   6 every cell in plant life requires nitrogen in the right form 7 5% of organic matter in soil is present as nitrogen 8 nitrogen joins carbon, hydrogen, oxygen as a main constituent of the animal body, other than the skeleton

5

Using the Nitrogen Cycle

AFTER THE REQUIREMENTS AND LOGISTICS of fertility management have been determined, some questions arise soon enough. When is the best time to put on fertilizer? If the crop to be grown in the spring is corn, when is the best time to put on phosphate and potassium? Is it better to supply phosphate and potassium in the fall, or would spring application better serve the purpose? Farm magazine ads and fertilizer company pitch sheets want fertilizer sales in the fall. This counsel has the benefit of avoiding a spring rush for the suppliers.

Essential elements for plants are several. Basically we get carbon, hydrogen and oxygen from air and water. Nitrogen, phosphorous, potassium, calcium and magnesium command a great deal of attention in this book. Also covered at great length will be sulfur, and then the trace elements—particularly boron, copper, iron, manganese and zinc.

Clashing philosophies govern terms used, the chief division being the difference between feeding the plant and feeding the soil. The concept of feeding the plant is flawed, of course, if the shape of the soil is unknown. Mere application is no assurance that the plant is going to assimilate the fertilizer anyway.

High yielding crops with adequate fertility use water more efficiently. In one case I often illustrate with slides for farmers where the fertilized area produced 118 bushels of corn, and the unfertilized area produced 80 bushels. The fertilized plot made 7.6 bushels of corn per inch of water, and the unfertilized soil made 5.3 bushels of corn per inch of water. Some farmers are familiar with a normal corn leaf, a nitrogen starved leaf, a phosphate starved leaf, and a potassium starved leaf. I call attention to such signs and symptoms because many farmers will say they need more nitrogen on their soil. They might be putting on 200 pounds of nitrogen, yet not achieving 150 bushel per acre corn—so they think they are not applying enough. All you have to do is walk into the field when corn is just past tassel to tell if this is true. Nitrogen deficiency starts with a "V" in the leaf at the bottom. A potassium deficiency also shows up in the oldest leaves. You can tell the difference easily. Still, most farmers see the leaves that are showing a potassium deficiency, and they think they have a need for more nitrogen. A nitrogen starved plant will exhibit its sign at the leaf tip and move down in a V shape. In a potassium starved plant, the edges of the entire leaf begin to die off, the damage moving inward. Almost all of southeast Missouri soils have potassium deficiencies. It is seldom considered economical to put on the amounts our tests show as most desired. Farmers should at least put on a maintenance level when such deficiencies are shown.

On many farms in our area, if you walk into the field after the corn starts to silk, you will see those bottom leaves with a brown edge on them. If you start to see the leaves die from the outside in, that means a potassium deficiency, not a nitrogen deficiency.

Some studies in the 1970s revealed that the higher the potassium in the ear leaf at silk, the higher the corn yield is going to be. As long as you don't get that potassium level to exceed the point where it starts tying up something else, you have the ability to take the potassium in and get a good high level at the time of silking. Farmers have grown a lot of popcorn in our area. Popcorn shows potassium deficiency very quickly. If you can keep potassium in the plant, you can get the yield. Potassium has much more to do with yield than many growers think.

In any case, nitrogen must rate first attention because it is the hardest fertility assist to deal with. It is also the most difficult to recommend properly. Nitrogen is essential for plant growth and is a part of every living cell. There are three major forms of soil nitrogen. Organic nitrogen is a part of organic matter, or humus, and it is not readily available. It makes up 97 to 98% of total soil nitrogen, and it is held there, albeit in a form the plant cannot use. When we measure manures, we measure organic nitrogen. When you measure organic nitrogen in manures, you have to cut in half the amount it contains before calculating the nitrogen you are counting on for the crop that year. Ammonium nitrogen is another form of nitrogen in the soil held by the soil colloids. The NH_4 attaches to the clay particle and is less available than nitrate. Less than 1% of the total soil nitrogen is generally in the form of ammonia in a natural system. Nitrate nitrogen and other soluble compounds are also available in the soil as 1 to 2% of the total soil nitrogen.

On the average, a plant contains 2 to 6% nitrogen. We can get large quantities of nitrogen from the nodulation on legumes. In an excellent situation, 70% of the nitrogen comes from the microbes. Under medium growing conditions, you only get about 50% from that source. Under poor conditions, you can get as little as 25%. As far as I am concerned, the better we can influence the chemistry and the physical structure of the soil, the more efficient we make those microbes. If we have a normal year and we have the soil in the right shape, the microbes are going to be able to do a better job. Therefore we don't decrease their efficiency as much as we would in a soil that doesn't have proper fertility. Non-legumes absorb NO_3 (nitrate nitrogen) and NH_4 (ammonium ions) from the soil. That nitrogen is used to form chlorophyll, proteins, amino acids and nucleic acids. In particular, we look at it for greenness. If a plant doesn't have enough green, farmers and growers tend to say it doesn't have enough nitrogen.

If you have yellowing corn or any kind of a grass crop and you don't see the tip of the oldest leaf show yellow, it is not necessarily nitrogen. It can be something else, because the yellow of nitrogen deficient plants will show in the oldest leaves first. That has to do with the greenness of the chlorophyll. That pale or yellowing plant can be needing phosphate, sulfur, or even boron. Nitrogen is needed to build proteins. If higher protein is desired for alfalfa, it needs to have enough nitrogen. If you don't have enough nitrogen and you have enough calcium and sulfur, you still won't get your protein. If you have a situation wherein microbes are only 50% efficient at taking nitrogen from the air and putting it into the plant, then alfalfa is not going to do its best. I see situations in which there is plenty of calcium and sulfur, and still there is a shortfall of protein in alfalfa.

If we can get the ammonia form of nitrogen into the plant, we can help build amino acids in the later growth period of grasses. If you can get ammonia into the corn after it already has silked, it will actually take the ammonia and build amino acids with it. That is one of the reasons why putting on ammonia forms of nitrogen late in the year will actually show an increase in amino acids in the plant—provided, of course, you don't overdo it.

We can take a measurement of nitrate and ammonia in the soil. This test measures the soluble nitrogens in order to tell where we are in terms of the crop cycle. Crops take up large quantities of nitrogen. Eight tons of alfalfa requires 450 pounds of nitrogen by dead reckoning. The crop has to get this nitrogen from somewhere. If it gets 70% of the nitrogen from the air, 30% still has to be accounted for. That means 135 pounds of nitrogen

Application of Fertilizer

It goes without saying that it is often desirable to feed growing crops. In such cases the best practice is to apply small quantities of the fertilizing materials at each application and then make the applications often. By following this plan, on an active, living soil the biotic workers will be able to complete the necessary conditioning very quickly and all soil operations will go right on harmoniously

In our farming and gardening our aim should forever be to obtain normal growth, for normal growth and quality are synonymous. A quick, falsely-stimulated growth may be pleasing to the eye, but that growth can easily be deceptive.

Remember our reference to Sir Albert Howard's Health Highway? The establishment of that highway in our food-producing soils should be our chief aim. And this desirable situation, as we will recall, obtains only when the beneficial soil fungi are actively on the job. When new stuff is added to the land, though it may be of the highest quality considerable conditioning of the materials will be needed by the soil bacteria as well as by the molds themselves before that "protein flow" will be at its efficient best.

By applying the "soil food" well in advance of planting time, or a little at a time to growing plants, as suggested above, the soil workers will be able to condition it and that "soil machine" discovered by Sir Albert Howard will not fail to function smoothly—which means no obstructions in our health highway.

How important it is not to be deceived by the appearances! We should strive to know what is going on down in the root zone of our crops. One question should constantly be in each of our minds:

Am I getting normal growth, or is this largely false stimulation? An over-stimulated crop will usually be far more attractive to the eye than a crop that is growing normally. It will, that is, unless you are able to detect the true quality signs. When a crop is growing on a dynamic soil, the quality indicators will be there, one of which is a darker and more velvety green in many crops. Over-stimulated crops often have a metallic green. One can learn to detect normal, quality growth if he is observant.

—*Joseph A. Cocannouer*
Natural Food & Farming *(1961)*

have to come from somewhere if there is to be an eight ton alfalfa crop. This does not mean we simply put it on. It does mean that we have to make the soil operative so that more than the nodulation on the legume supplies nitrogen. All those microbes in the soil can have a fantastic effect because more than the *Rhizobium* genus of bacteria supplies the nitrogen. Algae supply nitrogen, and there are various types of other soil life that also supply nitrogen. This supply chore is usually accomplished by working on organic matter. Huge amounts of nitrogen seem to be available based on a measurement of total nitrogen, but most of it is tied up in humus. There has to be some operative principle that makes it available. If we have a 5% organic matter soil, we already have roughly 100 pounds of nitrogen that is available for that year's crop. Put that 100 pounds along with the other 70%, and we now have to account for 35 pounds of nitrogen from somewhere else. This is not a tough job for the microbes as long as we give them the right environment. That is why it is so important to get the chemistry and the physical structure of the soil just right. By dead reckoning, a 150-bushel corn crop requires 200 pounds of nitrogen. Actually, it all depends on where the calcium/magnesium levels are. It depends on the soil's balance.

Soil high in magnesium means that a 150-bushel corn crop will require nitrogen calculated at 150 times 1.5. In other words, 200 pounds of nitrogen will be short, based on such an extremely high magnesium level in the soil. And yet in a good fertile soil, it is routine to get 150 bushels from 200 pounds of nitrogen or less—pounds taken up in the total crop. Thus the 200 pounds represents the total amount taken up in the crop either from the soil's organic matter or via application. In parts of Missouri, we do well to get 60-80 pounds of nitrogen from organic matter. This information is provided by soil testing. When we consider the nitrogen which is reported on the test as pounds per acre, we are not talking about any nitrogen from a commercial source that may have been applied or any nitrogen from any manures that have been put on. Every time we have 5.1 humus (termed organic matter on some soil tests) in a soil, the nitrogen figure will be 100 pounds. Every time we have a 2.3 humus reading, nitrogen is going to be 66 pounds. This is nitrogen to be released from the soil humus over the growing season. Subtract the amount that is shown sourced from humus, and supply the rest as required.

Do we add that by growing legumes? Can it be added via *rhizobium* on soybean roots? If a corn or grass crop is to be produced, where is the rest of the nitrogen coming from? That is what we have to look at.

I have clients who have used what I call biological stimulants between 1975 and the present for this job. If the soils are worked correctly, I have seen these products work on the same fields year after year. But if the soil fundamentals are not correct and in place, you can get into all kinds of trouble relying solely on biologicals.

In 1977 and 1978, a company that makes a biological product hired me to do all their troubleshooting east of the Mississippi

River. No one knew much about field application at that time because such products represented a brand new concept. The first problem referred to me surfaced in southern Illinois, which was close to where I was working. The company asked me to go up one day and look at a farmer's corn. I took a look at it. Right to the row where he used anhydrous ammonia, that corn was tasseled out and looked the best. Where he used the biological and no anhydrous or other type of nitrogen at all, the corn had hardly tasseled except in the low spots. That had been soil conservation land for ten years. He had plowed weeds as tall as his head under with a moldboard plow the previous fall. There was little rain during the winter. As a consequence, decay faltered, and the undecayed weeds were still there when he planted his corn. Where he knifed in anhydrous, the extra nitrogen broke down those plowed down weeds. The undecomposed materials in areas without nitrogen application were still there to compete with the crop for an inadequate amount of nitrogen. Though by August the corn without anhydrous looked like it had come out of the problem, it cost the farmer about 25 bushels of corn per acre in terms of yield because he starved his plants early in the season.

As a result of that consultation, the company sent me to farms spread from Missouri to the east coast. Over a two-year period I visited over 13,000 acres treated with these products to supply or help supply needed nitrogen. Out of these 13,000+ acres, 93% of the crops were properly represented and were as good or better than what the farmer had been doing. Only 7% had problems. I took a lot of pictures of the problems because I wanted to document them. There is always a logical explanation for problems. If this explanation can be discerned from the record, it can save a lot of money.

I know farmers who have never heard of biologicals. They won't hear about them from me because they have trouble just staying up with what they are doing right now. I don't try to come into an operation and say, "Look, you are doing this the wrong way and you need to do it like this." What I have learned by hard experience is to sit down with the farmer and say, "What do you want to accomplish? We will help you accomplish that with your soils as best we can. You will have to decide what approach you take."

I have farmer/clients who are completely organic, and I have clients who are completely commercial. The people who truly work with natural systems and use biological stimulants as a supply for plant nitrogen can come out ahead of the farmer who uses only commercial nitrogen sources, but some farmers just don't have the mind-set it takes to work with those natural systems. There are some clients I simply instruct, "Under the situation you are operating in, you are not going to do well with biologicals." Thus some companies don't want me talking to their customers. The further out of whack the soil is in terms of chemistry, the more that is true. On the other hand, I have clients who say they would like to try a little bit. Accordingly we work into it slowly. Some clients use biologicals on the whole farm. Usually I don't ask who is using what. I just come in and start talking about their program. Nothing is said or done to come in sideways or tell a farmer to do his job some other way. I just want to recite the basics. In terms of biologicals, the closer the chemistry in the soil is to being "right," the better they are going to work. If the chemistry is not right, then extra steps must be taken first to see that the basics are more perfectly in place.

I have clients who grow alfalfa and use ammonium sulfate, and I have other clients who grow alfalfa and use the biologicals. I have still other clients who grow alfalfa and do not apply either one. It all depends on the basics and the concepts a farmer understands. It is not my objective to govern the approach. But I will tell the farmer who is doing neither if either one would benefit his alfalfa, and which would likely do best for his circumstance.

A few years ago, in southern Illinois, the alfalfa weevil absolutely ate up not only the first cutting, but also the second. A farmer who attended one of my meetings had never heard of a biological approach. But his fertilizer consultant called me and

Microorganisms and Soil Structure

Flocculation and sedimentation of soil particles in an aqueous suspension, as a result of a change in charge of the particles, can account for the bringing together of primary particles of colloidal size (less than two microns). However, flocculation and sedimentation are of limited importance in aggregation under natural conditions in the soil. Drying of a wet soil tends to bring primary particles together, since the attractive charges are brought closer together when the water films between the particles are reduced. On the other hand, drying of the soil may result in the development of unequal stresses which may break the soil into particles. Other physical forces, such as freezing and thawing, also may cause fragmentation of the soil mass into smaller units. Tillage may break up the soil mass into various units such as clods, fragments, crumbs and granules. Plant roots certainly tend to push primary particles closer together to form aggregates or structural units in the soil, as do the mycelia of certain fungi. Earthworms, crayfish, ants, and many insects form aggregates and, in many cases, may stabilize them. Certain bacteria, through the production of gums, may have similar effects. Burrowing animals, such as moles, separate the soil mass into units. Thus in nature there are numerous ways in which lumps, granules, clods and other aggregates are formed from the soil mass into the many-sized units that are found in the soil.

Once the soil units are formed there are numerous ways in which they may be stabilized. Inorganic cementing materials, such as iron, may give extreme stability such as occurs in the Latosols. Also colloidal materials, such as clays and organic matter, through their chemical and physical effects stabilize the soil units.

Microorganisms, during the decomposition of plant and animal remains, produce numerous organic compounds and release inorganic substances that affect stability of the soil units. Some of the compounds produced and released exert a tremendous effect on stability. Other compounds have little or no effect. Some of the natural products produced by microorganisms are more effective per unit weight than are the synthetic stabilizers that have been produced. In addition to the foregoing microbial effects, the physical influence of certain fungal mycelia in holding together the soil units should be mentioned. Microorganisms vary greatly in their ability to stabilize the soil.

The soil fauna is also important in influencing soil stability. For example, the earthworm secretes slimes that render the cast several times more stable than the original soil. Under some mulching treatments, as much as 40 tons per acre of earthworm casts were produced and deposited on the surface of the soil. Thus there are many factors involved in forming soil structure units and in stabilizing them. The kind of soil structure will depend upon type of soil and all aspects of its chemical, physical, and biological makeup.

—T.M. McCalla and F.A. Haskins
Missouri Agricultural Experiment Station's
Research Bulletin 765

said the farmer wanted to plant some new alfalfa in the spring. He wanted to use a bio-stimulant, and wanted me to tell him—based on his soils—whether it was going to work. I said, "Not only will I tell you, but you have the best chance because you have excellent soils. If you put the product and an insect repellent together, then you are going to be able to get that alfalfa right through." I knew he could because I have seen other people do it. He planted his new seeding of alfalfa and the insects never touched it, even though they consumed his established crop that did not receive the bio-stimulant and the repellent.

There are other farmers who raise alfalfa in the same area. I wouldn't think of telling them to do the same thing because they do not have the proper foundation. Admittedly, these few remarks are getting far removed from commercial nitrogen, but some understanding of the topic is necessary. So, back to the numbers on basic crops. Soybean production factors out as follows: a 50-bushel crop takes 280 pounds of nitrogen. Some texts tell you that a 60-bushel crop requires 295 to 300 pounds of nitrogen. The same general rule governs both soybeans and alfalfa. For ease of computation, I like to think in terms of 300 pounds of nitrogen and 60 bushels of beans.

In a normal growing season, you are going to get 50% efficiency from the nodulation on your beans. If it takes 300 pounds of nitrogen to grow a 60-bushel soybean crop, and you are getting 50% efficiency, this means another 150 pounds of nitrogen must be accounted for. What if you have 2.3% organic matter? That factors in another 66 pounds of nitrogen. Subtract 66 pounds from 150. This leaves another 84 pounds of nitrogen to be accounted for. Without that extra nitrogen, you will not grow 60 bushels of soybeans per acre.

The first clue for a decent production level is calcium in the 60% range. If the soil colloid does not have a proper calcium level, nitrogen will not deliver a top yield. Once you have your basics in place—60 to 70% calcium, 10 to 20% magnesium—then and only then do you start looking at nitrogen as a factor in growing high yield beans. There are very few farmers on my

Hands-On Agronomy

program who raise 60 bushels of beans without obtaining some extra nitrogen above the amount supplied by the soil and nodulation.

A typical farmer question runs approximately as follows. If a grower wants to raise a 60-bushel bean crop and he is at a 60% calcium level, how many pounds of extra nitrogen would he have to add, the organic matter level being 2.5%? At 2.5% organic matter, such a farmer will have 70 pounds of nitrogen supplied by the soil. He will need 150 pounds of additional nitrogen in a normal year, after accounting for the 50% supplied by nodules. Again, if you have 70% efficiency from your beans, that goes up. We are considering a 50% efficiency factor right now because it is easy—and expected in a normal year. In other words, 150 pounds of nitrogen generated by bacteria goes into production. We have another 150 pounds to go. Take that 70 pounds from 2.5% humus off the equation and we have to come up with another 80 pounds of nitrogen from some other source. All this assumes that we have a good fertile soil and that there is a proper phosphate and potassium level.

It is not discussed generally, but there is a vicious nitrogen cycle that you can get into just by pushing nitrogen. And there are other things that can contribute to crop production for which nitrogen gets the credit. All things considered and all things in perspective should be a norm. We say legumes can get nitrogen out of the air, but we have to add that they don't get it all from the air. At least 30% has to come from another source, and that 30% either has to be supplied by microbial activity in the soil or by applying some type of N source. The farmer must decide, but when the choice is made, he or she has to deal with the consequences.

If you choose commercial nitrogen, that act will start making that soil more and more reliant on commercial nitrogen. If biology is the choice, everything else has to be right and in place, or else the biological activity will turn out to be the limiting factor. Before microbiology works properly, chemistry and physics have to be in place. Albrecht's percentages are what really make the microbes work. I have clients who do not know about microbial products and still can raise 60 bushels of beans without commercial fertilizer, but that is not the general rule.

Manures are an excellent source of nitrogen. I work with farmers, who use a lot of manures in some areas, and I have other areas under consultation where there is no livestock for thousands and thousands of acres, and nothing organic is applied. A real saving factor in my area has been a broiler production facility that generates more than 30,000 tons of manure a year. Most of it is moved out to farmers.

Most of the farmers in southeast Missouri didn't consider the value of manures when I settled in the area. It was generally not available to those who had gone out of the livestock business. In time some of us sat down and worked out some figures. One farmer tried it on 400 acres and another one tried it on a few less acres. Now the man who contracts for disposal of the manure has no trouble at all finding someone who wants it. In fact, my clients want it all if the quality is good.

Several items merit front burner consideration when applying manures. Number one, even the same type of manure can vary greatly in terms of fertilizer value, and the nutrient content will vary from fall to spring, depending on contents of the feed. Manures can be nutrient rich. Once you know what the total nitrogen content is, divide by two to compute the nitrogen potential for the next crop.

There are tremendous differences between poultry, cow and hog manures, and there is even a difference between layer and broiler manure. Layers are fed extra calcium to strengthen the egg shells. Broilers generally do not get this ration.

One client had 26,000 layers and farmed 160 acres. He had his soils analyzed because his fields weren't producing good crops any longer. He had put so much layer manure on his farm and pushed the calcium level so high, it started tying up all his trace minerals. He was destroying his farm with the manure. It took about five years to get that problem solved because he didn't choose to buy sulfur for remedial application.

His son raised turkeys down the road. The son needed calcium and was putting on turkey manure and his dad was putting on too much calcium using layer manure, so I had them switch. They both solved their problems.

Manures will drive calcium out of the soil except where calcium is highly supplemented, such as for egg production. The problem is that magnesium will take the calcium's place. The farm mentioned above didn't have excessive magnesium. In fact, it had basically the kind of magnesium levels needed. By the time we got finished with the switch, both were a little on the high side, but not extreme. When the calcium got high, it tied up his iron and certain other trace elements. This was what kept hurting his crops.

Every soil is different. You have to analyze what is going to happen to the several nutrients. When you analyze soils, you have to remember that just because a certain program works on one farm, that doesn't mean it is going to work on the farm down the road. Every time the numbers change, a new set of circumstances come into view, with a new set of possibilities and potential problems.

If you use manure and it reduces calcium, but magnesium goes too high, in the end if the proper nutrient balance is to be achieved, you will likely have to use some sulfur to get magnesium down to a reasonable point. So growers might as well start with sulfur in the first place, but be careful if calcium levels are low and magnesium levels are high. This inventory of facts should prompt us to remember that manure will take out some calcium. Manures will supply extra nitrogen, phosphate and potash to be certain, and is always a better source than physical measurements suggest. Nevertheless, an analysis gets you into the ballpark.

I worked with a ranch in Texas that began using legumes to supply all its nitrogen for pasture grasses. In the 1960s, the Extension Service said this couldn't be done because it wouldn't work properly. In 1973, when oil prices went up, the dialogue became, "How do you do this?" Within two to three years, an extension specialist in livestock management at Texas A&M was telling a veterinarian from Stephenville, Texas that this very ranch's program was an A&M idea.

Legumes will supply nitrogen. Regardless of the legume you are using, don't forget about what type of year it is. If you have a good year and growing conditions are right, then count on legumes to supply quite a bit of nitrogen. If conditions are terrible, you are not going to get more efficiency from the rhizobia than you get anywhere else. The more you work with the microbial population in the soil system, the better they are going to do in a poor year. The bland remark that in a poor year you are only going to get 25% efficiency from legumes in terms of supplying nitrogen may not be true. But if you have poor soils and a poor year, most likely you will not get as much. If you don't know for sure and you want to get some general ideas, do a nitrate and ammonia analysis. You can go three feet deep. But if you go that deep, at least take the top six inches separately. Put that in one sample bag. To look at the next increment, go down 12 inches. Put that in another sample bag. For corn, you can stop there. For cotton, in some areas roots go down 18 inches. Ask for a nitrate and ammonia analysis, and look at how much nitrogen is calculated for each of the 6-inch samples.

A client who made 45 bushels of beans per acre had a lot of rain through the winter. Come springtime, he planted corn. A little later he became concerned about his nitrogen stores. We had an analysis run for the area where he grew beans the year before versus where he grew corn during the same time frame a year later. He had 65 pounds more nitrogen on the side where he grew soybeans than on the side where he grew corn.

Several things could contribute to that. Generally, if you are growing soybeans in an area, you are only going to get about three quarters of a pound of nitrogen per bushel of soybeans for use by the corn. You can't just say, "Well, we are going to get one pound of nitrogen per bushel of soybeans produced." It depends on what you are doing to influence the microbes that build nitrogen in that soil.

Hands-On Agronomy

Quality Produce Demands
Proper Composting

Today we still notice that cabbage, cauliflower, broccoli and kale can give off very intensive aromas while cooking. This, too, depends on the fertilization of the soil.

The reason is that breakdown products contained in the manure, such as skatole, indole and other phenolic compounds (to the layman, that which stinks) are not further decomposed. They enter the soil, are absorbed by plant roots and migrate into the plant tissue. These breakdown products have been excreted by the animal or human organisms, are toxic wastes of their metabolism and imprint their history on the soil and the growing plant.

Night soil is particularly undesirable in this regard, but even sewage sludge contains many toxic compounds, unless properly decomposed by an aerobic composting process. The difficulty is that these byproducts are rather stable and can survive for a long time. Returned in food to the human upper digestive tract where they do not belong, they can cause many symptoms of indigestion, flatulence and maybe even allergic reactions.

Biuret is a contaminant or byproduct of urea and urine. It is extremely stable. In greenhouse and field experiments at Purdue University it was demonstrated that it was toxic to growing corn plants. It caused leaf chlorosis, hyponasty and it severely stunted, twisted and deformed plants with their leaf tips rolled together. All fertilizer salts, when placed with the seed, resulted in decreased length of primary roots. The ability to sur-

I had a client near Moses Lake, Washington call one November. He said, "They tell me that you have been working with this 'biological' product which helps supply nitrogen, and I want to try it on some land, but there is no need for us to put a fall application on because our ground freezes up. You can't tell me that if I put it on in November that it is going to do anything from now until next March." I responded, "There is one thing you need to consider. When the very top surface of the soil warms up to 28 degrees, certain microbes start to work. It doesn't have to be a case of putting a thermometer in the soil, and the whole thing being thawed out. When the sun is shining on the soil surface, a certain number of microbes start to work right then."

He said, "Well, I don't really believe it, but I will take this 30-acre field and split it into three parts. On ten acres I will put an application right now, and on the other 20 acres I will not do anything. Next spring on that first 10 acres I am going to make another application. Then I am going to put an application on the middle ten acres and use the last area for a control."

He was producing carrots. He made the application on ten acres, first taking samples for analysis to determine the nitrogen levels. The readout was very low. I already knew that during the winter it was common to cause an accumulation of 30 to 40 pounds of nitrogen by applying the "biological" in the fall. The Moses Lake client hardly made the application before it froze up. He called in the spring and asked me to come out and conduct a meeting. He said, "By the time you get here, I will have a nitrate and ammonia analysis because the soil is thawing out." When I got there he was really excited. He said, "You know, we have 35 pounds more nitrogen on this ten-acre treated plot than we do on either one of the other ten-acre plots."

If such a program is not begun in the fall, and you want to use this type of program, you must have at least 40 pounds of nitrate nitrogen in place, or else you have to come in with that much nitrogen. A nitrate and ammonia analysis can tell you what you need to know.

I have farmers growing corn and they don't know if they have enough nitrogen a week before silk. In such cases, pull special samples and have them analyzed. Almost any laboratory can provide a nitrate and ammonia analysis because that test is pretty well standard. One lab seems to be just as good as the next. A nearby laboratory can make a nitrate and ammonia test easier on you because the lab needs it within 12 hours. If you can't get it there within 12 hours, take the sample into the house and spread it on waxed paper. Put a fan on it and dry it out and then send it to the lab.

With reference to nitrogen, it is most difficult to properly recommend management because five things can happen to it.

1. It can be used by the crop, which is great.

2. It can become part of the soil complex, which means it can be *adsorbed* on the clay colloid or get incorporated into the humus. When it is on the clay colloid it is not too hard to get hold of, but when it is incorporated in the humus, microbial activity and chemical balance must attend to its release.

3. It can leach down in the soil and be transported away with drainage water.

4. It can be eroded away no matter what form it is in.

5. It can volatilize and escape as a gas.

When nitrogen from any commercial source suffers from water standing over the crop for three or four days, a big portion of it will be lost. After four days you probably will have lost almost all of it.

A new client put 90 pounds of nitrogen on his corn at planting time. A 14-inch rain followed when the corn was 12-15 inches tall. Even though the land was put to grade, one 20-acre field was covered with water on the low end for four days. A nitrate and ammonia analysis revealed that the ammonium sulfate—a stable nitrogen form—held on the end where the water hadn't stood. The readout showed a respectable 85 pounds of nitrogen in place. On the end where water stood for four days, only 18 pounds remained.

Under anaerobic conditions, microbes that can live without air will actually decompose plant residues, taking oxygen out of the nitrate nitrogen for life support. Nitrogen gas remains briefly before it comes up through the water and escapes into the atmosphere.

Aerobic microorganisms require oxygen to live and work. These critters generally work in the top six to seven inches of soil. Anaerobic microorganisms do not require oxygen. They break down materials in the soil by harvesting oxygen from parent materials in the soil. This means anaerobes can work without direct oxygen availability; aerobes have to have oxygen. We want to have the aerobes work because they are the ones that go into action when we have 25% air space.

Measuring nitrogen is both difficult and rewarding. It is difficult because nitrates leach easily. Nitrogen from manure is basically in the ammonia form. It goes from ammonia to nitrite to nitrate. When it reaches the nitrate form, it goes out with the water. Nitrate nitrogen is volatile, yet this is the form the plant can use most easily. Nitrite nitrogen is an anion. Nitrogen has a negative charge and attracts a positive charge. In terms of soil physics, such a compound won't attach to the clay particle. The same thing is true of sulfates and boron.

In any discussion of nitrogen, the subject of the tissue test comes up. A tissue test will tell you whether your plant is getting enough nitrogen, and helps determine whether an addition can be done in a timely manner. A lot depends on the numbers on the tissue test and the experience of the person making the test.

Crop needs and stage of growth are determining factors. In my case, it is easier to evaluate the nitrogen requirement from soil analysis than it is from tissue testing.

Many other considerations figure in making the nitrogen connection. If soils require aeration, the right amount of nodulation will not materialize. If there is too little calcium, nodulation will falter.

At the same time, consider the case of a client near Mason City, Illinois. He was growing edible soybeans for the Japanese market, but couldn't get good nodulation on his beans. He started to use one of the microbial inoculants on his soils. The plant nodules went from small to some as big as a thumbnail. The only change he made was to use the inoculant. Obviously, the other conditions were correct or this wouldn't have happened. This means he had his calcium level in place, and enough phosphorous. It means he had enough sulfur.

The title page in making the nitrogen connection might well be, nitrogen in the life of a corn plant. Nevertheless, a big spurt of growth is the time when a need for plenty of nitrogen for the crop is indicated. This puts the ball in my court as a consultant. I need to be sure that the nitrogen is breaking down at the proper time or that nitrogen is released in a timely manner. At tasseling and silk, the corn plant really needs nitrogen. Then it starts to taper off. For that brief moment in time, it is important to get that nitrogen in fast. Using a source that gets into the corn plant quickly or using a foliar type is important.

The soil has to have good nutrient levels; still, a quick release of nitrogen is required to take care of a deficiency. A rule of thumb is to make an application a week before tasseling if a commercial source is used. You can actually put that on when the corn silks and still get a response if you apply a fast releasing nitrogen such as ammonium thiosulfate through the irrigation water, or dry ammonium nitrate using a plane. If dry urea is used, absorption efficiency will falter, but small amounts of urea applied in water have been very effective as a foliar source of nitrogen for cotton. A small amount of foliar material at about the four leaf stage—especially slow acting material such as a microbial inoculant—can be chancy if the deficiency is considerable. Ammonium nitrate or urea in very small amounts, fed through the leaf at the six leaf stage with micronutrients, can be effective. Personally, I like a foliar best at silk, especially if micronutrients are a consideration, using nitrogen and potassium in combination with the trace elements.

The basic rule is to use a nitrate and ammonia analysis, or a tissue analysis, but don't count on a regular soil test to tell you whether or not you have enough nitrogen. Either utilize a special test, or rely on the art of getting it right by observation. Most people, when they rely on intuition, use too much. The usual propensity is to rather use too much than not enough, the cost in terms of lost bushels weighing most in the growers mind.

Deficiencies lend themselves to both laboratory and pragmatic analysis, especially in corn production. On this page is a drawing of a good healthy corn leaf, compared to what a leaf

Nitrogen deficiency in corn and grain sorghum is characterized by the "yellow V" which shows in the tips of the oldest (lower) leaves first, designated as nitrogen starved here.

Nitrogen
Starved

Normal
Plant

Hands-On Agronomy

looks like at the same stage of growth when nitrogen deficiency reveals itself. I tell farmers that they are well ahead of the game to get pollen down the back of the neck by walking through corn fields. At tassel time the cornfield becomes a veritable encyclopedia. Better yet, walk the fields a week or two before corn tassels, and then walk them again when in tassel. Then walk those same fields two weeks later. Even when the corn is starting to dry down, walk the fields again. If time is a governing factor, at least walk the fields between tassel and silk. See what you look at. If you start seeing the leaves pictured here at tassel time, you are in trouble. If you want to know how short you are on nitrogen for corn, whether you use a biological program or a commercial program, count the leaves that exhibit a nitrogen deficiency. If you have four leaves that exhibit these signs and symptoms, or worse, just understand that for every leaf starting with the bottom one and coming up, each leaf with a V or that is dead, you are short ten pounds of nitrogen. Let's say we find three leaves. That translates into a 30 pound shortage of nitrogen. How much yield is that going to cost if nothing is done about it? If you have over 20% magnesium, divide by 1.5. For every pound and a half of nitrogen, it is going to cost you a bushel of corn. If you have three leaves showing the telltale V, it is going to cost you at least 20 bushels of corn per acre. And yet it is not too late at tassel time to do something about it. Every leaf below the ear builds the stalk, and the ear leaf and those above it build the grain for corn. If you can stop debilitation before it gets to the ear leaf, the projected yield will be maintained. If you see three leaves at tassel, that means you need 30 pounds of nitrogen to take care of the problem right now.

If you are growing corn short of nitrogen and if the magnesium percentage of soil saturation is under 20—say 18 or 19—the divisor is 1.45. If the reading is 15, 16 or 17, the divisor is 1.35. If magnesium is 12, that sum becomes its own dividend since the divisor is 1. If you have the 68/12 recommended level for calcium/magnesium and you have three leaves showing nitrogen deficiency, it will cost you 30 bushels of corn according to that three leaf index, unless the deficiency is corrected.

If you have one part of a field that is high in magnesium, and another part where the magnesium is optimum, here's what will happen. Where the high magnesium shows three leaves, the 68/12 would only be showing two. So a high magnesium soil would show three leaves, whereas a good soil would only show two because we are going to be short 20 bushels.

If you are turning to a commercial source of nitrogen and you don't really have a lot of microbial activity—especially when you are below 2.5% organic matter—and if you do not accomplish that nitrate and ammonia analysis, you are not looking at the true picture. You are seeing three leaves. But by the time you take remedial action, you could have about five leaves. The cut off point seems to be 40 pounds of actual nitrogen. If you have a pivot system or access to an aerial applicator, you can still make a difference, but testing to determine needs is the best.

Once you see that V in the corn leaf, it is already too late for that particular leaf. If you analyze the leaves above it, a shortage of nitrogen will already be evident. Even though you put on the nitrogen required at that time, some yield will be lost. In fact, we do not want to see the visual effects of any nutrient on the plant leaves, not a trace element or whatever. Failure to see a nutrient deficiency in the leaves does not mean that crop is not short of a particular nutrient, because of what we call *hidden hunger*. It means that we do not have enough of a shortage to show up at visual inspection. Once you see that V it is too late to do anything for that specific leaf simply because it was short a long time before the V became evident. I have clients who fly on dry ammonia nitrate at tassel time. When applied to a part of the field, it takes only three days to see the difference. Even if it is put on dry, it will be taken up from the soil into the plant. This is one thing we can do when we have poor aeration and a microbial stimulating-type product is used to supply nitrogen, but for whatever reason has not sufficiently done the job.

When the farmer uses biologicals together with poor aeration, or he has an over-abundance of residues to break down, then if he does not get that nitrogen in place, he will lose the bushels.

That figure of ten pounds per leaf is not something I dreamed up. A lot of people have known this fact. Today it is simply a matter of delivering that information in usable form.

A summary of sorts is now in order. If you know what your calcium-magnesium ratios are, you can compute the efficiency of the pounds of nitrogen involved. Here are the different stages.

In the illustrations below, the leaf at the bottom starts to die back. Next the yellow V. Above that, a little bit of yellow. Finally, the solid green leaf at the top.

If you take these three leaves off a stalk and the one above is still green—counting from the bottom leaf—then you can be certain that you should have used another 30 pounds of nitrogen. Whatever the source, 30 pounds of nitrogen not applied earlier in the season is now the governing factor.

Normal (top) leaf compared to three with nitrogen deficiency's characteristic "yellow V."

Actually, if you had put on 30 pounds of nitrogen to get it utilized in that stalk before tasseling, the deficiency in the leaves would never have appeared. It doesn't have to be put on at planting time though. It can be put on as a top dressing, or if necessary, later in the season.

I have seen fields at tassel with no yellow leaves. Yet on a long, full-season corn, there would still be three leaves showing up as deficient before ripening. You can have an excellent green looking stalk at tassel and still have a nitrogen deficiency later on. A nitrate and ammonia analysis before tassel can suggest the degree of deficiency, if any, that will show up. Such a readout will give the relationship between the nitrate and ammonia in the soil and make its suggestion as to whether that corn is going to properly make it or not.

If you use ammonium sulfate, the very best time to get the most response on corn is to put it on as close to the day you plant as possible. It takes 60 warm days to get a maximum nitrogen release. Some clients ask if they can put their ammonium sulfate on in the fall for the next spring. If they do it, they usually waste money because they have to put on extra in order to have the proper availability in spring. If you put all that ammonium sulfate on in the fall and you get 60 warm days from the time you put it on, you are going to begin to get your major push about that time. This could be in February, too early to plant in the cornbelt, and for best results, you want it 60 days after planting.

Anhydrous ammonia also should be mentioned. It releases faster than ammonium sulfate. Many commercial growers will not give it up, even though there are many problems with this product. The best time for anhydrous use is as a side dressing after the corn is up and growing. Even then, I advise clients that it will require 20% more nitrogen from anhydrous to get the same yield as a good broadcast nitrogen source.

I know some farmers who put a nitrogen inhibitor with it. That inhibitor actually kills the nitrogen fixers in the soil and stops them from breaking ammonia down to nitrate nitrogen. The idea is to repopulate the bacteria after they have been annihilated. I don't think this is a good idea. Anhydrous ammonia can be defended for post-emergence use. The corn plant can take the ammonia nitrogen from anhydrous or ammonia nitrate or from ammonium sulfate or from any ammonium source. As the crop inches its way toward maturity, the full-season corn taps this resource. Short-season corn may not adequately convert the ammonia nitrogen directly to amino acids, which translate back to yield; it needs a faster release of nitrogen than full-season corn.

Time the nitrogen application rather than use an inhibitor. The nitrate portion of any nitrogen form, generally, is immediately available. The ammonia portion is going to find use farther down the line, say, 30 to 60 days later, depending on the soils. If you use ammonium sulfate and have a pH of 7.5 or less, it is going to be more of a case of that slow 60-day breakdown I have been talking about. If you use ammonium sulfate on a high pH soil, say pH 8, ammonia will break down just as fast as urea in such soils.

The bottom line is simple in the extreme. More nitrogen at the right time doubles corn from the same amount of water. Nitrogen applied with other needed nutrients at the right time can actually double a good corn yield.

pH / (')pe⁻'ach / *n* 1 the negative logarithm of the effective hydrogen ion concentration or hydrogen ion activity in terms of gram equivalents per liter to express acidity or alkalinity on a scale with values 0 to 14, 7 representing neutrality, less than 7 representing acidity, numbers greater than 7 representing alkalinity 2 in soils, acidity denotes deficiency—calcium, magnesium, sodium or potassium, or a combination 3 by bringing calcium, magnesium, sodium and potassium into equilibrium in terms of the Albrecht equation, pH becomes adjusted automatically in soil systems suitable for plant growth 4 in neutral medium (high pH), soil colloids tend to be stable (gel) 5 under conditions of acidity (low pH), a more mobile (sol) state is achieved 6 when molecules of clay and humus become mobile because of acidity, more nutrients are etched from parent soil materials

Hands-On Agronomy

6

Concerning Commercial Nitrogen Sources

THE ORGANIC FOLKS OFTEN WINCE when I detail the many facets of nitrogen application, especially when I describe the metes and bounds of ammonium sulfate use. I have to remind them as gently as I can that there are excellent sources of nitrogen for organic growing, even if compost is not available or should not be used, and that microorganisms need "go" foods as well as "grow" foods. Every plant cell needs nitrogen in the right form.

Ammonium sulfate is a synthetic nitrogen, usually containing 20.5% nitrogen for use in conventional crops. It adsorbs to the clay component of the soil colloid readily and is not subject to leaching. This nitrogen form gets on quite well with most soil microorganisms.

My purpose here is not to debate the nitrogen forms, or even to explain William A. Albrecht's concept of *Insoluble Yet Available*. Readers are directed to *Eco-Farm: An Acres U.S.A. Primer* for exposition and analysis of the subject. I will agree with the Primer that plants need their nitrogen cafeteria style, not as a whole-hog feeding at the beginning of the season.

There are clients who recite their records on nitrogen use with great aplomb, setting up goals and systems to achieve those goals. For instance, several 25-pound applications through irrigation for corn are both valid and feasible. In a Minnesota study, 100 pounds of nitrogen delivered as four 25 pound applications produced 154 bushels of corn per acre, or 1.11 bushels of corn for each pound of nitrogen used simply by spreading it out over a longer period of time. Two hundred pounds of nitrogen in one application at planting time provided the foundation for 158 bushels per acre, or .58 bushels of corn per pound of nitrogen. Eight 25 pound applications through the irrigation system made 192 bushels per acre, but the efficiency was not as good—three quarters of a bushel of corn per pound of nitrogen. These data are quoted to show that spreading out applications of nitrogen, even on corn, account for much better efficiency. If the total application is made before planting time, less efficiency per pound of nitrogen will be the norm, not more. It is going to take more nitrogen to do the same job, because of the way the conversion is accomplished.

I have already mentioned ammonium sulfate. A number of farmers in my area have been told that the ammonium sulfate people have paid me because I have so many farmers using the product to buffer their high magnesium levels. In fact there was a rumor that I received ten cents a ton for every bit of ammonium sulfate that was sold. After I was in the area for about two years, the sales rep who sold ammonium sulfate to fertilizer dealers caught up with me one day. He said, "I need to shake your hand. We weren't selling any ammonium sulfate at all in this area until you came here." About three years later he made the following comment in my presence, "The first year that Neal started working in this area, we sold maybe a semi-load of ammonium sulfate. The next year we sold 4,000 tons." (I would like to have received ten cents a ton for that, but I didn't receive a penny, and still don't.)

Many of my clients grow significant amounts of wheat and corn in soils with high magnesium levels. Everything they had ever learned told them to use commercial nitrogen. This being the case, ammonium sulfate was the first recommendation. If you need sulfur and nitrogen, there is no source at a lower price. Second, ammonium sulfate takes 60 warm days before you get a major push for the crop. Ammonium sulfate put on a month before corn planting is still there after two to three rains. But I never recommend its application a month before corn planting. In one case the farmer intended to plant when it began to rain, got wet, and stayed wet. It was a month before they could go back into the fields.

The fields were checked for nitrogen using a nitrate and ammonia analysis. Virtually none of the nitrogen had been lost in that time frame—maybe five pounds per acre. Still, for corn and cotton, application should be made as close to planting as possible, otherwise the release will come before the crop most needs it.

I have clients who will wait until they begin planting their cotton and corn, and then use a buggy to spread the ammonium sulfate over the top. This is not too late. Ammonium sulfate and ammonium thiosulfate belong in the same category. Ammonium thiosulfate (12-0-0-26) is even used late in the season on irrigated corn.

The above are the most stable forms of nitrogen in terms of application ease and lasting effect. On the other hand, if you are growing wheat and you are using ammonium sulfate, you've got to keep in mind that it is a slow release material on soils below pH 7.5 (this is water pH). You have to get the nitrate nitrogen to that wheat at a specific time because it has a nitrate requiring enzyme that determines how many kernels are going to develop in a head of wheat. Unless there is an adequate amount of nitrate nitrogen for that enzyme at all times, it can run short and cut the yield accordingly. If ammonium sulfate is used as a nitrogen source in wheat production, a rule of thumb calls for application at least four months before normal harvest date. This may seem to be a long time, but on cold soils it works out just right. In warmer climates, application two months before the normal harvest date is sufficient. Basically, in our area we want nitrogen available in March and April for wheat. The last date we should consider for application in southeastern Missouri is February 7. The normal early harvest date for the area is June 7. We can apply the material as early as the first of January. The soil will be cold at that time of the year, so loss due to a warm soil is not a problem. I tell farmers near my home that any time between January 1 and February 7 is appropriate for the last ammonium sulfate application to the wheat field.

Ammonium nitrate is half nitrite nitrogen and half ammonium nitrogen. We use it when we need a quick push. If low spots start to yellow out, say, in April, and the wheat hasn't headed yet, you can expect the nitrogen content of the rest of the field to be short as well. The low spots usually leach out nitrogen first. When normal sized wheat in the low spots starts to yellow, use an airplane to apply the last 30 pounds of needed nitrogen in the equation as ammonium nitrate. Those 30 pounds applied on one part of the field and not on the other will normally produce an extra ten plus bushels of wheat to the acre. I have farmers who put four or more applications of nitrogen on wheat. If the soil is not dry enough to accommodate ground-level application, they will hire a plane.

In northeastern Arkansas, the average wheat yields run about 60 bushels or less per acre. One farmer, who monitors his wheat, goes out and takes the leaf samples himself. He makes sure that the nitrogen is in it. When the nitrogen drops below the proper level, he makes another application. He had an 80 acre field. The north 40, the better of the two, made 108 bushels of wheat to the acre. The south 40 made 96 bushels. Not many farmers there enjoy that kind of yield. Building the correct fertility is the answer.

That is one thing I learned working with wheat growers in Germany. They have higher fertility levels for wheat than we find

Insoluble Yet Available

The soil's behaviors, like those of many other things in nature, do not conform completely to the "laws" we learn in laboratory chemistry and by which we have been explaining the natural nutrition of plants. In the laboratory, the solubility of a substance in water, in alcohol, or in certain reagents is commonly the foremost criterion for its description and classification. We are mentally disturbed, then, when we find that some natural substance or commercial product, commonly soluble in the laboratory, behaves as an insoluble one, or vice versa, when put into the soil.

We experience similar confusion when, for example, some insoluble substances on coming in contact with the mucous membrane of our body, like that of the lungs on inhalation, is soluble and harmless there. We are more disturbed when some so-called soluble substances are as disturbing (and fatal) to the lungs as the insoluble silicates of rock dusts are in the case of the disease known as "silicosis." Land plaster, consisting of the mineral gypsum, or of the chemical compound calcium sulphate, is considered soluble in the laboratory. Yet its inhalation brings a breakdown of the lung tissues which on X-ray examination suggests silicosis or even calcification by its accumulations there.

—*William A. Albrecht*
The Albrecht Papers, Volume I *(1975)*

in almost any of the soils in the U.S. They have used manures on their soils for years, if not centuries. In terms of certain trace minerals and other basics, they simply leave American growers behind.

In terms of phosphate and potassium, they can actually have levels that are so high they should forego manure applications.

Too much can inhibit yields instead of contributing to them. In fact, I had to get some clients to stop using phosphate and potassium in order to get their yields up. Those farmers in Germany who are making 120 to 200 bushels of wheat per acre are putting their nitrogen on three, four or five times each year. Most of them put it on four or five times.

Ammonium nitrate is a source of nitrogen that will work in grass type crops in about three days. If an emergency situation develops and it comes down to the proposition that if you don't do something you are going to lose yield, you can apply ammonium nitrate on corn, and in three days that corn will begin to show the effects. If urea is used, it becomes a case of "Can you water it in?"

I learned this from Dr. Roland Hauck, a research scientist at Tennessee Valley Authority in Muscle Shoals, Alabama. He pointed out that urea can be the worst form of dry nitrogen if application is to be made on top of the soil. There are two reasons for this. Number one, there is a chemical reaction between pellets of urea that touch each other. They actually start to volatilize nitrogen immediately, which means you start to lose nitrogen immediately. But this does not have to happen; the bigger loss is generally due to a biological reaction that breaks down the urea into ammonia gas. If an application is not worked in or followed by the half inch rain needed to carry it in, the result can be a dead loss. Urea converts from urea to ammonia to nitrite to nitrate. When it converts from urea to ammonia, it becomes a gas. If the material is deep enough in the soil, the gas will adsorb to the clay and humus. But without incorporation into the soil or adequate rain, you can lose an average of 25% of urea nitrogen in three days. In seven days, 50% can be lost. Many fertilizer dealers used to insist this was not true, but not anymore. Simply do a nitrate and ammonia analysis and see the situation as it is.

As for the nitrate portion of ammonium nitrate, the plant has to take it up or the soil solution will carry it away just as soon as water moves through the soil. Nitrate moves with the water. If you put on 100 pounds of ammonium nitrate, 34-0-0, then you have 17 pounds of nitrogen that either the plant has to use or it will

Hands-On Agronomy

leach away with the water. The other half is in the ammonia form. It has to go through the conversion from nitrite to nitrate. Basically, the process comes right back down to that 45 to 60 days.

Carrying nitrogen through a sprinkler system to the crops calls for 32-0-0 or 28-0-0 or else ammonium thiosulfate. The 32 form, generally, is half urea and half ammonia nitrate if it is less than 1% ammoniated, which most of it is. I tell farmers that when they order a semi-load, get up on the semi, lift the lid and smell. If it sort of knocks you back, you don't want it. There is a whole lot more than 1% ammonia in it. The part that gives the ammonia smell means it is getting away. At times suppliers inject anhydrous ammonia into the nitrogen to get the level up to 32-0-0. That is why you should buy a 32% less than 1% ammoniated.

The consideration that brings this topic together is well stated in the saw—a pound of nitrogen, is a pound of nitrogen is a pound of nitrogen and the source makes no difference. Admittedly, once you get commercial nitrogen into the plant, a pound of nitrogen is a pound of nitrogen in terms of how it affects the plant. For years and years, I have told farmers, don't topdress urea if you can use ammonium nitrate. Others said it made no difference. All at once ag research came up with a nitrogen inhibitor that could be applied to urea that would cause it to break down more slowly. All of a sudden the universities made a new discovery. Researchers everywhere who worked with urea inhibitors discovered it. They set up plots of corn with the usual control. They used ammonium nitrate on one experimental plot, and paired it with the same number of pounds of nitrogen from urea with and without an inhibitor. The control was way down, of course. The next worst was urea. Next was urea with the inhibitor and ammonium nitrate. Urea with the inhibitor and ammonium nitrate yielded the same. The highest yield was with ammonium sulfate. They showed this via slides and wrote it up for the journals.

Here is the way they approached it. For urea to be as good as ammonium nitrate, you have to use the urea with inhibitors. By the time you put the inhibitor in it, it costs about the same as ammonia nitrate. That says that when they were previously telling us that urea works just as well as ammonium nitrate, the economics were not right. At one meeting they talked for 30 minutes about this corn experiment, and the last comment was that the highest yield was with ammonium sulfate, but that it was too expensive for the farmer. The reasoning, I suppose, was that it has sulfur in it, and "the farmer does not need sulfur." Universities are actually on record in several states as saying that farmers don't need that much sulfur for corn. Our work shows that sulfur is one of the most under-rated nutrients in farming.

Once you establish that sulfur is needed, ammonium sulfate becomes the most inexpensive of all the forms of nitrogen to use. Instead of saying it is too expensive, just tell the facts and let the farmer try it and find out how much effect it has on his field for the price. Again, the researchers did the same thing with cotton. They exhibited the same nitrogen sources and the same type of results as the National Cotton Council Meetings. Again the highest yield of cotton was with ammonium sulfate, but it was dismissed as too expensive. The reason it was too expensive was not given. Could it be because sulfur is not needed for cotton either? I wrote these lines to tell you that almost all soils that I check need sulfur. Most soils need so much sulfur, in fact, that many farmers are not going to take care of the problem the first year.

Some farmers put urea on after the corn is growing and plow it in. If you add an inhibitor to urea, then you can expect more efficiency from this form of nitrogen. I also work with farmers who use anhydrous ammonia. More importantly, I have farmers who tell me if I can show them a nitrogen source other than anhydrous for the same amount of money, they will switch.

I often ask farmers who tell me this to run a 40-acre test, split it into 20s, and if they have the capability of using broadcast nitrogen they can cut the amount of nitrogen they use by 20% over using anhydrous as the source of nitrogen. I've done it time and time again. A big advantage in such cases is reducing the dangers associated with overuse of nitrogen. When you

Hands-On Agronomy

overuse nitrogen or any other nutrient, consider that every time you put too much of something in a soil, something else suffers.

It is a fact that free ammonia is toxic to living organisms. When you knife anhydrous ammonia into the soil, you are injecting free ammonia, and you are going to burn out some of the organisms. If anhydrous is applied in only a six-inch band, the assumption is that it can populate back. This is true. Just the same, the more you spread free ammonia, the harder it is on microbes. Also, the reaction of ammonia with soil moisture produces ammonium hydroxide, which raises pH. A raised pH has an effect on microbes. The most beneficial soil fungi, for instance, do not like a high pH. In fact, many can't survive in such an environment, and so they die. Later, the conversion of ammonia to nitrate is accompanied by a production of acid, which lowers pH. Now the soil bacteria have problems.

Let's consider anhydrous further. With anhydrous you should use the nitrate and ammonia test differently from when you broadcast. On a medium to heavy soil, even on a clay loam or a silt loam soil, properly testing the anhydrous can validate the following information. In, say, two to four weeks after application, a soil probe can be used to get a 12-inch sample, three inches out from the row. Another 12-inch sample should be taken the next three inches out, and so forth, to the middle. Sampling design should call for one probe exactly where the anhydrous knife ran, other probes being taken three inches either way. All should be analyzed separately. A 36-inch row will call for 13 samples. Starting with the sample from the middle, tests will reveal that 96% of all the nitrogen that the anhydrous knife inserted generally remains in a six or seven inch band. Only 4% moves out of that band—it hardly moves! In other words, the bulk of the nitrogen moves only three inches either way from the knife. In a heavy soil, it does not move further. This suggests that when you apply anhydrous as a sidedressing, the roots had better be able to move out and pick it up. You don't want to wait very late. If this weren't the case, you could actually

The pH Equation

As each of the equations for each of the chief cation elements fall into place, a principle of eco-farming becomes transparently clear. pH becomes self-adjusting when calcium, magnesium, potassium and sodium are in proper equilibrium. To answer low pH with lime regardless of the character of that lime rates attention as frustration agronomy.

pH means acidity to some people, but to eco-farmers it means a shortage of fertility elements, the same fertility elements named in the paragraph above. Professor C.E. Marshall of the University of Missouri once designed electrodes and membranes to measure ionic activity of calcium and potassium in the same way hydrogen ions are measured to determine pH. Marshall's pK and pCa illustrated clearly that ionic activities of a mixture of elements were not independent of each other. Taking calcium and potassium in combination, he discovered that potassium gained ascendancy in relative activity as cations become narrower. Magnesium, pound for pound, could raise pH up to 1.67 times as high as calcium. A soil high in magnesium and low in calcium could test pH 6.5 and still be entirely inadequate for the growth of alfalfa. Any of the major cations—calcium, magnesium, potassium and sodium—in excess can push pH up, and any one of them in lower amounts can take pH down. They have to be in balance, or the pH reading is likely to be meaningless. An equilibrium of pH at 6.2 or 6.3 for farm crops (based on these four elements in balance) will prompt plants to grow well and

> produce bins and bushels in tune with both the pedi-
> gree of the seed and the character of the soil.
> —*Charles Walters & C.J. Fenzau*
> Eco-Farm: An Acres U.S.A. Primer *(1979)*

put the anhydrous on very late and get a tremendous response for corn.

These data make their own suggestions. That is why it takes 20% more nitrogen to grow the same crop via anhydrous than when nitrogen like ammonium sulfate or nitrate is broadcast. The efficiency of uptake is increased by at least that much.

One of my clients, comparing anhydrous (82%) and ammonium sulfate (21-0-0-24), told me that by the time he figured the cost of the sulfur and the cost of the anhydrous, ammonium sulfate still saved him money. He said it saved him $5 an acre to use ammonium sulfate as compared to anhydrous ammonia and the purchase of sufficient sulfur to go with it.

What about that six-inch area in which the knife inserts the nitrogen? How much havoc do we create by putting that huge amount of nitrogen in one place? Certainly roots are going to bypass a lot more nitrogen than they do if the nutrient is spread out. This, indeed, is why it takes 20% more to do the same job. But consider what happens if nitrogen is over-supplied? First of all, too much nitrogen can induce a zinc deficiency. Zinc is instrumental in moisture absorption; therefore it takes more water to do the same job in, say, corn production. Also, excessive amounts of nitrogen tie up copper. Copper is what confers stalk strength to the plant. That is why the field that gets the nitrogen in the proper amount will exhibit quite a different scene from the one that gets too much nitrogen. In the last case, you can actually cut the stalk near the ground once tasselling has occurred and see the inside starting to disintegrate. By the time this plant has matured, there will be hardly anything left at the bottom of the stalks. The stalk falls over. One of the things that causes this is a copper deficiency. It is well documented that too much nitrogen stops copper uptake in citrus. All the manufactured nitrogen forms are guilty. But when we have to use one fifth more product in an anhydrous application, the worst effect of all can be expected. And right in the area where the roots have to feed, anhydrous will be held in escrow, which means the least amount of copper and zinc will be released.

Furthermore, the higher the concentration of nitrogen, the more humus will be lost in the soil. If you have a soil with a magnesium level above 20%, and you want to raise that elusive 200 bushels of corn, it is going to take 300 pounds of total nitrogen to achieve that goal, based on the formula of a pound and a half per bushel of corn. A total of 5% organic matter will deliver 100 pounds of nitrogen. This computes out a remainder of 200 pounds of nitrogen. Application of exactly the amount of nitrogen the corn crop needs should comply with this rigorous computation, except that enough additional nitrogen to break down residues is still required. The old rule of thumb is that it takes one pound of nitrogen per 100 pounds of residue, and this rule will work very well for corn, wheat, and other similar crops. Corn on corn will often mean 2,000 pounds or more of residue; therefore 20 pounds of nitrogen will be required for its breakdown in addition to the 200 pounds mandated by the commercial crop. Add all these figures together and the summation says 220 pounds. But it is not possible to put on 220 pounds of nitrogen with anhydrous ammonia and get the computed response. In fact, 20% more is now required. That is just a rule you have to know.

You may think this rule is way out of line, but based on university experimental plots in DeKalb County, Illinois back in the 1980s, that is what farmers were told, namely that it takes 240 pounds of nitrogen to grow not 200 bushels of corn per acre, but 175 bushels. The reason it takes so much nitrogen is that those DeKalb County soils had 40%+ magnesium and 45% calcium on the soil colloids.

Now, if your calcium is 85 or 90% base saturation, and the magnesium is 7%, it is tempting to say that since magnesium is 7%, I won't need that pound and half of nitrogen. Magnesium still affects the soil so that air and water space is not right. The magnesium may be tied up in terms of availability to the plant, but it still has an effect on the physical structure of the soil. At 85 or 90% between calcium and magnesium, there is too much effect from the magnesium, meaning you still have to use that pound and half of nitrogen. As a result, we get an over-concentration. Every pound of nitrogen used over what is needed to supply the crop and break down the residues gives false stimulation to the microbial populations. It is a lot like pushing down on the accelerator and giving your car more gas to take off and go faster. Why?

Because this added source of energy on the protein side of the equation turns microbes into feeders rather than fixers. As long as the microbial workers have residues in the soil that require digestion, the residues remain their food source. When they run out of crop residues, they don't just fall over and say, "Well, too bad, we have no more to eat." Quite the contrary, they look for another alternative food source. The next available source of food is seated in the humus content of the soil. But the microbes will not turn to humus as long as crop residues remain on-scene. When crop residues are used up, they turn to the humus and start to break it down as a food source. Humus is thus incorporated in their bodies. Extra nitrogen causes this sequence to unfold.

Plenty of nitrogen with yellow colored plants may mean there is not enough magnesium, sulfur, boron, or phosphate. When humus starts to break down, microbes start dying. Plants in turn start to pick up a portion of all the other elements that are released out of the humus. Most of the time, nitrogen gets the credit. But this isn't nitrogen alone. It is the products microbes are breaking down out of the humus.

This is how many farmers mask their trace element deficiencies. Unfortunately, this works only as long as there is a good humus supply. The lower the humus gets, the shorter the time for this crutch's survival. That is why farmers with high organic matter have the buffering capacity we are talking about. They can have a micronutrient deficiency and seemingly get by with it, whereas the grower with a lower humus content is sandbagged.

These several observations unveil the big dangers associated with nitrogen overuse. Anhydrous in the strip suggests 20% more nitrogen, but microbial breakdown of humus is enhanced dangerously. Any nitrogen source can be dangerous if overused.

Nitrogen drives out calcium. When the soil is open and nitrates leach out and go with the water, it is never a solo journey. It always takes along a passenger. If there is a cache of sodium, nitrogen may take sodium. Otherwise it takes calcium. Nitrogen never takes out magnesium, but as nitrogen leaches downward, the passenger status of calcium is assured. If calcium levels are excessive, this may be a solution of sorts. There is a corollary. For every percent calcium taken out by nitrogen, magnesium goes up 1%. Removal of 10% calcium by a nitrogen over-supply will increase the magnesium level by 10%. This is one reason nitrogen from anhydrous ammonia has a reputation for tightening soils.

In the area where I live, some of the soils are light sands. Many farmers still use anhydrous. Anhydrous (NH_4) was introduced in the southeast Missouri area by 1955. By 1965 most farmers had quit using it on their heavy black soil. Observant farmers had already concluded by then that anhydrous use made the soils harder.

Some farmers may question this statement. After all, research has determined that using anhydrous does not cause soil to be harder. This intelligence has been printed in almost all farm publications. It is nevertheless my observation that any form of nitrogen—when it drives out the calcium—contributes to making soil harder simply because it brings the magnesium level up.

Let us now consider the pH factor. Recall that pound for pound, magnesium influences pH more than calcium. Thus removal of calcium from the soil—with magnesium taking its place—will actually cause the pH to reflect less of a decrease than the actual amount of calcium removed. This means that the use of pH to calculate whether or not to lime should be questioned. If you lime back to the same pH you had before, this must be backgrounded by the fact that you no longer have the same soil you had before overusing nitrogen. What you actually have is a soil with the desired pH that is higher in magnesium and lower in calcium. It will be tighter than it was before.

That is the situation with any corn farmer who limes according to pH. Over the years, soils worsen if pH is the sole criterion, and the ability to produce goes down. Plus, it requires more and more horsepower to pull the very same implements over the very same soils.

In the panhandle of Texas, they use tremendous amounts of nitrogen on their grain sorghum and corn. The pH is still high, but our tests often suggest the need for another ton and a half or two tons of lime. The university says, "You don't need any calcium, you don't need any lime, because your pH is fine." And still those soils will not have enough calcium to support yields that could otherwise be attained. The farmer who will pay attention to this advice and put on the needed calcium will actually get his yields back up to where they used to be or even better. But growers who believe that pH is the only worthwhile index will con-

pH and Availability

The labeling of calcium as fertilizer element of first importance was delayed because scientists, like other boys, enjoyed playing with their toys. The advent of electrical instruments for measuring the hydrogen ion concentration gave tools and slight provocations and causal significance widely ascribed to them, when as a matter of fact the degree of acidity like temperature is a condition and not a cause of many soil chemical reactions. Because this blind alley of soil acidity was accepted as a thoroughfare so long and because no simple instrument for measuring calcium ionization was available, it has taken extensive plant studies to demonstrate the hidden calcium hungers in plants responsible in turn for hidden but more extensive hungers in animals. Fortunately, a truce has recently been declared in the fight on soil acidity. What was once considered a malady is now considered a beneficial condition of the soil. Instead of a bane, soil acidity is a blessing in that many plant nutrients applied to such soil are made more serviceable by its presence, and soil acidity is an index of how seriously our attention must go to the declining soil fertility.

Now we face new concepts of the mechanisms of plant nutrition. By means of studies using only the colloidal, or finer, clay fraction of the soil, it was learned that this soil portion is really an acid. It is also highly buffered or takes on hydrogen, calcium, magnesium, and any other cations in relatively large quantities to put them out of solution, and out of extensive ionic activities. It demonstrated that because of its insolubility, it can hide away many plant nutrients so that pure

> water will not remove them, yet salt solutions will exchange with them. This absorption and exchange activity of clay is the basic principle that serves in plant nutrition. This concept comes as a by-product of the studies of calcium in relation to soil acidity.
>
> *—William A. Albrecht*
> The Albrecht Papers, Volume I *(1975)*

tinue to experience faltering yields and higher fertilizer requirements. Nitrogen, in fact, is driving out their calcium.

If you use 100 pounds of nitrogen from ammonium sulfate and 100 pounds of nitrogen from ammonium nitrate (or a similar source), the ammonium sulfate will take out the same number of pounds of calcium as the 34-0-0 or as urea or as 32% or any other nitrogen form. An additional thing that the ammonium sulfate does—if the calcium is above 60% base saturation—is take out magnesium. When it takes out magnesium, it lowers pH. But when schoolmen see the pH go down, they discern no association with magnesium because the universities believe it is impossible to remove the magnesium from the soil. Based on this fiction, they count every bit of that as calcium. They rely on pH, and fail to measure what is leaving. They translate this into loss of calcium, which is not the fact. Use of ammonium sulfate when the calcium saturation is above 60% means taking out magnesium at the same time, and better control of any excesses. The farmer who has adequate calcium and uses ammonium sulfate—even without measuring calcium and magnesium—when he limes to adjust pH is taking magnesium out with the calcium. Yet, if he has excess magnesium, he is better off than the fellow who uses straight nitrogen and no sulfur. Sulfur does not have to come from ammonium sulfate. Any sulfur source has a measure of merit. Using nitrogen and sulfur together has a far greater effect on keeping a good soil as it should be than does using nitrogen by itself. This is true because sulfur takes out magnesium. If you have less than 60% calcium and use ammonium sulfate, the procedure is not going to take the magnesium out. In this case both nitrogen and sulfur will contribute to calcium losses. Growers using sulfur under such circumstances will be in the same position concerning calcium losses as the grower who is using excessive amounts of nitrogen. In compacted soil sulfur accumulates, but if soils are such that sulfur will be leached out, it won't take the magnesium because sulfur can't reduce magnesium until calcium is at least 60% saturated on the soil colloid. It will take out calcium. It will not take out potassium. It will not take out sodium or any one of the other cations, and it won't take out the magnesium, until 60% calcium is achieved and fully maintained.

If you take calcium from 85% down to 80% base saturation, then you are going to raise an 8% magnesium level by that many percentage points (5). However, if you use enough sulfur to control the magnesium at the same time (roughly two pounds of sulfur will remove a pound of magnesium when calcium is adequate), then you are not going to get into that problem.

Anhydrous ammonia is NH_3. The ammonia that attaches to the soil colloid is NH_4. NH_4 is ammonia that is already stabilized. NH_3 is ammonia gas. When urea goes from urea to ammonia, it goes from urea to NH_3 ammonia gas and then to nitrite and then to nitrate. This becomes the observed result because microbes convert it into a gas, after which it goes from nitrite to nitrate. Urea will hold, of course, if there is at least a half inch of water— rain or irrigation. Otherwise, the material must be applied and incorporated in the soil.

NO_3, nitrate, is an anion with a negative charge. Chloride has a negative charge. Sulfate, SO_4, has a double negative charge. That means it is stronger and more difficult to dislodge from the soil. Chloride leaves the soil easily. Nitrate also makes an easy exit. Sulfate stays around longer. That is good because we want it to stay put.

Sulfates move with soil water, but not as freely as nitrogen. If the sulfate didn't move out, it would never carry out the magnesium. Only the materials that move through are going to carry out those things we have in excess. That is why nitrogen can carry out calcium and why sulfur can carry out calcium, magnesium, potassium, or sodium—because they do move with the soil water. As a result, it is not good thinking to apply huge amounts of these nutrients when growing conditions are correctly maintained because they represent money thrown away.

The operating principle is to open the soil so that water can move through, or else those negatively charged elements are never going to leave and take the excesses of sodium, magnesium, calcium, etc. from the topsoil.

We'll get back to sulfate. But next to be considered is phosphate, P_2O_5, the subject of the next section.

Phos-pho-rus / 'fäs-f(e-)res / *n, often attrib* [NL, fr. Gk *phosphoros* light-bearing] 1 a solid non-metallic element of the nitrogen family existing in at least two allotropic forms, one yellow (poisonous, inflammable, and luminous), the other red (less poisonous, arid less inflammable) 2 chemical symbol:

3 release in soils depends on decomposition of organic compounds 4 contained in all tissues with concentrations most pronounced in young plants (seeds and flowers) 5 superphosphate, triple-superphosphate, rock phosphate, and organic fraction phosphates, proteins, phospholipids, etc. are labile—undergo chemical and physical change while not necessarily available 6 essential for building sound bones and teeth, and for assimilation of carbohydrates and fats 7 necessary for enzyme activation

7

The Reluctant Nutrient

PLANTS NEED PHOSPHORUS FOR PHOTOSYNTHESIS, for respiration, for energy storage and transfer, and for cell division. There is a pregnant paragraph in *Eco-Farm—An Acres U.S.A. Primer* that merits reproduction here, and an instant replay at least once a year. It says...

"When farmers talk about phosphorus, they usually talk about phosphorus deficiency. Indeed, phosphorus deficiency in humid soils has become legend. It is an anion, but it is united rapidly with divalent calcium, a cation, to become insoluble, and therein lies the whiff and whoof of phosphorus fertilization. The weak carbonic acid from a plant root can't seem to activate bound up phosphorus. Apatite is quite insoluble. Rock phosphate in any form becomes available reluctantly, and this is one of the reasons why soils should be at least slightly acid. But the fact is science still does not have a clear picture of what happens with phosphorus in the soil."

Perhaps this is why we see soils with a pH in the 7.0 to 8.0+ range that will still show an available root acid-soluble phosphate increase when rock phosphate is applied.

Phosphate has a triple negative charge, which makes it strong enough to stay put. It can attach with calcium—which has a positive charge—for which reason the two can be held in the soil. Phosphate, as generally considered in the past, has to be placed where it is needed. Depending on the form, this is still true. But phosphate applied in large amounts of manure or compost can be built to excessive levels and leached downward through the soil. Even so, if placement is restricted to the top quarter-inch of soil, it will not feed the plant once that soil dries out.

Most plants contain 0.2 to 0.4% phosphorus. Though it is considered a major nutrient along with nitrogen and potassium, the amount is small by comparison. There is only 0.2 or 0.4 pound—or not even a half pound—of phosphorus in 100 pounds of average plant material. Still phosphorus is considered the workhorse of plant nutrition because it has to be there for cell division and growth, for photosynthesis and for energy transfer from ADP to ATP. It is absorbed into the plant as orthophosphate ions. In other words, H_2PO_4, with a single negative charge, or HPO_4, with a double negative charge. But the phosphorus and the hydrogen do not do it all by themselves. As my friend, Zoell Colburn, used to say when he taught agronomy courses, "The soil is the plant's stomach." That stomach, for eight tons of alfalfa, has to process 450 pounds of nitrogen as well as 95 pounds of phosphate. A 150 bushel corn harvest takes 85 pounds of phosphate. Soybeans require 55 pounds in terms of a 50 bushel crop. Wheat, at 60 bushels, takes up 55 pounds of phosphate.

Spring or fall application is governed by the crop you intend to grow. If the crop is winter wheat, then conditions change versus growing a spring crop, especially one like corn. If you are going to grow soybeans, then a different situation comes to the fore. If in doubt, and it is a crop to be planted in the spring, the suggestion is to apply phosphate in the spring. If applied in adequate amounts on the day of planting, and if it is the right form of phosphate, it will be taken up by the crop as needed.

Fall applications are special cases as far as specific crops are concerned—special cases having to do with the type of crop and the type of phosphorus to be used. Phosphate type in turn differentiates between plant feeders and soil feeders. A plant feeder type of phosphorus must be applied close to the time it is needed by the crop. Plant feeder phosphates are usually the cheapest; 0-46-0 (triple superphosphate, called 0-20-0 in Australia) is a plant feeder. You can apply 500 pounds, or 1,000 pounds, as a fall application and it ties up quickly. Next spring you won't have any more phosphate than you had the spring before. The product is a plant feeder, not a soil feeder. Within one to two months after it is applied, it reverts back to tricalcium phosphate, a form that the plant cannot easily pick up unless it is a legume.

Phosphate value depends on availability. When farm publications tell about phosphate tie up, they are talking about plant feeders. The other phosphate product that used to be talked about in the same category is superphosphate, 0-20-0 (called 0-9-0 in Australia). It is not used much in U.S. production agriculture these days. Phosphates in this form won't leach out of the soil. They either get tied up or remain available for a relatively short period of time.

The condition of the soil will help determine how available the phosphate will remain. A reserve of phosphorus in the soil is always best. In fact, it is always better to have more than the crop requires. When test figures reveal a phosphate deficiency at least the minimum desired value for crops should be provided. You can get by with a little less on soybeans, but if you are raising 150 bushels of corn or more, you normally won't get by on the minimum, often shown as "desired value" on soil tests. With just the minimum of phosphate farmers can actually limit yields, especially in the years when you have cool, wet seasons or when all the other conditions are there for top yields.

Because phosphate is not easily moved, the most common ways to lose it completely is via wind or water erosion. If you need it on top, then put it on top. If you need it down under, then try to put it on so that you can get it worked and mixed into the top six or seven inches of soil. I am not suggesting that you work it down 12 inches. Work it in as deep as the fencepost rots because that is how deep the microbes are going to work on it and keep it available. If you put it down deeper, chemical reactions in the soil take place, none of them of necessary benefit for getting phosphate to the crop.

Some crops need more phosphate just to make the kind of yields farmers have now come to expect. It used to be that 100 bushels of corn was considered a good yield. For some areas it still may be, but not generally. On the other hand, if you have a soil with excellent phosphate readings, it is human nature to think you don't have to worry about phosphate "this year." That always depends. If you start working the field wet so that some mud holes survive, and you run through those, then it turns cool for three or four days, you are likely to see a phosphate deficiency in those areas. Whenever that soil gets packed and the roots can't move out, the plant will not get the phosphate unless you put it right there on the spot. This has been observed to happen on entire fields. If you already know that you have to plant corn and work that soil wet or you will never get over all your acreage, you might just as well say, "When I do that I need some starter phosphorus!" In such cases, 0-46-0, 0-20-0 or a liquid starter can be extremely beneficial.

In southeast Missouri, every so often we have such cool, wet weather. The farmers who put on no phosphate, or actually put too little on their corn, show a phosphate deficiency to the point that the corn turns purple and at times even brown. Many farmers in the area are told they don't need much phosphate, just a little triple super for a starter. I have a reputation in the area for saying that farmers need more phosphorus than others claim they really need! That is what the people who don't use our program tend to say about my recommendations. There are some labs that tell these same farmers they don't need any phosphate at all.

Well, a few years ago, a fertilizer dealer called me and said, "Neal, on every farm you don't work with in this area, the corn is turning brown."When that shows up in corn, you have already missed your top yield. When that purple color comes into the leaf of the corn plant, you have probably lost 15 bushels of corn. You don't ever want to get to that condition. As a consequence, some reserve phosphate is a good practice. When you are growing 150 bushels of corn per acre using the type testing we use, 240 pounds of phosphate is not testing high enough. If you are above 300, then if you don't work it wet that is enough. If you are going to work it wet, especially if the weather turns cool again, you need to put a starter in there anyway—not necessarily very much, but a little! Phosphate availability in the soil is affected by the amount and type of clay. Availability is also affected by application time and method. If you put it on top, it is essentially going to stay there, and it is not going to be available except when there is moisture at the top.

Phosphate availability is also increased or decreased with aeration, compaction and moisture. If you have plenty of moisture, the roots will feed right at the top and go on down as far as there is moisture. When you have compaction, the root can't move out. Roots have to move and come in contact with phosphate. If you don't have adequate aeration, microbes are not going to be able to do their work properly. Then you are not going to accomplish proper P conversion in order to assure there is enough hydrogen present for the phosphorus, so as to keep it in a form the plant can use. Availability is also affected by the level of phosphate and other nutrients in the soil. If you have high sulfur, you need high P levels, and vice versa. If a soil has borderline phosphorus and high zinc, the zinc can actually cause a problem—and you don't get enough phosphate.

Actually, it works both ways. I once worked with an Illinois farmer. He had this one field with good soil based on past soil tests. He raised good crops, but never made as much yield as he expected there. When he put this field in corn, yield was always short compared to his other fields. Soil samples were taken and sent to the lab, and the audit agreed that this farm had a tremendous soil. His calcium was right and his magnesium was right. All the micronutrients were there. Then I got to the last nutrient on the list—zinc—6 ppm zinc being enough; 50 ppm zinc reportedly can kill a 50 year old grapefruit tree. He had 275 ppm zinc in the field. He supposedly had five times more than enough to kill an old tree, and he was still raising corn. That field was located near a glass factory. Smoke coming out of the stack was showering zinc on his field. Although phosphate tested excellent, the only thing I could tell that farmer to do was to put on some extra phosphorus. He applied extra phosphorus that year. After harvest he reported that this field—for the first time ever—was just as good as his other fields in terms of yield. The zinc was so high it was keeping the phosphorus from doing the proper job.

Usually, soil out of kilter and containing excessive zinc will not produce good corn yields. But balance in the top six inches—other than the high zinc—will make it possible for the plant to tolerate an unusually high zinc level. You can have an excellent phosphate level and have zinc levels so high that the phosphorus is not getting into the plant properly. When the weather gets cool, the plant can't pick phosphate up very well. When the soil temperature gets cool, the ADP conversion to ATP is slowed down or stopped.

Also remember, phosphate availability is affected by soil pH. With a pH of 6.5, phosphate availability from that influence is generally going to be as good as it can be. Another element that affects it is calcium availability. Most phosphate in a crop is contained in the fruit or the seed. In a 180-bushel corn crop there are 78 pounds of phosphorus in the grain and 30 pounds in the stalks. In 60 bushels of soybeans there are 48 pounds of phosphorus in the grain and 16 pounds in the stalks. Every time you harvest a 180-bushel corn crop, you are taking off roughly 78 pounds of phosphorus. In and around southeast Missouri, our corn yields run 165 to 200+ bushels per acre. The old rule of thumb for our corn soils calls for maintenance of phosphorus at 70 pounds of P_2O_5 per acre. If growers don't put on a maintenance level of 70 pounds on such a corn crop, yields won't stay up. If double crop soybeans follow wheat, you will lose ground on 70 pounds of phosphate. If you have 500 pounds in the soil and you remove 70, then you are still not in such bad shape. If you have 300 pounds in the soil and take out 70, that puts the level down to 230, and there is not a soil I know where high yields will not go backward with such a low phosphate level if sufficient phosphate fertilizer is not applied.

Of course, there will always be cases cited that seem to contradict this as being true. One such study may help demonstrate the point. A research farm received 40 pounds of P_2O_5 per acre for four years and came out with two bushels less than where no such fertilizer had been applied. The second four years had 19 bushels more yield. The third four-year period had 28 bushels per acre more yield. When the fourth set of four years ended, there was an increase of 43 bushels per acre. How can 40 pounds per acre of P_2O_5 make such a difference, when we advise using 70 pounds per acre each year as maintenance? Results will depend on the soil's original P_2O_5 level (which was not provided with this university research report), the crop to be grown, and what phosphate type has previously been applied to that soil.

When considering soybeans, there is a possibility this could easily happen. It is still not recommended when levels are extremely deficient. Eventually though, the phosphate level could be built up if growing legumes where hard rock phosphate, or 0-46-0, or 0-20-0 have been applied over a number of years. My advice to each farmer or grower is start with a soil test and use the proper phosphate where the need is indicated. If the numbers begin to decrease, not enough phosphate is being used, or else it is not the correct form with which to build phosphate levels.

Now let's consider what materials should be used to increase phosphate levels in the soil. In the U.S. concentrated superphosphate (triple superphosphate or 0-46-0) is generally the most common, lowest priced source on the market. Two other popular commercial sources are diammonium phosphate (18-46-0) and monoammonium phosphate (which is 11-48-0 or 11-52-0). Also considered are normal superphosphate which is 0-20-0, hard rock phosphate, which is roughly 33% P_2O_5, and soft rock phosphate. Soft rock is sometimes called colloidal phosphate.

If you take concentrated superphosphate (0-46-0), and diammonium phosphate (18-46-0), and superphosphate (0-20-0), and run the same type of test Dr. Albrecht advocated as needed to show phosphate availability, the following conclusions would prove true. Of course, you don't have to use the 0-20-0. You could do the experiment with the other two, or even use 11-52-0 in comparison with 0-46-0 if desired. Just remember, a P_1 water soluble phosphate test will not show these results. The type of test that measures water-soluble and root acid-soluble phosphate in the soil, the type of test Dr. Albrecht actually used, is required here. With this point kept in mind, consider a study the

---

The Corrective Treatment

The most ideal situation, therefore, is for the farmer to work into his soil the total amount of rock phosphate recommended in his soil report, and then apply from 20 to 80 pounds per acre (according to his phosphorus values) of a water-soluble P_2O_5 fertilizer in the first season, and to continue applying from 10 to 40 pounds per acre of water soluble P_2O_5 yearly thereafter until the analysis of the soil shows that he has attained the desired level of active phosphorus in the soil. At this point he may live upon the interest only, not touching the principal itself.

On the other hand, there are some farmers who have the honest conviction that rock phosphate is not effective as a phosphorus supplement to soil. They insist on using only the water-soluble forms of phosphorus fertilizers available on the market.

Many do not realize that the phosphorus thus supplied them comes from rock phosphate in the first instance. For example, by treating 1,400 pounds of a 33% rock phosphate material with 1,200 pounds of sulfuric acid, a 20% superphosphate fertilizer is produced in which the tricalcium phosphate form of phosphorus in the rock phosphate is converted to the water-soluble monocalcium phosphate form. Such chemical reaction causes 20% superphosphate to be represented by approximately 45% of monocalcium phosphate and 55% of calcium sulfate (gypsum).

Thus, in 100 pounds of the usual 20% superphosphate (0-20-0) fertilizer, two separate materials are provided in the one package, representing approximately 45 pounds of water-soluble monocalcium phosphate, which is desired and approximately 55 pounds of calcium sulfate which may or may not be desired. In 100 pounds of the concentrated triple superphosphate (0-45-0) the acid treatment is made with phosphoric acid. This eliminates the calcium sulfate from the fertilizer material. Ammonium phosphate such as 8-32-0, 11-48-0, etc., involves the use of concentrated phosphoric acid in its processing.

However, the fact that such unstable monocalcium phosphate is subject to natural reversion to the stable tricalcium phosphate form must be given practical concern. This rate of reversion to the stable form differs greatly in soils, and is usually subject to the amount of organic matter, the pH, and the free calcium in the soil.

—Rudolf Ozolins
private papers, Acres U.S.A. collection

Tennessee Valley Authority published back in the 1950s, that should be of benefit when there is a need for phosphate.

In order to correctly verify the results, test your soil first. Try to select a field that will test relatively even throughout in terms of phosphate availability. Take separate soil tests from each area that will receive the phosphate materials as well as a control area where no P fertilizer will be applied. This will assure that you know what the original phosphate levels show. (Some studies on fertility have been conducted and quoted as fact, where the researchers did not even check for and report the levels essential for crop production in that soil first.) Then whatever forms of phosphate you intend to utilize—and this is speaking in terms of a fall application to be tested again the next spring—apply each source on one of the tested areas of the field, leaving at least one area as the control which receives no phosphate. Another note is needed here for those with soil pH levels above 7.5. Phosphate as 11-52-0 will work on such high pH soils, but 18-46-0 is not recommended for use there.

If you use 11-52-0 or 18-46-0 with the pH criteria in mind and apply 250 pounds of material per acre in the fall, then the following spring run a soil test on the area that did not get any phosphate and on the area or areas that did. You will find a greater phosphate increase using the test we employ where the 11-52-0 or 18-46-0 was applied than on the area where nothing was applied. If you use 0-46-0 and put on 250 pounds of it per acre (the same amount of phosphate as from the 18-46-0) and test again in the spring, the side that did not receive any phosphate will contain just as much available P for the crop as the side that received 0-46-0 at 250 pounds, or even 500 pounds per acre, or whatever amount was applied. This is because 0-46-0 (triple superphosphate) ties up in the soil within one to two months after it is applied. And that is just what the TVA studies revealed.

The TVA study determined this by taking those materials and treating them with a radioactive substance before application was made. Tissue analysis measured the uptake of phosphorus.

Because it was tagged with a radioactive substance, they could measure how much of the phosphorus came from the commercial source and how much of the phosphorus came from the soil. With 0-46-0, in a year that had excellent growing conditions, 20% of the phosphorus came from applied phosphate, and 80% came from P sources already present in the soil. Incidentally, in the year with good growing conditions, that phosphate kept on being taken up by the plant for two months. In the years when they had poor growing conditions, the phosphate that was tagged would only be taken up for about four weeks. Under poor growing conditions fully 90% of the phosphorus in that plant came from a source that was already in the soil and 10% came from the factory fertilizer. But with the 18-46-0, the phosphate did not tie up. It continued to remain in an available form and to be taken up by the plant. This is the same as we see from the tests we use. Here is another way to test the value of your soil test in correctly measuring your soil's fertility. Does it show a sufficient increase when 18-46-0, 11-52-0, or soft rock phosphate is applied, as compared to 0-46-0, and perhaps in some countries 0-20-0?

With 0-46-0 under poor growing conditions, it remains available for four weeks. Under good growing conditions, it stayed available for eight weeks. At best, only 20% had its tag mark. The rest came from sources already in the soil. For crops such as wheat, corn, cotton, trees and grass, if you must use 0-46-0, use it like a starter fertilizer. It is a plant feeder, not a soil feeder.

The fertilizer industry has access to this research as much as I do. Most people simply do not pay attention to the research. As a matter of fact, I had a fellow who spoke at one of my seminars in St. Louis on corn production, namely 200-bushel corn production. He was a researcher for one of the commercial fertilizer companies. He was from Germany, where he earned his doctorate. He addressed our group because he understood base saturation and exchange capacity. He made the comment at a meeting I attended that if you balance out your soils by using the proper amounts of all the nutrients and get your base saturation percentage right, it will take less fertilizer to do the same job and you can raise much higher yields. At lunch one of the farmers said, "You are researching all this, but I never hear any of this from your company." He said, "You know, it is an amazing thing to me. They pay us this money to do all this research and the marketing arm never pays any attention to any of the research that we are doing. The people in marketing, even though it is written up and printed and shown, never say anything about this because the executives are too busy avoiding a loss to be concerned about helping the farmer. I don't mean they are trying to make a profit, I mean they are too busy avoiding a loss. In the fertilizer industry today it is a matter that the prices are such that they are just trying to stay where they are and keep from losing money."

Facts about fertility are not highly rated in importance for most fertilizer companies it seems. If you attend a two-day industry sponsored fertilizer conference, you will hear perhaps two lectures on fertility. They will tend to concentrate on getting new accounts, holding and keeping current accounts, keeping up with receivables, and the rest on how to meet government regulations.

If you are a conventional grower planning to apply phosphorus in the fall for crops to be grown in the spring, use an ammoniated phosphate. Use diammonium phosphate (18-46-0), monoammonium phosphate (11-52-0), or liquid polyphosphates. If you use enough, polyphosphates will build just like the ammoniated phosphate. But you have to put on enough polyphosphate to get 70 pounds of phosphorus if you are going to need 70 pounds for making that next crop. Normally, by the time you compare diammonium phosphate or monoammonium phosphate with polyphosphate, the liquid is so much more expensive that it is not going to be used to build your phosphate levels.

When a "plant feeder" fertilizer source is used in the fall, the key to increased springtime soil phosphates is residue. Phosphate levels will go up if microbes have enough residues to break down. The increase is from breakdown of the residues, and not from phosphate that is applied. That is why a check is important.

Why does a soil system tie up triple-super (0-46-0), and why doesn't it tie up 11-52-0? Triple superphosphate has a pH of 3.0 or less. When you put something that has a pH of 3.0 on a soil that has a pH of 5.5 or 6 or 6.5 or 7 or 7.5, how long would you think it is going to stay in the form it is in? The answer is, "Not very long!" In a year with adverse conditions, it is not going to stay more than a month. In a very good year, it could last as long as two months. When you put on that pH 3.0 material, it will start to combine with calcium because phosphorus is attracted to the calcium and is drawn to it the way many southerners are drawn to black-eyed peas. What you wind up with in four to eight weeks is tricalcium phosphate. Tricalcium phosphate is the parent material in hard rock phosphate.

To make triple super (0-46-0), they take hard rock phosphate and process it with sulfuric acid, the resultant product being styled 0-20-0. To get sulfur and calcium out, and a higher concentration of phosphorus in, they process the parent material with phosphoric acid. This yields a straight phosphate material, but the pH is 3.3 or less. Unless your soil will break down and use rock phosphate, or unless the crop you are growing there will break down and use rock phosphate, then you are not going to get any more good for the immediate crop out of that phosphorus after the first four to eight weeks. That is bad for wheat, corn, and grass-type crops. It is not so bad for legumes; because as older literature will tell you, when you put on hard rock phosphate, legumes will take the phosphate they need beginning the first year. So if you have places where you have used triple superphosphate, the legumes can actually start to process some nutrient out and make it usable. Once the legume processes it out and gets it in the right form, it is not going to easily revert back to the unavailable form again. After the plant picks it up and once it dies and decomposes, that P will be the first source the next set of plants will tap.

In Florida, I ran some samples on soils that had pHs as low as 5.5. If you are going to get triple superphosphate availability, you are going to get it on 5.5 pH soils. Area farmers grew cabbage, and their customary practice for cabbage was to put on 600 pounds of 0-46-0 per acre per year. The soils where they had grown cabbage 20 years ago had finally come to the point that with poultry manure applications the superphosphate was breaking down and becoming available. When you put on phosphorus and you are not growing legumes, use an ammoniated source.

I grew up on farms, mostly rented land from 500 to 1,200 acres. But when I started to learn about soils from William A. Albrecht, I actually didn't remember whether P stood for phosphorus or potassium.

Back then farmers tended to order by the number of pounds of N-P-K desired, not by requesting specific product. They would call up and say, "I want 120-50-90," or whatever, and the fertilizer dealer would send it out. There are probably farmers who still do it this way. It is the easy way. With the exception of costs, pricing and where to get it, sometimes the fertilizer dealer knows no more about fertilizers than most farmers. Too many dealers don't generally know how fertilizers work in the soil. When you go to the fertilizer dealer, don't say 18-46-0, say diammonium phosphate or ammoniated phosphate.

What a fertilizer dealer may do—if you don't specify—is take 0-46-0 already on hand and mix it with some urea so that the analysis won't be exactly 18-46-0. All you have to do is have 18% nitrogen in it. So he mixes the urea and the concentrated superphosphate and spreads it on your soil and says, "You've got 150 pounds of 18-46-0," but you don't. That superphosphate still has a pH in the 3.0 range. For diammonium phosphate, the pH will run in the middle sixes. When you put triple superphosphate down, you are instilling pH 3.0 or so and it is going to tie up quickly. If you apply 18-46-0, it will remain available because it is already matched into the pH range and is not grabbing for calcium to balance itself out.

In my meetings with farmers, I always make the comment that if you put on 150 pounds of 18-46-0, you are applying 69 pounds of available phosphorus for the next crop. When you put that on and do a soil test the next year—if you have grown a 150-bushel corn crop—the phosphate will be about the same as where you started. So, fertility-wise, you really have gained nothing. On the other hand, if we put on 250 pounds of 18-46-0, which is 115 pounds of phosphate, rather than 69, when we come back next year and take the same 150 bushels of corn off, instead of being where we were before, we will actually have gone up by 100 pounds of available phosphorus. This represents an increase of 100 pounds when putting on only 115 pounds per acre.

When making presentations, I always tried to point out that I didn't know why this happened. An attendee, who used to teach horticulture at Purdue University, sent a paper by a Dr. Fox from Columbia University, who went around the world studying phosphates. What he found was that when you put phosphorus on a soil, a certain amount is actually "absorbed" by the soil and then after you saturate the soil with phosphorus, the rest will stay there and be used by the plants. That partially answered it, but could the true answer be that when you put the smaller amount on, the microbial population in that soil uses up the phosphorus? And in effect, applying the larger amount enables the microbes to breakdown or release some extra phosphorus. Otherwise, how are you going to be able to apply 115 pounds and still have 100 pounds left, suggesting that you took out only 15 pounds to grow that 150-bushel corn crop? It will happen year after year after year. A maintenance level in general for diammonium phosphate or monoammonium phosphate is about 70 pounds per acre, whereas larger applications will begin to build levels in the soil.

If you are using 30 pounds of phosphate every year and already have a good phosphate level, that means you have good microbial activity and you should have a good phosphate release in that soil. If your levels aren't going down, then you don't have to change those 30 pounds. Just monitor it. If you see that you are using over 30 pounds, and the soil keeps steadily declining, it's time to do something.

A good friend once consulted in the area of Marion, Ohio. At a seminar in Texas he came up to me literally with tears in his eyes. He was 64 or 65, and he said, "You are the first man to say what I have understood about soils and have used all these years."

He had no love affair with some of the liquids that people used in place of basic fertilizers. He said, "If you have never used them before and you don't know what your soil situation is, you can use them for one year and be pretty safe if you have been putting on fertilizer regularly. If you don't know what your soil situation is and you use them two years in a row, you are pressing it. The fellow with poor soil who doesn't know his soil situation and uses them for five years, by the third year will start saying, 'Well, the weather is not the same or this condition is not the same.' It will generally take six or seven years before he realizes what is happening." This is talking about where a liquid product containing phosphate is marketed, and the company tells you that you don't need anything else for phosphate, and you have low fertility levels. If you have medium fertility levels and you start out that way, then it depends on how fast you are taking the nutrients out. In theory, you can last for several years. If levels are excellent, nothing would be required for several years longer.

I am not saying that people selling these materials are hurting soils on purpose because they have farms that show their findings, and some of them deeply believe in their hearts that it works. But do they take a soil test that shows the whole story? A soil test that reveals exchange capacity and base saturation percentages would be more to the point. You can have tremendous levels of phosphate and potassium that will remain so for years. Yet some will see high levels gone in three years. Some may last five years or even longer. There are farms that I work with right now on which it has been seven, eight or nine years since any

Hands-On Agronomy

form of phosphate or potash have been applied, all without manures or biologicals, and more than adequate levels are still there. But such cases are the rare exceptions.

I had a client up near Gibson City, Illinois. He called me during a drought year. He said, "I have rented 160 acres next door to me, $125 an acre. I want you to analyze the soils." His neighbor had been farming it for years and he didn't have any idea what the fertility levels were. The soil was analyzed and shown to be extremely deficient in P and K. In fact there was a 150+ phosphate deficiency. He had a 200 to 300 pound potassium deficiency. Percentage wise, the potash was below 2%. His dilemma was self-evident. "I have already rented it," he said, "and next year the owner's son-in-law hopes to farm it. I probably won't get it again. How can I grow a crop here without spending a huge amount of money that I am not going to be able to get back?" I asked him to find out if the landlord had ever used a product such as 9-18-9 or 10-20-10. The answer came back: he never had. I told the farmer, "You can grow a fine crop as long as you put either product two inches beside and below the seed, and put on plenty of nitrogen as far as the corn is concerned. He bought the material and put it on all of his corn. He applied the nitrogen that was required. He also made a liquid application on his beans. When he got to his last tank, he saw he wasn't going to finish the field. So he began on the other side of the field to finish up. Therefore he had a little area in the middle of the field that didn't get any treatment. He told me later that this was his check.

My wife, Linda, comes to many of my meetings and helps with registration and the like. She seldom pays attention to the fine points of fertilization. She would let me handle that while she concentrated on doing all the things a good wife and mother does. We were visiting with this farmer and his wife and in time we went out the back door for something. Here were his soybeans with the check strip out on the ridge. She looked out at them and said, "Jim, what did you do to those soybeans in the middle? Why are they so yellow?"

Later, Jim said, "Neal, where I came in and applied that small amount of liquid fertilizer like you said, I made 16 bushels more soybeans to the acre over where I didn't." That was a situation where I was trying to get him by for one year.

Now let's conclude on phosphate, specifically with rock phosphate. I put rock phosphate into two classifications—hard rock and soft rock. Hard rock is not generally available in the market these days. If you do have access to hard rock phosphate, keep in mind that while it can raise the phosphate level in the soil, if it isn't ground extremely fine, the only type crop that can easily benefit during the first year is generally a legume. It takes the second year to release enough for wheat. And it requires a third year to bring the release sequence up to where you can expect to be. Once the pH gets above 6.5, it becomes more difficult for hard rock phosphate to remain available. But it can still build even at 8.0+ pH, although the often used P_1 phosphate test will not show such to be the case. Consequently, and because it may be slower to release, hard rock phosphate has gotten a bad reputation.

Commercial fertilizer people and some concerned with the environment who knew no better used to say to avoid soft rock phosphate because it has so much aluminum. In 1973, when the fuel crisis came along, we also developed a "phosphate crisis." Farmers had to find some new answers. One consultant took a sample of soft rock phosphate and sent it in. There was nothing in it that was toxic. Growers started using it by the carload in Iowa, where I originally learned about it. I had some of my clients start using it. Accordingly, several lessons emerged. If we had a slight phosphate deficiency and a corn crop to be planted, we could put on 300 pounds of soft rock or colloidal phosphate in the spring and still have the phosphate available in time for the corn. There would be no deficiency that year. The minimum amount indicated is 300 pounds, and that is much like putting on 150 pounds of diammonium phosphate. You just maintain where you are and the next year you will have to do it again. When you put on 250 pounds of diammonium phosphate, which is 115 pounds of phosphorus, you raise your levels by 100 pounds. If you put on 500 pounds of soft rock phosphate, you can also raise that same phosphate level by 100 pounds per acre. The levels will actually go up from one year to the next if you use 500 pounds. On the test we always use if you have 200 pounds of available phosphorus and you put on 500 pounds of soft rock phosphate, next year you will have 300 pounds of available phosphate. If you have excessive calcium levels, rock phosphate should be ruled out for building up P levels. This is because 500 pounds of soft rock phosphate will also supply 100 pounds of available calcium. So with the soft rock, we put on 100 pounds of available calcium and you increase the phosphate store by 100 pounds per acre. If you need calcium and phosphorus, this is a terrific source. If you already have too much calcium, application of more is not a viable option. There is a drawback. A mere 500 pounds of that material is not "commercial" as far as many handlers are concerned. They have to order it by the carload.

Protection by Proteins

Plants also protect themselves by means of proteins. Experimental trials have demonstrated that by increasing those fertility elements in the soil which were serving for increasing proteins in the young plants, there was provided increasing protection against the attack by a fungus, suggesting one connected with the "damping off" disease. In another experiment, more nitrogen and more calcium offered to vegetable plants for higher concentrations of proteins in these food crops, gave more protection against attack on the plants by leaf-eating insects. Here was suggested the possible converse of this demonstration, namely, that the increasing fungus diseases of our crops and the increasing insect attacks on them seem to be premised on deficiencies of protective proteins in the plants, and these in turn on the deficiencies of the fertility in the soil.

Shall we not, then, open our minds to the possibility that the shortages of proteins and shortages of all that is associated with them in their synthesis by microbes, by plants, and by animals, are prohibiting us through a kind of malnutrition from collecting and creating the necessary list of proteins by which our bodies can protect themselves, or build their own immunity?

—*William A. Albrecht*
private papers, Acres U.S.A. collection

The dealers do not want to get stuck with unsalable product. This often puts sourcing into the farmer's corner. In terms of availability the product rated 18-46-0 doesn't seem to last as long as the soft rock phosphate. Soft rock seems to break down over a longer period of time. I have clients who use soft rock. They simply figure that once they attain the proper level on a good soil, it is going to be five, eight or maybe even ten years before they have to make an application again. Growers should not assume this to be the case, use the soil test to be sure.

Crops need phosphate for rapid seedling development. If you want to get a crop started, you have to have plenty of phosphorus, not only for winter hardiness, but also for disease resistance, efficient water use, early maturity and maximum yields.

When it comes to crops and animal nutrition, don't skimp on soil phosphorus. I learned this from a good friend of mine in Virginia who has a master's degree in animal nutrition, but also works with soils. He used the same soil test I use. He said, "We had a new clover that was introduced in Virginia for pasture and livestock. Some farmers loved that clover. Others cursed it because they said it caused terrible bloat in their cattle." He started looking at his client's pastures. Most farmers check all their cropping fields, but if the permanent pastures ever get checked at all, they come last. Anyway, what he found was this, any farmer who had 500+ in phosphates, his cattle didn't bloat on the clover. When there was less phosphate, the cattle were far more prone to bloat. With this excellent level of phosphorus in the soil, there was no bloat problem.

What am I talking about when I say 500 pounds of phosphate? There are said to be over a dozen ways to run a phosphate test and there are several different ways to report the results. A low number on a phosphate test, say, 50 to 70 pounds, is considered adequate, and 80 pounds could mean excellent in terms of the P_1 water-soluble phosphate test. The P_1 or water-soluble phosphate test tells you what you have right now, this minute. It

---

Calcium and Phosphorus

Calcium and phosphorus are deposited in the bones and teeth in chemical combination with each other. If one is lacking, there is nothing for the other to combine with, therefore one without the other is of little value. Phosphorus is found in meats, dairy products, foods made from grain, and vegetables. Of the eight major soil minerals, phosphorus is by far the least abundant. A deficiency of calcium, the most abundant mineral element in the animal body, is associated with the lack of phosphorus. The importance of having an abundant supply of these minerals in the soil is at once apparent when we consider that 95% of the inorganic bone material in animals is composed of calcium phosphate. Sea water contains 0.1 ppm, and although much less than its calcium content, it serves a very important function.

—*Charles B. Ahlson*
Health from the Sea & Soil *(1962)*

---

does not measure the amount of phosphorus that is going to be released over an entire growing season. Moreover, this test is not accurate after a 74% calcium saturation has been reached. Once you get to 74% calcium, a P_1 phosphate test will show a much lower P level than is actually the case.

The test we use for phosphate is a water-soluble and root acid-soluble test. The reason for the test is to see what the phosphate availability is for the entire growing season. This is a P_2 test. Since it is a water-soluble and root acid-soluble phosphate test, it does calculate the root acid-solubles that are going to be released over a growing season. If pH is above 7.5, then this test is not always accurate either. Automatically, when you send a soil for analysis if it is above 7.5, a second phosphate test, namely the Olsen test will be run. Relying on the Olsen test, if your calcium is correct and your other levels are there, 80 pounds per acre is enough. If you have 120 pounds, it is considered enough no matter what.

When we say 300 pounds per acre is the minimum you need for phosphate, the subject is water-soluble plus root acid-soluble P. And this is the minimum. I like to see phosphate levels in the 500 to 750 range. At 500 pounds per acre, the P level is considered *excellent*, but at more than 750 pounds, problems are coming down the pike on the other side. When phosphorus gets too high, it starts tying up copper and zinc. Above 1,000 pounds per acre, problems come in platoons. I have seen trees in citrus orchards die because phosphate levels were above 1,000 pounds per acre on the test we use. The conventional wisdom says nobody ever gets there. There are many growers who use too much manure or compost and get there.

For phosphate availability the Olsen test is used above a pH 7.5. And with our phosphate recommendation we must consider whether the calcium level is excessive or excellent or good or deficient. We must do the same with the tests for magnesium, potassium, phosphorus, sulfur and the trace minerals. We always hear about getting phosphorus on and keeping it there early, except for corn. With corn we don't just want it there early. After about 30 days for growing corn there is a good, even uptake of phosphate until almost the 100th day. Corn uses phosphate from start to finish, and it takes more between the 30th or 40th day to about day 100. A severe phosphate shortage will be revealed by a reddish-purple color. Younger plants tend to exhibit more pronounced signs and symptoms. Most of the time the plant can compensate, still it is possible to have phosphate deficiencies and never see purple in the leaf. Phosphate shortage interferes with pollination and kernel fill. It causes the ears to be small and curved to one side. The key to getting ear development is phosphorus in seed production. I have clients who show 400 and 500 pounds of phosphorus per acre. Still they will say they need more phosphorus because the last half inch of the cob didn't fill out. For the particular analysis we use, a reading of 300 pounds per acre is enough to completely fill the ears of 150+ bushels of corn.

When you have 400 or 500 pounds of phosphorus, you are well past having enough. When you fail to get fill on the tip of the cob, the first order of business is to look for a phosphate deficiency. If phosphate reads 300 plus, the problem may be borate as from boron. The first fellow I ever heard about who used boron on corn was a man up in Illinois. According to University of Illinois Extension, two pounds of boron will kill corn. This fellow used four pounds of actual boron to the acre, and if he couldn't get it on any other way, he would hire an airplane to fly it on. He said it made him more corn. When asked exactly what four pounds of boron did for him, he said, "Well, it makes the cobs longer." It looked like the ears actually got longer because it filled them all the way out to the end and put a kernel on the tip. Consider phosphate first, but do not let the lack of borate fool you into buying more phosphate when more than enough is already present. Test your soil to see what level of phosphate is there, and be sure it is a test that is measuring and reporting the information that is required for obtaining a proper response.

Po-tas-si-um / pe-ˈtas-ē-em / *n, often attrib* [NL, fr. *potassa* potash, fr. E *potash* sometimes fr. *kalium*] 1 a silver-white soft light low-melting univalent metallic element of the alkali metal group, abundant in nature esp. combined in minerals (see Mendeleyeff Periodic Table of Elements) 2 chemical symbol:

3 a catalyst and a prime requirement in chlorophyll construction 4 a governor for taking free nutrients from the air—carbon, hydrogen, oxygen 5 needed so plants can make starches, sugars, proteins, vitamins, enzymes or cellulose 6 may be dangerous to microorganisms when embodied in muriate of potash 7 in animal life, promotes normal growth and muscle function, also a cell regulating element 8 regulates osmotic pressure in cellular tissue and fluids

8

The Freelancer
in Plants

IN THE PARTICULAR COPY I HAVE of *The Fertilizer Handbook*, it says on page 97 that potassium will leach in certain soils. Yet ads in agricultural publications tell you to apply potash in the fall so that you don't have to do it next spring. Some will tell you that potash doesn't leach. But when you put potassium on, if you don't have the right conditions in the soil, you are always going to lose it.

The Fertilizer Handbook does state that potassium will leach under certain conditions. "Conditions" here translates into sandy soils. Actually, in most cases, it is easier to build potassium levels in good sandy soils than in heavier soils if commercial sources are to be applied. But when adequate amounts of manure or compost are applied, potassium levels can generally be increased in any type of soil.

Considering medium to heavy soils, where commercial sources of fertilizer are used you can build potassium only when there is enough room in the soil for it to be held on the clay colloid. How do you know there is enough room on the clay colloid? The pH reading is the key. If pH (speaking of water pH) is above 6.5, don't put potassium materials such as muriate of potash (0-0-60 or potassium chloride), sulfate of potash (0-0-50 or potassium sulfate), or sulfate of potash-magnesia (potassium-magnesium sulfate, K-Mag or Sul-Po-Mag) on the soil in the fall to grow a crop in the spring. As a matter of fact, I tell my clients when the soil pH is above 6.5 not to put potassium on in the fall unless they have a significant deficiency, even if they are going to plant winter wheat. Otherwise, wait until you make your winter application of nitrogen and then apply potassium. An excellent example of when to recommend it be done that way is where farmers are going to raise a second crop. If a double crop behind wheat is planned and you put potassium on in the fall, the wheat will pick up some of it. However, by the time you get to the double crop, that added potassium is no longer available and will not be available under conditions of pH levels higher than 6.5, and a TEC higher than 8.75.

Fertilizer researchers generally know when pulling a soil test in the fall—while all the residues are still on the ground—phosphate and potash will exhibit a tremendous increase between fall and spring, once decomposition of the crop residues takes place. Nutrient levels in soils tend to be at their worst just after harvest. If you want to see your soils at their best, pull the samples after all stover and organic matter have decomposed. May and June are prime periods for the northern hemisphere in this regard.

If you haven't taken a soil test in three or four years, the best time to do it is *now!* If you are going to set up a program and already know the soil audit figures well, then you can make your choice. Do you want to see it at its best so that you know the minimum amount to put on, or do you want to see it at its worst so that you will know what you are going to face in terms of building up percentages? I advise clients when and where possible to test soils when at their best. In this way it is possible to know exactly what to put on to reach the minimum requirement or build to the excellent level. But some prefer to see the soil at its worst sampling just after harvest, which is fine too, if that is preferred for decision making purposes.

The biggest phosphate and potassium deficiencies will always test out in the fall. A soil sample taken in spring will reveal a better level than in the fall. If you pull a full soil test in the fall and again in the spring and apply no fertilizers in between, phosphate and potash levels will still be better in spring as a consequence of phosphate and potassium release from breakdown of residues. If you put potassium on that entire field, take a soil test beforehand, come back next spring and take another soil test, the uninformed

Potassium-Bearing Minerals as Soil Treatments

The acidity in the soil, created by the plant roots (and by the soil microbes), is nature's chemical reagent for processing the rock and mineral fragments there much as we process rock phosphate with sulfuric acid. This root acid converts their contents of unavailable nutrient elements into forms more readily available for plant and microbial nutrition. While the clay separate of the soil is the intermediary between the roots and the silt-sized mineral fragments; and while it is the clay that carries the stock of nutrients we measure when testing soils for their "available" supplies of these; it is the finely ground mineral and rock particles serving as the reserve fertility from which the clay is restocked. The clay is the means of passing the acid from the roots to the minerals and, in turn, the nutrients in the reverse direction, or from the mineral fragments to the plant roots. The nutrients held on the clay are the "starter" fertilizer for a single crop. It is these reserve minerals—mixed with the clay—as the soil skeleton that are the sustaining fertility for many crops over many years.

. . . there were pronounced differences in the amounts of potassium delivered to the crop by the different minerals applying equal amounts of potassium to the soil. Also it is evident that in many cases these minerals were undergoing transformation as a result of incorporation into the soil, resulting in the additional amounts of potassium going to the crop. It is evident that in this soil with a degree of acidity no more severe than that represented by a pH of 6.6, the reaction rate between this soil growing the crop and the various minerals was rapid enough to provide significant amounts of potassium in the cases of some of the samples used.

—*E.R. Graham & William A. Albrecht*
private papers, Acres U.S.A. collection

guess will be that you applied potassium, so consequently you have more potash. Therefore the potassium is bound to be working. But this isn't true when the pH is above 6.5.

Muriate of potash or potassium chloride, are basically the same, regardless of whether it is the red 0-0-60 or the white 0-0-62. If pH is 6.5, it is possible to build the potassium level a little. If pH is 6.6, this product won't build the potassium level very much, if any. At pH 6.7, there is not much chance to build the level at all. At pH 6.8, there will be no buildup to the sampled depth even though 2,000 pounds are applied to each acre over a five year period. There simply is no place for that potassium to attach to the soil colloid. If you have pH above 6.5, few negative sites remain. Consequently, potassium cannot find enough sites to push hydrogen out of the way, and attach to the soil colloid.

Hands-On Agronomy

Rarely can you get a little bit of an increase, and even then it is generally because something has changed the other cation levels.

Calcium, magnesium and potassium are always evident in soil water. The textbooks call this the soil solution, but we are really talking about water in the soil, and that water carries various nutrients. Potassium floats along. It finds the hydrogen and pushes it out of the way, taking its place. Hydrogen has a single plus charge but potassium can replace it. Along comes a calcium ion, and it has a double plus charge. It is stronger than the potassium. It can actually push two potassium ions out of the way and replace them on the colloid. At a high pH, few negatives occupied by hydrogen remain; hence potassium can't find a parking place. At pH above 6.5, don't spend a lot of money trying to build up potassium levels with commercial fertilizers. Consider only a maintenance program if potassium is shown to be needed in the topsoil at the higher pH levels, when you must buy it as commercial fertilizer.

If you do not have sandy soils, don't spend a lot of money for potassium buildup when the pH is 6.5 or higher. In general, the potassium levels are not going to build anyway. On the average, if we are targeting a 200-bushel corn crop, or 60 bushels of beans, or 80 bushels of wheat, and potassium is needed, the farmer should put on a maintenance level of 90 pounds of potassium. Those 90 pounds will take care of the crop for one year. Building the potassium level should be held in escrow until pH is maneuvered below 6.5, or until something is available other than a commercial source.

Compost and manures will not fit this rule. Only so-called commercial materials comply. If you have a pH of 6.8 and start using manures, you can build up your potassium levels because manures work on a completely different principle. If potassium levels are above 6.5% of base saturation and you have an exchange capacity in the 8.5+ range, be careful. This means there is no need to throw money away trying to build potassium, without manure, compost, etc.

Two brothers who were clients were having problems with their soils, and they thought the common denominator was a lack of potassium. I didn't know they thought it was potassium. They farmed north and east of St. Louis. Without knowledge of the histories of those farms, one of my friends sent in two samples from their fields along with his to be tested. We met to deliver the results. The last thing I explained was the potassium needs. They had something like a 300-pound potassium deficiency. I told them to apply 90 pounds of potash. The one guy looked at me and said, "What do you mean? We have been putting on 500 pounds of 0-0-60 each year. We can't get our potash levels up, and you are telling me to cut back to 150 pounds. There is no way that is going to take care of our corn." I explained how much potassium corn took up, and detailed why the pH was too high, and that if he had some other land that had a pH that was below 6.5 the potassium level would build. The problem was not potassium. It was sulfur and boron. They had three different farms. They pulled samples on each field and sent them in. Every place the pH was below 6.5, potassium levels were substantially higher.

The average Midwestern soil—if you measure every bit of potassium in it—will have 30,000 to 50,000 pounds in the top seven inches. This potassium will generally be in the wrong form for the plant to use. If the soil can be managed to turn loose some of this mother lode of nutrients in very small amounts over a period of time, it is possible to go a long time without potassium inputs. We can take off crop after crop without running out of potassium. The key is to get microbial activity going in the soil. That is why the man who uses manures on his soils can actually raise the phosphate and potash levels by more than can be accounted for by the manure content alone. However, always make sure there is an adequate supply for the next crop. If not, apply it; don't wait for the unavailable K to release. It may require several years to accomplish and the crop will require a sufficient amount this year.

Earlier, we looked at nitrogen and said that nitrogen ran from 2 to 6% of plant content. Phosphate was a fraction of a percent,

0.4% at most. Potassium is determined at 2 to 10%. This means a lot of material goes into plants as potassium. The intake can be higher than the amount of nitrogen percentage-wise.

Potassium is called a free-lancer in plants because it doesn't actually form any compounds. It helps with photosynthesis and the transport and storage of carbohydrates. That means it helps get reserves into the roots, greatly improves winter hardiness, and foundation cell development, including cell wall construction, and therefore reduces stalk lodging. In the case of cell development and strong wall construction, we have to look at potassium in relation to sodium. We can actually cause problems in the soil because we don't have enough potassium in relation to sodium.

If you see white, glistening spots in your field, always make sure your soil tests measure the amount of sodium. It is possible to get into trouble by having too much sodium in relation to potassium because of cell wall development.

Crops take up large quantities of K_2O. In an eight-ton alfalfa crop, the nitrogen numbers are 445, potassium 440. A 150-bushel corn crop takes 200 pounds, the same as nitrogen. A 50-bushel soybean crop takes 120 pounds; 60 bushels of wheat takes 80 pounds. Again, I am not suggesting that we make that much of an application. The reason we don't have to apply that much is the one that often puts us in a corner with organic producers. Almost any soil has a nutrient content that is unavailable. Microbes and plant root secretions convert these nutrients into available forms as long as the biology and chemistry and physics are in place.

There is a soil audit called a total nutrient test. Usually, we talk about the Albrecht method which utilizes an available nutrient test. This last details what plants can pick up and use immediately. But if a farmer is interested in how much potassium is present there in every form, the total nutrient test has the answer. In a light, sandy soil with anywhere from five to six feet of sand, we can still find 14,000 pounds of potassium in the top seven inches. Using that same type of total nutrient test, it is unusual to find more than 1,000 pounds of phosphate. Nevertheless, it is not unusual to find over 500 pounds. Regardless, it is possible to do a total analysis and scrutinize what there is to be released from that soil. Most of the time it is much higher than what you have in an available form which is actually showing what is present that the crop can utilize. I tell clients who have no good reason to run a total analysis to consider it carefully, because it can get expensive. A standard tab for a total soil analysis is often over $100. Once the total analysis has been determined, it is still a matter of testing to determine whether it is there in the form plants can utilize. Some understanding of the exchange capacity and how the exchange capacity works is necessary before a determination can be made as to why potassium is needed in large amounts and why at times it can be built up in the soil or recovered and other times not.

Here is the dilemma. We put on only 90 pounds of potassium at a time, yet an eight-ton alfalfa crop takes out 440 pounds. Some of the universities have farmers put on as much as 350 or 400 pounds of potash in a given year. Yet the growers who listen to academia will only build the potassium up when the pH is below 6.5 (using a water pH test). On soils with a higher pH, the alfalfa will not benefit from all that extra potassium if applied all at once. Just keep this in mind, although the reserves of potassium may be huge in your soil—don't count your chickens before they hatch. Always supply what the Albrecht Model will show to be needed for the next crop. Even if the unavailable potassium can eventually be released it will generally not be in time for the next crop. Once the soil test reveals you have enough to properly grow the next crop, then, and only then, should you consider skipping a potassium application.

Potassium has important roles in crop production. It is vital to photosynthesis, essential in protein synthesis, and improves water use efficiency. There is a saying that potassium is the poor man's irrigation. It is a key nutrient to improving water use efficiency. It also increases yields, improves crop quality, and reduces disease. Potassium is sourced from solid rock or soil rocks and minerals.

This is a Midwest theory: potassium gets around in water and finally gets trapped between the colloids, and it can't get loose until something is done to change the soil chemistry. In that form, it is unavailable for plant use because the soil colloid has trapped the potassium. Perhaps that is why whenever magnesium gets higher and higher and the soil gets tighter and tighter, potassium availability gets lower and lower. As you bring the magnesium level down and the soil loosens up, you can actually release potassium that is trapped between soil particles. Potassium moves out into the soil water and then onto the soil colloid. As you bring magnesium down, you make more sites available on the clay for potassium to attach. This potassium then becomes available in soil water and from the colloid to feed the plant.

Below pH 6.5, potassium attaches to the soil colloid. A certain amount moves with the water. Factors that affect potassium requirements may not always be identified by soil tests. Soil temperature does affect it, but dry soil means it takes more to do the same job, and the plant has to feed from deeper down. Wet soil, if it is saturated, will annihilate aeration. High cation exchange capacity (CEC) affects the potassium requirements. The higher the CEC, the more potassium is required to assure the minimum percentage is available. When you have pH 6.5 or better, there will be a greater chance of tie up of potassium. It will be tied up in calcareous soils because it does not have room to attach to the colloid.

Subsoil potassium does have an effect, especially if the topsoil is completely dry. Under such conditions, moisture in the subsoil may be the only source of potassium mobility because soluble potassium that moves with the water is all a plant can acquire. In the presence of ammonium nitrogen, there will be a problem with microbial fixation and attachment to the soil colloid. The higher the nitrogen, the more potassium it will take to do the same job.

Crop rotation, high yields, forage use, any of these can have an effect on potassium levels. But the key to potassium availability is the CEC and pH levels. I used to think a high CEC was between 20 and 30, but then started working with swamp soils in Arkansas and the Red River Valley soils of North Dakota, and found a high CEC to be 40 to 50. There are farmers who say they farm sand and heavy land, but their "heavy land" is lighter than many sandy soils as far as the exchange capacity is concerned. On the other hand, some clients in Iowa refer to their "light" soils as those with exchange capacities in the high teens. They are so used to working with heavy black soils that they think of upland forest soils as light. For our purposes, anything from CEC 8.75 and up is medium to heavy soil. The point here is that you have to have a pH below 6.5 before potassium will build in soils with a CEC above 8.75 or so. There are exceptions, especially when manures and composts have been or will be used.

But then, some soils are just naturally high in potassium. Potassium influences pH even more than lime does. That is one of the reasons why you can't tell by looking at pH whether or not you need lime. In some areas, potassium can influence pH more than calcium or magnesium.

On soybeans, first look at the percentage of potassium to tell whether any more is needed. It takes a lot of potassium (K_2O) to grow beans. If you have more than 100 pounds per acre deficiency and you put on 90 pounds per acre, that application will make about seven bushels more beans. If there is ever a 125 pound deficiency, in general, the 90 pounds per acre application will make you ten bushels more beans to the acre. If you are above 2% and have less than 100 pound potash deficiency, you don't really have to worry about it if you plan to raise beans that year. You could skip a year. But if you get above 100 pounds deficiency, it can make a yield difference.

The most common fertilizer source for potassium is muriate of potash or potassium chloride, and it is the cheapest of all sources. Potassium sulfate is 50% potassium and 18% sulfur. Sul-Po-Mag or K-Mag is 22% potassium, 11% magnesium and 22% sulfur. These last two are most effective when all three elements are needed. Potassium nitrate is 44% potash and 13% nitrogen. Many farmers want to know about using potassium

Hands-On Agronomy

chloride versus potassium sulfate. I don't have much to back up the idea that potassium chloride hurts the soil. I do have some comments that make me more cautious. I know that on soybeans and cotton, moderate to high rates of potassium chloride, 0-0-60 or 0-0-62, can kill the germinating seed. If it is possible to get a level that is high enough to kill germinating seeds, then what does it do to the microbial activity in that soil? It is bound to affect it.

At sensible rates the potassium side won't burn anything. You will never kill a germinating seed with potassium sulfate applied prior to planting. I know a farmer in southeast Missouri—a fertilizer dealer—who has studied the potassium chloride versus potassium sulfate issue for years. Several years ago, on his entire 3,000 acres, he used potassium sulfate. After two years, he said he couldn't really tell the difference where one was used versus the other. If you are raising soybeans and you have a 100 pound deficiency, and you don't want to use 0-0-60 and wonder about whether potassium makes much difference or not, then at least try some potassium sulfate. Use 200 pounds or so of potassium sulfate versus 150 pounds of potassium chloride to get basically the same analysis. That is going to be 90 pounds from the KCL and 100 pounds from the K_2SO_4, potassium sulfate. If the farmer says K_2SO_4 is too expensive then I tell him there are at least three choices that can be made. If he'll put on 90 pounds of potash, even as 0-0-60, he is going to make another seven to ten bushels of beans. From that profit he can then afford to use 0-0-50. If he skips the potassium, it will mean losing that yield. On the other hand, if he believes what I'm saying, he could use the more expensive 0-0-50 and make enough extra soybeans to more than pay the difference.

Potassium reduces sorghum lodging and harvest stress. Experiments on sorghum have proved that without application or a proper level of potassium, 88% of the plants lodge for a 95-bushel yield. Application of 40 pounds of potassium results in a 105-bushel yield and 71% lodging. With 80 pounds, there is 45% lodging, and with 160 pounds there is 16% lodging, all

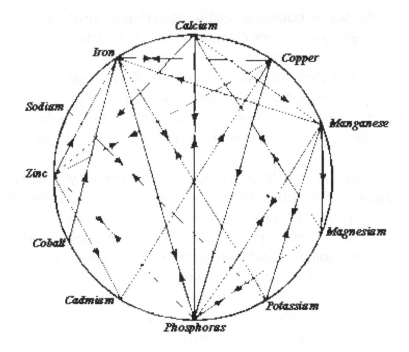

according to experiments. It is not necessary to go that high in order to get some good effects. Keep in mind, you can put on the entire 160 pounds, and if you have a manganese or copper deficiency, you could still get lodging.

Potassium is the first key for stalk strength, but the crop also has to have enough copper and manganese. Also, mineral interrelationships can underwrite problems because of the complex ways nutrients work in a soil system.

There are interrelationships between all the different elements in the soil, as illustrated above. Follow each line to see the interrelationships. Look at sodium and potassium. The only line that goes from sodium is to potassium. It doesn't go to any other mineral. The only relationship to be concerned about in terms of sodium is the sodium-potassium relationship. When the potassium and sodium base saturation percentages total above 10%, the plant is not going to get as much manganese. It isn't a matter that the manganese is tied up. The soil test may show excellent manganese levels. It is simply a matter of a combined

10% saturation of potassium and sodium blocking manganese uptake from the roots. If you have 6 or 7% potassium, at that point you should become especially watchful concerning the potassium-sodium percentages.

Any time you have sodium in a field and the percentage saturation of sodium is higher than the percentage saturation of potassium, you already have trouble if you experience both heat and humidity at the same time. When sodium exceeds potassium in the soil, the plant will take the sodium instead of the potassium. Plants do not distinguish between the two. As long as the plant is getting potassium, it incorporates potassium into the cell wall. But the day the percentage of sodium exceeds the percentage of potassium in the soil, adequate potassium stops getting in and sodium is incorporated into the cell walls instead. As long as it stays nice and cool everything works—or as long as the humidity is low this is no problem. So in various parts of the world, they hardly recognize this problem if it ever surfaces. However, when it gets hot and humid, the sodium incorporated into the cell walls begins to cause expansion. When that expansion is too great the cell walls burst, killing the plant cell by cell. This phenomenon shows up easily in peas and beans. It sets the stage for a problem that looks like nematodes, but is not. The lighter the soil, the worse the problem.

Certain farmers and consultants have determined in their minds that if you have nematodes and you apply potassium, you eliminate the nematode problem in your soil. I have clients who have problems with nematodes and they put on plenty of potassium. Where we have nematodes, we never eliminate nematode problems just by putting on potassium. It can make the plant look better and do somewhat better, but the nematode problem stays. You have to use other materials for nematode control. Where we have sodium that is higher than potassium, it can look like a nematode problem. But if you solve the problem by adding potassium and thus building the potassium level above that of sodium, too much sodium in relation to potassium was the problem.

What does a soil test look like when sodium is causing that type of problem? Let's take a typical scenario. Say you have base saturations of 33.07% calcium, 40.38% magnesium, 1.51% potassium and 1.82% sodium. If that sodium was merely 1.52% we'd already have a problem. But all you have to do is put on 90 pounds of potassium and that solves the potassium-sodium problem. We have to do several other things to completely solve this soil's problems altogether. Any time the magnesium is higher than the calcium you can't raise a good crop without supplying additional calcium. Even Iowa and Wisconsin researchers—who say high magnesium is not generally a problem in their soils—actually admit that when magnesium is higher than calcium, nothing grows well.

In any case, any time you see sodium higher than potassium, you're going to have a problem. The sodium will be causing a problem with cell wall expansion. Apply enough potassium to raise the level above sodium, and the problem melts away. Again, it's a matter of following through on the required nutrient corrections.

These two relationships between potassium and sodium need to be brought into focus. When the percentage of sodium exceeds the percentage of potassium in the soil, then heat and humidity will begin to kill growing plants. And when you put on enough potassium so that the combined percentage of K and Na total above 10%, the plant is not going to get as much manganese. At that point manganese availability starts to be affected regardless of whether potassium or sodium is the predominate percentage. Manganese, of course, is essential to grain formation. Two such crops that exhibit a terrific response to manganese for seed production are legumes and small grains. If you are in wheat production or growing soybeans, you can decrease yields on either one faster without sufficient manganese than on corn. If manganese is missing, corn yield will suffer, albeit not as much as soybeans, dry beans and wheat, when deficiencies are only slight.

For those farmers or growers who already have excellent potassium, be especially careful—more so as levels rise above 7%. Anytime the base saturation of potassium gets above 7.5%, weed pressures increase. This is proven most easily on organic farms where compost applications have driven the potassium levels too high. But it is just as true on conventional farms where stronger herbicides or higher rates are required to control the same weeds than is the case on fields or areas where K is not excessive. Where pasture grass grows versus where weeds take over, especially sticker-type weeds (a red root weed which resembles a smaller version of Palmer Pigweed with stickers), or where such types of weeds thrive, potassium generally will test extremely high. (If you are interested in how nutrients govern the parameters of weed control or proliferation, read *Weeds: Control Without Poisons*, by Charles Walters.)

One fellow told me that if you want to find out what a soil program is like, chew on the stems of the clover or the legumes that the cows have to eat. He said if you get a bitter taste then you know you're not doing the right thing. If it's sweet then you know that's how the cow is going to taste it, too. That also applies to vegetable gardens. A lot of organic gardeners believe that you can't overdo manure. I am a serious organic gardener and am not making fun of that. At home we don't use anything on our garden that we feel is not 100% natural. To me that's important. You may not feel that it is, but that's a matter of choice. Too many choices that were once considered safe have proven to be unsafe over the past few decades. But a lot of organic gardeners say you can't use too much manure. Yes, you can, and the way you can tell is when even though they look good in appearance you start to taste radishes that are bitter, or squash that is bitter, or cucumbers that are bitter and turnips that begin to have a bitter taste when you cook them. And the same is true if you use too much compost.

On acid soils, the pH actually helps point to the real problem. It is getting too low because there is not enough calcium in the soil. The calcium is not sufficiently controlling the potassium and perhaps even the phosphate. Timely application of high calcium lime, where needed, can help take care of the problem. Bitterness in the plant means potassium or phosphorus, or both are getting unusually high. I have worked with the soils of people who have lived for years out of their garden only to learn that their plot needs lime. They will tell that after two or three years they actually feel better. And this should happen because they are finally getting a serious nutrient imbalance out of their soils.

When potassium and sodium in the bloodstream starts to increase, the doctor will tell us that we have an electrolyte imbalance. But livestock can't tell us that. We can safely extrapolate from plant to animal in this case. When the potassium-sodium level gets higher than the calcium-magnesium level in the blood, a cow dies.

We have probably all heard about the fellow with a small enclosure, maybe 20 to 40 acres, with all of his dairy cows on those acres. He buys his feed. The only green grass his cows get is what grows on that small acreage where all the manure is falling. If that dairyman had analyzed that pasture and kept calcium up, what will be described here would likely never occur. But because he doesn't keep the calcium up, potassium gets out of control. As manure amounts and the effects accumulate over the years, the potassium levels go up, but the cows will still eat that grass. It is bitter, but it is the only green grass they have. Over a period of time, the potassium levels get too high. A lot of dairymen feed salt. As a consequence the sodium and potassium go up. The day the potassium-sodium level exceeds the calcium-magnesium level, that animal dies.

I have had dairymen tell me that their cows simply started dying, and the veterinarian couldn't find an answer. Unless there is a blood analysis, there will be no true answer given.

I told this to a Huron, South Dakota group one winter. One of the men came up and said, "I got out of the dairy business. I have had all my row crop soils checked for years, but I have never checked a pasture." About three years earlier, he lost some of his best heifers, then his cows began to die, but no one knew why. This was the first he had ever heard about the calcium and potassium connection. Hogs can die, cows can die, and horses can die because of this. We would also die, I am told, if the

As with nitrogen, potassium deficiency (top leaf) begins in the oldest (lower) leaves first. But unlike nitrogen, which moves downward from the tip in a "yellow V" shape, potassium shortage shows up along the outer edges of the entire leaf.

sodium and potassium exceeded the calcium and magnesium in our blood and we did nothing about it quickly.

But too little potassium can also cause problems. Take a corn plant. Do most farmers and growers recognize potassium deficiency in corn?

The leaf illustrated in the picture above represents a potassium deficiency. Remember, the potassium deficiency starts on the side of the leaf and moves in. The leaf dies from the outside in. Discoloration on the stalk around the internodes also represents a potassium deficiency. When potassium is short, problems in the nodes of the stalk (that black color seen at the internodes) are on the way.

A lot of people look at potassium deficiencies, but they don't recognize them. On soybeans, old crinkly leaves and coloration are dominant features, much as with corn. The damage starts at the edges and moves in. When you start to see leaf edges die, start thinking of potassium shortage.

Every field has something limiting its yield. It may be the seed, but generally the field is limited by fertility long before anything else surfaces.

Concerning potassium, getting the minimum levels corrected is most important. A new client from Iowa set the highest corn yield made in the state one year. He had come to a meeting two years before that. He sat through it and took a lot of notes. When I got to trace elements, I recited what the minimum levels of the trace elements were, and suggested the ideal levels for corn. At the time he and his dad were farming 4,000 acres on the Mississippi River between Fort Madison and Burlington, Iowa. Before he left he told me he was going to pull samples on some of the poorer yielding areas and send them to see if I could help him.

I advised him to send at least one good producing soil, perhaps even a couple, and not just samples of the problem spots. This farmer had a huge swine operation. Pig manure was put on every acre of the farm, albeit not every year. He and his dad raised 2,000 acres of corn and 2,000 acres of beans in rotation, except on irrigated land. On the irrigated land they produced continuous corn.

From the soils he sent, you could tell why problem areas were problems and why the good ones were good. When we got to the last soil, I said, "Well, I am glad I met you because otherwise I wouldn't know what to say to you, or how to make it believable. If you ran a pH, phosphate and potassium test, anyone looking at the test would say this field is the worst of all the fields you sent in." Because they used the hog manure on their fields, they didn't show any place where they had a phosphate or a potassium deficiency, except in the last field. It exhibited a 100-plus-pound phosphate deficiency and a 120-, 130-, or 150-pound potassium deficiency depending on the area of the field. All the rest of the acres had high to excellent levels for phosphorus and potassium. I said, "If you just looked at pH, phosphate and potash, you would identify this as the worst field of all we looked at, but viewed in terms of the aggregate, this one suggests itself as the best field I have ever seen in Iowa." Then I said, "With normal fertilization, I have never seen a field with as good a yield capability as this field." I didn't know the history and didn't know whether they had farmed it for years or not.

He was quiet for a minute, and then he said, "It is our best field. We made 215 bushels of corn per acre on this 90-acre field. We have only farmed it for two years. The guy we bought it from never really farmed it. I can tell you that last year on our other irrigated corn, the best we did was 198 bushels. On our non-irrigated corn, the best we did was 98 bushels. I would like to take that field and see what we can do in terms of corn yield."

That field had 68% calcium, but it also had 24% magnesium—a not unusual profile in Iowa. It had a phosphate and potassium deficiency, and in the trace elements department there was a boron deficiency. In Iowa some say that if you have more than 200 ppm iron, it will be toxic to corn. In this field, test results identified 1,224 ppm iron. High iron is not a problem, at least in terms of yield. Manganese registered in at 125 ppm—excellent. Zinc was about 11 or 12; 10 to 20 is excellent. Copper was exactly 5 ppm, also excellent. The next year, the son and father team again raised corn. Several other clients joined me for a trip to see the farm. They planted Pioneer and Garst corn. The Garst people had been out. They said, "You have 275 bushels of corn in this field." Every stalk had two big ears on it. That fall they harvested the corn, taking care not to run over the bean field in-between. In fact, they harvested the beans so they could get into the corn.

It started raining, and it was after Thanksgiving before they could harvest the corn. They had a lot of lodging by then, but they still averaged 225 bushels of corn per acre. Here is what we did to change that field. I had them switch to ammonium sulfate as a nitrogen source, and recommended boron as well as 70 pounds of phosphate and 90 pounds of potash per acre. In other words, I did not suggest big amounts of phosphate and potassium. This really didn't take care of the potassium deficiency, but it was enough to supply what was needed for that crop. Limiting factors prior to this crop had been sulfur and boron. These farmers were putting on enough nitrogen.

The Freelancer in Plants

Cutting back on needed fertilization won't ever save you money. But cutting back on needed fertilization will eventually decrease soil fertility which can lower yields, potential income, and crop resistance to drought, disease and insects. Potassium plays a big role in this regard.

Ma-nure / me-'n(y)ü(e)r / *n* [ME *manouren,* fr. MF *manouvrer,* lit, to do work by hand, fr. L. *manu operare*] 1 material that fertilizes land; esp. refuse of stables and barnyards consisting of livestock excreta with or without litter 2 material suitable for fermentation, with Actinomycetes and Streptomycetes first digesting sugars, with other organisms creating a mesophilic condition that raises temperatures sufficient to destroy pathogens 3 raw materials capable of breaking down, then building up for the production of humus for plant nourishment and nutrient release from soil stores

9

Considering the Use of Manures

ORGANIC MATTER, MANURE, COMPOST—these are three of the most recited and the most misunderstood words in agriculture's lexicon. The late Ehrenfried Pfeiffer handled at least one of these mystery words in one of his talks which became an article, then a reprint, finally a fixture in the literature.

"Some old folks," he wrote, "remember that the odor of potatoes, when boiling in the pot, indicated very specifically the kind of manure—cow, hog, horse or poultry—which had been applied when preparing the soil for the growth of potatoes. Today we still notice that cabbage, cauliflower, broccoli and kale can give off very intensive aromas while cooking. This, too, depends on the fertilization of the soil.

"The reason is that breakdown products contained in the manure, such as skatole, indole and other phenolic compounds are not decomposed further. They enter the soil, are absorbed by plant roots and migrate into the plant tissue. These breakdown products were excreted by the animal or human organisms and are toxic wastes of their metabolism. They imprint their history on the soil and the growing plant.

"Night soil is especially undesirable in this regard, but even sewage sludge contains many toxic compounds, unless properly decomposed by an aerobic composting process. The difficulty is that these byproducts are rather stable and can survive for a long time. Returned in food to the human upper digestive tract where they do not belong, they can cause indigestion, flatulence and maybe even allergic reactions.

"Biuret is a contaminant or byproduct of urea and urine, and it is extremely stable. In greenhouses and field experiments at Purdue University it was demonstrated that it was toxic to grow-ing corn plants. It caused leaf chlorosis, hyponasty. It severely stunted, twisted and deformed plants, causing their leaf tips to be rolled together. All fertilizer salts, when placed with the seed, resulted in decreased length of primary roots. The ability to sur-vive germination damage was severely reduced by increasing the biuret content. The rate of growth and the yield were also reduced."

For the past several decades, many of the intellectual advisers to the farmer have sought to shut down the use of manures on farm acres. Some have characterized this raw material as low value fertilizer—a liability rather than an asset. Others, enchant-ed with the upgraded values inherent in well digested compost, have declared raw manure nearly worthless. One fellow, speak-ing at an eastern seminar, even recommended one day of jail time for each ton of raw manure spread on farm acres.

As usual, the best assessment rests somewhere between the extremes. In fact, manure has value far greater than a test of nitro-gen, phosphorus and potassium numbers might indicate. Even so, considering the cost of such nutrients, they represent a bargain if phosphate and potassium needs are great. Indeed, when calcium and magnesium levels are correct, levels of phosphate and potassium will be enhanced by more than the amounts indicated by the manure analysis.

Moreover, manures have characteristics that are not always apparent. Use of manures requires analysis, and if large amounts will be applied, it is best to get such analyses in both the fall and spring.

Manures help to release nutrients already in the soil. This is where too many farmers miss out on computing how much manure is really worth. It is not appropriate to use an average of the nutrient content, or tons per acre applied. This leaves too much to chance. First measure the amount of nitrogen, phosphorus and potassium in manure. With a good handle on the quality and character of the product, it is possible to spread manure on the field for sheet composting. Broiler litter and rice hulls—with proper handling—can account for 50 pounds of potash and 70 pounds of phosphate per ton of material.

Let's say you could spread three tons of litter per acre and work it into the top few inches of soil at spreading. If you come back next year after taking off a good crop and analyze the soil, you would expect the crop to have taken out more nutrients than applied. Instead, after one to three years of this, levels of certain nutrients would be higher.

I first saw that happen in east Texas with the use of feedlot manure. The operators brought in old sawdust. Manure would be mixed with the sawdust by the cattle tromping on it. About every three months the lot was cleaned out, the manure being spread on a field scheduled for silage production. First the field was analyzed, and then the farm manager put down the indicated amount of manure. Next year the phosphate and potassium levels were up by more than the numbers represented by the applied amount of manure, and he had taken off a crop. No other source of phosphate or potassium had been used. The year after that, the same thing happened. I didn't understand about total nutrients versus available nutrients at the time.

This concept is constantly overlooked when evaluating the need for manure and its value in terms of purchase price, and in

The Restoration of Fertility

The night soil and urine of the population is at present almost completely lost to the land. In urban areas the concentration of the population is the main reason why water-borne sewage systems have developed. The greatest difficulty in the path of the reformer is the absence of sufficient land for dealing with these wastes. In country districts, however, there are no insurmountable obstacles to the utilization of human wastes.

It will be evident that in almost every case the vegetable and animal residues of Western agriculture are either being completely wasted or else imperfectly utilized. A wide gap between the humus used up in crop production and the humus added as manure has naturally developed. This has been filled by chemical manures. The principle followed, based on the von Liebig tradition, is that any deficiencies in the soil solution can be made up by the addition of suitable chemicals. This is based on a complete misconception of plant nutrition. It is superficial and fundamentally unsound. It takes no account of the life of the soil, including the mycorrhizal association—the living fungous (sic) bridge which connects soil and sap. Artificial manures lead inevitably to artificial nutrition, artificial food, artificial animals, and finally to artificial men and women.

The ease with which crops can be grown with chemicals has made the correct utilization of wastes much more difficult. If a cheap substitute for humus exists why not use it? The answer is twofold. In the first place, chemicals can never be a substitute for humus because nature has ordained that the soil must live and the mycorrhizal association must be an essential link in plant nutrition. In the second place, the use of such a substitute cannot be cheap because soil fertility—one of the most important assets of any country—is lost; because artificial plants, artificial animals and artificial men are unhealthy and can only be protected from the parasites, whose duty it is to remove them, by means of poison sprays, vaccines and serums and an expensive system of patent medicines, panel doctors, hospitals, and so forth. When the finance of crop production is considered together with that of the various social services which are needed to repair the consequences of an unsound agriculture, and when it is borne in mind that our greatest possession is a healthy, virile population, the cheapness of artificial manures disappears altogether. In the years to come chemical manures will be considered as one of the greatest follies of the industrial epoch. The teachings of the agricultural economists of this period will be dismissed as superficial.

—*Sir Albert Howard*
An Agricultural Testament *(1943)*

determining both its capacity to benefit or cause harm to the soil. William A. Albrecht explained this one. He said that when you put on manures, you stimulate microbial activity and also create mild organic acids that free up nutrients considered unavailable. That is how extra phosphate, potassium and sometimes trace minerals are released.

Now consider the different types of tests available. Tests are generally concerned with measuring plant nutrient availability for crops to be grown. A standard soil test such as the one we commonly use measures nutrients according to categories characterized as major (nitrogen, phosphorus, potassium, sulfur); secondary (calcium, magnesium); and trace elements (boron, iron, manganese, copper, zinc, cobalt, and sometimes molybdenum or chlorides).

Another test is available, though at greater cost, called a total nutrient analysis. It shows that soils vary widely in their make up of nutrients. This test measures all nutrients in a soil, including those available for plant use, and those present in forms which cannot be utilized by growing crops. The total amount of nutrients *present* in a soil can be many times greater than those in *available* form. For example, an average topsoil from the corn-belt can have 30,000 to 50,000 pounds per acre of potassium, yet all except 200 to perhaps 600 pounds per acre will be present in forms plants cannot utilize. Unavailable forms of phosphate, calcium, magnesium, sodium and certain trace elements are also found in higher amounts when total nutrient analysis is involved.

A caution must be inserted here. Manures seldom increase available calcium in the soil. The only condition under which you can expect an increase in available calcium levels occurs when calcium is added to the feed ration, under which condition some of it comes out with the manure. Manure from laying hens is a good example.

The total amount of calcium in a soil is usually very close to the amount of *available calcium*. But there can be thousands of pounds more magnesium in a soil than are *available*. There can be thousands of pounds more potassium in a soil than are *available*, and also there can be thousands of pounds more sodium than the amount characterized as *available*. Usually calcium will have less than the equivalent of two extra tons of fine-grind limestone (1,200 pounds of calcium) to the acre tied up, or present in an unavailable form. This is true unless something like a calcareous soil is involved, one that has rocks containing calcium. Such rocks slowly break down. Obviously, we don't include the rocks when we check a soil. All we ever consider is calcium that will break down in a reasonable period of time. To measure available soil calcium—that shown on our normal soil test—

reports show only what can presently be picked up by the crops being grown.

When manure is applied to a soil, it certainly adds the nutrients contained in the raw product. But while stimulating microbial activity in that soil, mild organic acids are formed that work on and break down the nutrients plants need. These can be converted in this way from the unavailable forms into forms needed by the crop. In soils that contain reasonable calcium and magnesium levels, this is a process that can be observed via soil analysis to add to the soil's nutrient level over a period of time.

When you apply manure, compost, or even some type of protein meal, always keep in mind both available and total nutrient levels in the soil. Remember that calcium, due to its general availability, cannot be expected to increase. But it can be expected to decrease when any material except manure from laying hens or other such large amounts of calcium containing materials are being used. Phosphate will increase, on the other hand, and if used to excess, it can tie up other nutrients. And potassium can do the same if increased to the point of excess.

The application of manure can increase the availability of phosphate and potassium well beyond the amounts removed by crop production if the soil is otherwise in good shape. Compost can do the same thing.

When it comes to applying manure or compost, don't overdo a good thing. Too much can be detrimental to crop yields, but not using enough can hurt production. As a rule of thumb, fields that already test high in phosphate and/or potassium should not receive indiscriminate applications of manure or compost. Only when a soil test shows the soil to be ready for more manure or compost should an application of either be considered. Finally, keep in mind that when manure or compost has been used repeatedly, and must be stopped, the amount of nitrogen usually supplied by manure or compost must be accounted for from other sources, especially for crops with high nitrogen requirements.

If a farmer continues to apply manure or compost and increases unneeded phosphate availability, and copper or zinc levels are barely adequate in comparison, the phosphate level can interfere with the uptake of these two minor elements.

As potassium levels continue to rise, boron and manganese uptake can be restricted, and if excessive—especially in lighter soils—even a magnesium deficiency can be triggered by too much available potassium. On some soils manure or compost can unduly increase available zinc. When not too high, this is fine, but when zinc is already very high in a soil, greater availability can cause problems associated with zinc toxicity — particularly phosphate deficiency.

Farmers with livestock in confined areas should be especially concerned about the ability of manure to release or convert elements for plant uptake. Crops produced in such areas can cause health problems. For example, dairy cattle that are confined to a relatively small area will consume grass that grows there even though under normal conditions they would not consider such material palatable, and leave it alone, as mentioned in the previous chapter on potassium.

Certain problems can be traced back to the cumulative amounts of manure allowed to decompose on the land. Soil pH drops as available calcium is leached out of the root zone by the manure. At the same time phosphate and potassium levels rise higher and higher as manure releases forms previously unavailable. Plants that grow in such areas become bitter, and this indicator worsens as soil acidity increases. The danger in such cases cannot be overemphasized.

Here when it comes to testing and fertilizing, most farmers tend to neglect their pastureland until the bitter end, if they test it at all. Keeping such areas properly limed can help as long as manure accumulations are not excessive. But in too many cases, circumstances have gone so far that even properly liming the soil will not always solve the problem. The situation can deteriorate to the point that farm animals actually die as a consequence of the long term effects of eating plants that grow in such areas.

What happens in the end is that potassium levels in plants become so excessive they harm livestock. As potassium levels accumulate, calcium levels decrease. Also, excessive potassium can cause magnesium deficiency in growing plants. As these levels drop and potassium levels rise, levels of each in the bloodstream are affected.

In the blood, calcium/magnesium must always be above potassium/sodium levels. The day potassium/sodium levels exceed calcium/magnesium levels, the animal dies. Unless a blood analysis is done, there will be no apparent reason for such a death. No outward sign will signal the problem.

Too much manure and/or compost, as with anything else having to do with building fertility levels, can cause problems. Those who have gardens especially need to heed the lessons of too much manure. Not only can excessive use of manure increase phosphate and potassium levels and hinder the uptake of micronutrients, it can also contribute to health problems for people who rely heavily on garden food production. An indication that

Our Compost

Our compost is an earthy-like substance, which is the result of a controlled fermentation of feedlot manure by implanting certain aerobic organisms. As in the brewery or cheese industry, where selected organisms are used to cause specific action, we use an inoculation of over 40 different specific organisms which each have a specific function to perform in the compost, and later in the soil in which the compost is applied. This process has been used successfully throughout the world over many years. The organisms were selected from leading productive soil types of the world starting some 65 years ago and analyzed in the laboratory for their function in the soil and compost matrix before inclusion in this inoculum culture. These organisms, under favorable moisture, temperature and other environmental conditions created and maintained in our compost piles, go through a whole series of actions and reactions, some of which are mentioned below.

Actinomycetes and streptomycetes first work on the easily digested sugars present. This is the same family of organisms used in making the antibiotics so widely used medically today on both man and animal.

These and other organisms create a mesophilic condition which carries the body temperature of the compost pile above 100° F where thermophilic organisms then become active and generate temperatures up to 150° F. This action has proven so effective in the removal of pathogenic organisms that the poultry industry has turned to the practice of composting the old litter and manure for use as litter under baby chicks, with resultant decrease in death loss over where new litter is used. This fermentation destroys weed and undigested grain seed, hence eliminating that objection of the raw manure. There are cellulose digester organisms which work on decomposition of high carbon plant fibers. These work in conjunction with nitrogen fixers (normally recognized as in association with leguminous plants, but in our inoculum are ones independent of this symbiotic association) to produce humus of high plant nourishment because of the resultant good carbon nitrogen ratio attained. This organic material, unlike the inorganic form, in addition to its value as a soil conditioner, is stable and remains in the soil until needed, as opposed to the rapid leaching away and/or locking down as occurs with the N, P, and K fertilizers commonly used.

The benefit comes from the processes of the living humus. We do not recommend the occasional application of large quantities of feedlot manure (observed applications have been ten tons or more) which often causes distressing conditions in the soil during the first year.

We recommend the addition of a small application of compost which is stable living humus of balanced value to the plants and serves as an effective inoculum to the soil of these beneficial soil organisms. In this compost are organisms that consume organic chemical residue, (such as DDT and other insect poisons having a residual effect) and other contaminants of the manure and soil.

—*Fletcher Sims*
private papers, Acres U.S.A. collection

the problem has reached an advanced state is a bitter taste in cucumbers, broccoli and even turnips. The bottom line is the one William A. Albrecht repeated so often. A test is required, one that indicates the saturation of each soil in terms of calcium, magnesium, potassium and sodium.

Withal, the shortfalls mentioned above have a natural add-on. There is a tendency to apply manure on dry areas closest to the barn, to "pile it on" the garden every year, and to disregard small confined areas where livestock live out their lives. The degree of problems created depends on the condition of the soil to start with, and what it requires for equilibrium status.

Still, there is no need to shy away from the use of needed compost and manure in the garden or on the field. Always keep in mind, you can get more than you pay for when you buy manure, but if you keep putting it on and putting it on, you can actually cause certain toxic conditions to develop. Different manures call for different application rates, according to the soil's needs.

Manure, of course, can contribute considerably to the soil's organic matter content. For example, a ton of beef manure containing 80% moisture will hold almost 400 pounds of organic material. Organic matter in manure helps control the slow release of nitrogen bound up in that organic matter. This nitrogen must be converted to ammonium before it can be used. Only about 50% of the nitrogen in manure is available for crop use the first year. Soils receiving manure with naturally high levels of undecomposed organic matter, will not deliver much of an increase in crop yields at the onset. But in shallow or leached soils, the initial response to well-decomposed manure is generally very good.

For effectiveness and availability, manure should be incorporated quickly. Its relative value in increasing crop yields is reduced by about 50% after four days exposure under field conditions.

Hog manure makes it possible to build phosphate levels far more easily than potassium levels. Some Iowa farmers use large amounts of hog manure, with resultant improvement in phosphate levels, but some can't get their potassium levels up accordingly, and they can't understand why. If the soil pH is above 6.5, the higher the cation exchange capacity, the harder it becomes to significantly raise available potassium levels. In the case of such soils with low phosphates and high potassium, hog manure makes it possible to build phosphorous without building potassium levels by that much.

When crop residues are involved in soil management, the objective being to build humus, the carbon-nitrogen ratio must come into focus. Roughly, when you have corn stalks or bean plants or wheat stubble on a field, the carbon-nitrogen ratio will be 30 to 1, or greater. This complex has to be reduced to between 10 and 20 to 1 before you can build humus. Microbes attempt to do that, but the carbon to nitrogen ratio in crop residues is different from the ratio in manures.

Dairy manure mixed with straw will deliver a carbon to nitrogen ratio of about 18 to 1. Provided phosphate and potassium are not overdone, dairymen should use their dairy manure almost anywhere they can get a good spread, albeit not in large amounts on legumes such as alfalfa. Some clients say they get a good spread. Yet in too many cases too much is piled out right behind the spreader. A heavy spread is certain to give weeds a signal to increase and multiply. Why do weeds come through? Is it because weed seeds are transported with the manure? Not necessarily! Number one, farmers can have a weed problem because they spread so much manure that it drives the soils' potassium level up above 7.5% of base saturation, an open sesame for weed pressure. Number two, nitrogen is present in excess, and it enables certain types of weeds to out-compete alfalfa.

Some farmers hire custom operators to spread manure. I have seen an even spread at one ton per acre, the appropriate equipment being the key. Spread evenly at such low rates, manure does not generate weed problems, even in alfalfa fields that need the extra phosphorus and potassium. The key is an even spread and control over how much is used.

Horse manure is called a "hot" manure because it breaks down fast. The carbon-nitrogen ratio is around 32 to 1. Nitrogen in horse manure is generally estimated at about 1.6% times the dry matter. Sulfur, on the other hand, is about 0.2%; phosphorous, 0.7%; potassium, 1.2%. Calcium is not quite as high, but it is not too far off the potassium level at 1.1%. You may get quite a bit of calcium for crop growth via horse manure, but not enough to overcome any serious shortage. Generally, the carbon-nitrogen ratio of feedlot manures is a lot lower than 32 to 1. This means that you are much closer to humus formation with feedlot manure than would be the case if you composted straight horse manure. You get more nitrogen out of it—something like 2.3%—but the highest source of potassium, other than from sheep and poultry, is from feedlot manure. Expect it to run between 2 and 2.5% potassium. Sheep manure runs even higher.

Poultry manure, in turn, must be considered as turkey or layer manure or broiler litter. Layer manure may have a high calcium content if oyster shells are fed or some other form of extra calcium is used in the feed ration. Overuse of such manure is never suggested; otherwise the calcium can tie up other needed nutrients. Broiler manure is much like turkey litter. On soils needing phosphorus and potassium, either can be used without ill effect. As far as poultry litter is concerned, where six or eight tons of other

---

What Compost Does in the Soil

The soil, having been inoculated with the desirable soil organisms, then becomes a compost medium itself. There are very few crops grown on the high plains which don't leave a sizable residue. Some, as wheat and milo, often leave many tons per acre of stubble, roots and crowns. In barren soils, as most of the high plains region soil series have become, this residue is often considered a liability rather than an asset. The cellulose digesters in our compost change this condition. They consume this material converting the carbon and banking it for later use in growth. The nitrogen fixers securing their nourishment from the atmosphere, or where inorganic nitrates are in excess in the soil, stabilize it with the carbon for use by the plant as organic nitrogen when needed. It appears that more free ion nitrogen has been applied to the soils locally than the crops have been able to utilize and it has leached to lower levels of the soil, now causing trouble to deep rooted crops, such as sugar beets. With the soil organisms of our compost this excess nitrate would be stabilized for later crop use, thus avoiding this particular problem and possible contamination of underground water.

Hands-On Agronomy

Another group of organisms, the phosphate and potassium releasers, serve a very essential function. Since our soils are high in these elements it would be ludicrous if not so serious to observe that they are being purchased in such great quantities. Likely a large portion of those purchased join the ones present in this highly mineralized soil in becoming "lock up" or plant unavailable. Our compost organisms implanted in a similar soil under a controlled demonstration, increased the availability of phosphates 6,500% in 12 weeks. Their presence in our local soils will supply all the available phosphates any locally grown crop needs.

—*Fletcher Sims*
private papers, Acres U.S.A. collection

manures would be applied, you only need three to four tons. Both poultry litter and cage droppings incorporate urine, for which reason the saying has it, *poultry means hotter manure.*

Sheep manure is rich manure, right behind poultry manure. Other than nitrogen, sheep manure runs neck to neck with poultry manure. And even the nitrogen is comparatively high in it.

When manure is to be used, consider its properties carefully. Nitrogen conversion in the soil produces acidity. If you apply compost, soybean meal, alfalfa meal, cotton seed meal, or any kind of manure, without also adding the required limestone or other cations, increased acidity will result. The same thing is true for ammonium nitrogen fertilizers. Consider the chemistry. Two ammonia and three oxygen ions convert to two nitrate nitrogen and six hydrogen ions. The six hydrogen ions contribute to acidity. In other words, more hydrogen ions mean more soil acidity because hydrogen is the basis for all acids. Nitrogen conversion in the soil produces acidity. When you use nitrogen—whatever the source, manures included—pH is lowered because of hydrogen atom production. When nitrogen is applied and the nitrate leaves, it doesn't depart by itself. It takes along principally calcium, sometimes sodium or possibly other cations present, magnesium being excepted. Taking away these cations and their replacement with hydrogen is a recipe for increased acidity in the soil.

Secondary nutrients in manures should receive far more attention than is usually the case. Calcium and magnesium have already been mentioned, but it may be good to cover a few more points. Crops require considerable amounts of secondary nutrients. Eight tons of alfalfa with 445 pounds of nitrogen and 440 pounds of potassium, also has 175 pounds of calcium, 40 pounds of magnesium and 40 pounds of sulfur. Look at corn. Corn contains 42 pounds of calcium, 44 pounds of magnesium per 150 bushels—and 25 pounds of sulfur. Forget manure's undeserved reputation for sulfur content. I find that

Comparisons of Manures

At my lectures I am frequently asked to make comparisons in manurial values. One question that some of my listeners often ask is, "What is the difference between the manurial value of fresh farmyard manure and compost?"

Farmyard manure generally is made up of a solid and liquid excrement of farm animals, together with straw or litter. Animals cannot manufacture phosphoric acid, potash and nitrogen. The value of the manure, therefore, must depend to some extent upon the character of the food the animals consume. Indeed, the character of the food is easily the most important factor

Hands-On Agronomy

in determining the constituent value of *fresh* manure. When food is digested and assimilated by an animal, its manurial constituents are separated. In animals living on vegetation, the phosphoric acid and the undigested nitrogen of the food appear usually in the solid excrements, while the digested nitrogen and most of the potash are excreted in the urine. Fresh farmyard manure takes much of its chemical value from the nitrogen which it contains. If the food is difficult to digest, the chief value will be in solid excrement; on the other hand, if the food is easily digested the urine will have the greater value.

When cows are in pasture, or fed on concentrated food, the urine will contain about three times the value of solid manure so far as chemical fertilizing constituents are concerned; that is why it is important to make a liberal use of litter so as to absorb the liquid portion and avoid losing this valuable part of the manure. The values of manure obtained from the consumption of one kind of food can easily be calculated, and there are many authorities which have established figures.

—*Friend Sykes*
Humus & The Farmer *(1949)*

farmers who use manure still tend to have too little sulfur in their soils.

Most manures used today are not good sulfur sources simply because it is not possible to get anything out of manure except what is put into it. Since sulfur is not being put into rations, and since it is not adequately present in most soils, we do not increase sulfur levels very much by applying manure.

As suggested early in this chapter, there are several philosophies regarding the use of manure on the land. In a class on agriculture during my college days, we heard that manure in the barn wasn't worth cleaning out and hauling to the field. Commercial nitrogen, phosphorus and potassium were just as good and cost less. On the other hand, Earnest M. Halbleib, while operating Halbleib Orchards, McNabb, Illinois, would have manure applied on the land to be out of production for that year, in order to give it more time for breakdown before being tapped for food crop production. Since animals refuse to eat where they leave their fresh droppings, should human beings pay less attention?

Even in the Bible, the word dunghill is often used, but closer study with particular sources of commentary will show that the translation would be better rendered compost. The term does not refer to a fresh manure pile. In this regard, I never noted the order of use mentioned in the parable of the fig tree in Luke 13:6-9 until after an opportunity to discuss his problem of natural orchard production with the late Dr. Paul Kritchkovich of Zagreb, Croatia (formerly Yugoslavia). The successes of those using his program over decades of production from the same set of fruit trees provided the proof of its effectiveness. He advocated that any use of fresh manure on fruit and nut trees be from cattle, applied in prudent amounts, and always applied on top of mulch, never worked into the soil. Working in the fresh manure causes excessive growth in trees and results in a weakening of tree limbs, according to his work experience. In the parable of Luke 13, the dung is mentioned after the digging. Whether composted or not, could it be that for tree and vine growth even in the time of Christ it was actually left on top as Kritchkovich discovered was most beneficial in his work?

Regardless of the system invoked, agriculture and the environment will benefit far more from the use of manure—even in its crudest form—when it is worked into the soil, rather than left on top. Some will object that manure has to be treated before use, but again, perhaps an example from the Bible should be considered. Moses directed that even fresh human wastes be covered by soil, Deuteronomy 23:12-13. This is not meant to advocate the use of human waste for crop production, rather to illustrate that even in those ancient times they understood the importance of quickly handling a large volume of waste manure with adequate amounts of soil. There is no contradiction here, with small amounts being applied on top or larger amounts being composted or covered to prevent waste and disease.

Manure handling is an ancient art. Still available in libraries throughout the United States is the 1938 USDA Yearbook of Agriculture entitled, *Soils and Men*. One entire section is devoted to manure handling.

The work is intensely practical. It appears to square with what I have observed in every area of the country. It seems far more important to have manure used presently, rather than to insist that it should only be considered for use after it is digested in a certain way, even though several improvements may be accomplished by doing so. I tell farmers to use manure where it is needed, and then progress from there.

Sul-fur or Sul-phur / 'sel-fer / *n* [ME *sulphur* brimstone, fr L. *sulpur, sulphur, sulfur*] 1 a nonmetallic anion element that occurs either free or combined esp. in sulfides and sulfates 2 chemical symbol:

| 16 |
| S |
| 32.06 |

3 is a constituent of proteins and exists in allotropic forms, including yellow orthorhombic crystals 4 resembles oxygen, yet less active and more acidic 5 its release in soils is governed by the size of the organic matter bank account 6 its transformation is under the auspices of the decomposers of the biotic pyramid which take proteins and organic combinations—of which hydrogen and sulfur are simple forms—and turns them into sulfates and sulfites 7 essential to formation of sulfur containing proteins, a constituent in thiamine, biotin, glutathione

10

The Sulfur Connection

WHEN I FIRST STARTED TO WORK AS A CONSULTANT in 1973, the lab and my mentor, Dr. William A. Albrecht, taught about the importance of sulfur. As a consequence, from the beginning of our work with soil fertility sulfur was always tested right along with phosphorus, potassium, calcium and magnesium. It was always considered by Albrecht, and had been for years, the point being that long before I even got started, there was already a good track record on sulfur testing. There may be some laboratories that "aren't sure" about the accuracy of the sulfur tests they can run, but even in 1973 we could be sure because of instruction by the few who knew from experience. Perhaps if the "authorities" on fertility spent more time in the field working with sulfur instead of quoting other authorities, production would not be so hindered by dissemination of improper information about this extremely important and much needed nutrient.

The fact is, sulfate is needed for growing plants just as badly and in much the same amounts as phosphate. Yet farmers put on far more phosphate than sulfate. Furthermore, phosphate is more stable than sulfate in the soil, and when the two compete for absorption, sulfate is the loser, especially when phosphate levels are very high. Consequently soils either high in phosphorus or on the receiving end of high rates of phosphate fertilizer will need more sulfur to produce as they should—otherwise, growers won't get their money's worth for all the phosphate they put on.

Another point—based on all these years of cumulative experience with sulfur testing—is that almost every soil tested does not have enough sulfur to produce the top yields that crops are capable of making today. Even soils that have been receiving manure, including heavy clay and loam soils, and soils with a high humus content, rarely show enough sulfur unless the farmer is specifically adding it in his fertility program.

When all the confusion about sulfur is settled, there still remains the question of how much to apply. Some fertilizer dealers tell their clients that 20 pounds per acre will kill the crop. Yet if the grower could justify the cost and the soil exhibited a need for it, even 200 pounds per acre would not harm corn if applied at planting time, and 300 pounds per acre could be applied on growing alfalfa without harmful consequences. This is not to say anyone should do this without testing to determine nutrient levels first. But any farmer can be assured that 20, 30, 50 or even 100 pounds per acre will cause no ill effects if circumstances determined by a reliable test suggest a need and the sulfur is properly applied.

Just what does sulfur do for crops anyway? For one thing, when present in adequate amounts, it helps seedlings survive in cool, moist soils. Especially consider sulfur when soils are still cold for the earliest planted fields of crops such as cotton and corn, and for conservation tillage fields. Adequate sulfur helps provide more rapid root development during early periods of growth. I've seen 50% more root development in the same fields with than without adequate sulfate on wheat. The same is true for all crops, with many specific examples in citrus, corn, cotton, nut trees and winegrapes. Sulfur is also important for increasing the protein content of crops. If there isn't enough sulfur, alfalfa will not contain the best level of protein that is otherwise possible.

Of one thing you can be certain—more certain than the conceit some years ago that Midwest soils needed no sulfur according to most agronomists. Sandy soils need sulfur. Before too many years it will be recognized that farmers should use far more sulfur in order to harness the crop's ability to produce at a maximum.

Some farmers know that it takes equally as many pounds of sulfur—in the sulfate form—as phosphate to grow 150 bushels of corn. Some will say that this is not right because it takes three times more phosphate than sulfur to raise a crop. In terms of pure elemental sulfur, perhaps it does. But I am not talking about phosphate as phosphorus.

If you reduce phosphate down to phosphorus and sulfate down to sulfur, then we are talking in the same terms again. Otherwise you should convert sulfur to sulfate, the form of sulfur the plant actually uses, to get it up to the phosphate denominator. The big difference is that when some agronomists talk about phosphate, they talk about P_2O_5, and when they talk about sulfur—instead of talking about SO_4, sulfate, they talk about S, sulfur. To get the equivalent amount, it is necessary to multiply sulfur by three, which yields 75 pounds of sulfate for a 150-bushel-per-acre corn crop. Phosphate runs something like 85. Unit for unit, it takes about one pound of sulfate and one pound of phosphate to grow the same amount of corn. According to some, the big difference is the time frame in which either nutrient is used. Some say 90% of the phosphate can be used by the time the corn completes tasseling, 10% afterwards. With sulfur, 10% can be used before the corn tassels, 90% afterwards. The objective is to have the phosphate on-scene early, and the sulfur in place in the sulfate form later on.

The yellow striping that designates a lack of sulfur is often confused with magnesium deficiency in corn. Magnesium deficiency causes whitish stripes along the veins and a purplish color on the underside of the lower leaves. When you see that striping, you are long past hurting the yield. It is the same situation talked about with potassium on corn earlier. Severe nutrient deficiencies look very similar. I have seen zinc deficiencies that look almost exactly like a textbook description for magnesium deficiency. If in doubt, a leaf analysis to identify the problem is indicated. But never discount the possibility of a need for sulfur in your crop.

There is no substitute for sulfur. If you need it, you will have to supply it, or the crop will suffer. It is the fourth major nutrient in terms of the amount required for most crops. Please note that it is required in amounts higher than calcium and magnesium. It should be compared with nitrogen, phosphate and potassium as a major requirement. Plants need sulfur to make protein, to craft chlorophyll, to fabricate enzymes and vitamins. The first consideration for building protein in alfalfa is calcium. Another

A magnesium deficiency in corn shows yellow stripes of varying widths on the tops of corn leaves (above). Though similar to certain other nutrient deficiencies, it may be differentiated by a purplish tinge on the bottom side of the leaves.

consideration is sulfur, along with phosphorus. Any one of these nutrients can be a problem, or *the problem*. Just keep in mind that plant content for phosphate phosphorus is close to the same as for sulfate sulfur for many crops.

Sulfur is also a component of several amino acids. Deficiencies are increasing because yields are being pushed higher. In fact, varieties in use today can give much higher yields than those used in the past. But less sulfur is included in the fertilizer program, so what we grow has less potential for acquiring sulfate sulfur from the soil because fertilizer fabricators process it out.

Sulfur is worth more as such these days. Fabricators can process it out of raw materials and sell it. Also, they process it out of some fertilizers because of transportation cost considerations. Another sulfur source is being diminished as a consequence of public policy. Sulfur emissions are lowered by pollution control measures. Also, we don't use nearly the amount of sulfur-containing manures that we used to spread, and even if utilized, they were once a better source of sulfur than now.

Farmers who use manures still need to apply sulfur. We do not have a high humus level in most soils today. Humus is what holds sulfur in the soil. If you get down to 6 ppm sulfate sulfur, as measured on the test we use, it should be remembered that there is no plant that will not respond to a proper sulfur application. Once you are below 20 ppm, begin to think about doing something to get the sulfur level up. At that level you don't have even the minimum amount of sulfur required—which is 40 pounds of actual sulfur in the sulfate form—to assure that crops requiring even moderate amounts of sulfur are sufficiently supplied.

Sulfate sulfur leaches. By way of contrast, phosphate does not leach. In the correct form, it stays put until roots pick it up. Sulfate can be lost rather quickly, albeit not as easily as nitrate. Yet in agriculture today so many worry about adding phosphate, which does not leach easily, and overlook sulfates—which should be on the same par for corn, citrus, winegrapes, etc.—

which will leach away. Until this approach is corrected, both quality and quantity of production is adversely affected.

The response from an appropriate level of sulfur can be tremendous. Considering the various nutrients discerned by tests to be missing from "fertile" soils today, sulfur gives the best response of anything, albeit only when the big three—nitrogen, phosphate and potassium are adequately supplied for the crop to be grown—and calcium and magnesium for the long-term effects are present in the proper amounts.

If you have a balanced soil, or a soil that is within the tolerances related in these chapters, what should be the ratios of one nutrient to another? A particular ratio may work for one soil but not another because we still haven't established the

---

Chelation, a Unique Union of Metals and Organic Molecules

In the form of salts and ions, the larger amounts of trace elements may be hindering, rather than helping, life processes. They may be poisons, but when there are gross dangers, there are often gross advantages if and when the conditions responsible are understood. Emphasis on trace elements as poisons inclines us to close our minds to their large service when so little of them are present. But only trace amounts may also be anti-catalysts. They may be displacing the helpful metals. When "enzymes are carriers of vitamins, minerals, and amino acids," ["Minerals in Nutrition, Present, Fast and Future," by John J. Miller, in *Journal of Applied Nutrition*, 1962] the failure of the mineral part as only a trace may pervert the enzyme.

"The essence of this situation is that the minerals are tied into the enzyme by special bonds—called coordi-

---

Hands-On Agronomy

nate bonds—and when so bound the entire molecule takes on new properties. Soluble forms of minerals may become insoluble, and vice versa; color changes may follow; speeds of action of a mineral salt may be multiplied a thousand fold, and mineral elements, which otherwise cannot enter a cell, may participate readily in the intracellular activities when the metal becomes partly or completely surrounded by the organic portion of the enzyme. A partial surrounding of the mineral with the organic part of the enzyme is called a 'complex,' whereas a completely surrounded mineral is said to be 'chelated.'

"In view, then, of the discovery that strategic metals may be trapped (complexed or chelated) by certain organic substances and of the fact that all biological activity depends on enzymes that use the minerals in 'complexed' or 'chelated' arrangements, it is vital to ask 'whether the body can absorb and utilize the complexed and chelated forms of minerals more readily than the inorganic forms.' Logically the answer is that the complexing and chelating remove the positive charge from the metals as they become dissociated in the stomach or intestine—through combining with the chelating materials (organic)—thus permitting the neutral or slightly negative complexed molecule to slide through the pores of the intestinal wall. These pores are negatively charged; hence cause some degree of fixation of positive minerals at the pore entrance whereas the negative complexed or chelated mineral is induced to enter and then to pass into the blood stream."

—*William A. Albrecht*
private papers, Acres U.S.A. collection

necessary chemistry and physics there as yet. For example, one statement made by the Sulphur Institute is that you need one pound of sulfur for every ten pounds of nitrogen. That isn't necessarily true. If you start looking at those ratios and try to match the soil—and you don't have the same chemistry in the soil that the so-called norm had in the adage creation experiment, that ratio is not going to work the same way. Farmers should look at the base saturation of the soil, the usable amount already contained in the soil and the crop requirement based on proven yield potential to determine the practical side of things.

The minimum amount of sulfur for any soil is 20 to 25 ppm, meaning 40 to 50 pounds of sulfur per acre. Once this level is achieved, and if there is no excess magnesium to be leached out, and no excessive phosphate to cause a problem, or some other factor that can drive sulfur out of the soil, no more sulfur is required for some crops. In short, the indication is to use sulfur when it drops below the desired level. That situation will occur almost every year if 25 ppm or less is the normal reading: cropping will use up the sulfur that year. If a good high humus content is in place, the level will hold a little longer, but it is not possible to keep sulfur for long because it will be used up or leached out when it is present in the sulfate form. Expect to need a maintenance level of sulfur on a regular basis.

For high yielding crops, woody-type plants (including fruit, nut, timber and other types of trees, shrubs and vines), as well as pasture and hay meadows, 50 ppm is the minimum level to achieve the best results from sulfur. For example, soils with 50 ppm of sulfur, as measured by the specific type of testing we use, will increase trunk size by an extra 25% for trees and vines.

If you don't receive large amounts of rain and the leaching it can cause—it isn't just extra irrigation water that causes leaching—then you won't have to buy as much sulfur as the farmer who gets a lot of rainfall or who has to use greater amounts of irrigation water. If your soil is such that you want sulfate to leave so you can take out the magnesium with it, then it becomes a case of having to observe how much of an effect it has. In western Kansas, down around Sharon Springs and south near Leoti, they count on as little as eight inches of rainfall a year. They still have sulfur deficiency. Whether or not it is because the sulfur is leached out or used up by the crop or tied up somehow remains a question. They still need to use sulfur.

Farmers often wonder aloud whether pH affects the availability of sulfur. Actually, the calcium-magnesium balance is a pH governing factor. The closer the calcium-magnesium balance, the less fluctuation in the sulfur level. Once equilibrium is achieved, it is not as easy for sulfur to be leached away. So what we actually see is a leveling out of the sulfate in a soil once we get a balance of the cations. But as long as we have something in excess and adequate calcium is present, we can apply higher amounts of sulfur and it will continue to disappear along with excesses such as sodium, magnesium, and/or potassium. (For those interested in the methods and how to accomplish this, it requires a specific set of procedures that are taught in our advanced soil fertility training courses.) At a point where there are no more excesses to drive out, we have only to apply the needed amounts to that same soil in order to keep the sulfur nutrient load in the proper range.

It should be emphasized here that the sulfate reading on our test would not necessarily relate to what it should be on tests from other labs. There are perhaps a dozen ways or more to analyze and report sulfur levels. Therefore to try to apply one formula to another lab's test report can translate into one big mistake.

Although sulfur occurs in the soil as a sulfate ion, the major soil source for sulfur is humus. The higher the humus content, the less likely a need for sulfur. Therefore, the humus level and the rate of its increase or destruction is an index to sulfur availability. The bottom line remains the same: overuse of nitrogen will burn out the humus supply, and equally will destroy the sulfur storage system. Heavy use of nitrogen to cover for sulfur will translate into less humus, ergo less sulfur to sustain future crop production. At

7% humus content, it is possible to get by with a lower sulfur level than if the humus content is 5%, or only 2.5%.

On the basis of soil analysis results, it will generally require at least 10 to 20 pounds of sulfur a year for most soils as a maintenance. Along with nitrogen and boron, sulfur generally has to be added to the soil on a regular basis. A few numbers may be of possible interest; grain sorghum, to avoid a deficiency, takes 34 pounds of sulfur for a 180-bushel yield. In turn, 60 bushels of soybeans requires 27 pounds. But a 75-bushel wheat harvest takes only 17 pounds of sulfur. That may be why wheat responds to sulfur at lower rates of applied material than crops like winegrapes, citrus and vegetables.

University research at various state experimental stations in the Midwest helped make this last piece of information more credible. Shortly before the turn of the century, five states ran three years of replicated sulfur tests on wheat. Only one concluded that sulfur had absolutely no significant effect on wheat yields. Officially, that university got no response between the control and where they used sulfur.

Since this had not been the case in neighboring states, the consulting agronomist in charge of overseeing all these sulfur experiments visited the site to learn more details. During his visit, the farm manager observed: "When they tell me to use triple superphosphate, I always use 0-20-0, superphosphate because it always does a better job here." Now 0-20-0, superphosphate, has sulfur in it. Therefore his control had sulfur as well as the rest of the field used for wheat production tests. So here was a situation in which people doing the experiments didn't realize their farm manager was applying sulfur all the time. They didn't see any response to sulfur on wheat because adequate sulfur was used on the control as well as on the test plot. A reliable sulfur test would have helped here.

Most soils we test have less than 15 pounds of sulfur per acre unless it is being applied. Under such conditions, levels do not usually increase with soil depth if sulfur is not being applied on a regular basis. We have taken a number of subsoil samples for analysis. In most cases, less sulfur is detected in the subsoil. Either it survives in the topsoil, or it is generally lost. If you can keep a supply in the subsoil, roots will pick it up. But this will not be the case under normal circumstances unless sulfur is being regularly added to the soil.

Sulfur, in times past, was replenished primarily from atmospheric sulfur dioxide gas, from fertilizers and certain pesticides. As a practical matter, we can forget about sulfur dioxide gas because we are not getting as much of that these days. We can also discount most fertilizer sources because, as pointed out earlier, sulfur is no longer much of a component in the most common trade products. Certain pesticides contain some sulfur, many do not. All things considered, without the sulfate forms of fertilizers, this leaves only manure as a prime sulfur source. And we have previously outlined what has happened in that regard. Without sulfur in the soil where plants are grown, the manure resulting from the use of those crops will also fail to supply the needed sulfur. Until the soil is adequately replenished to the point that our crops can pick up adequate amounts of sulfur, the lack of sulfur will continue to be a serious fertility problem.

Adequate sulfur improves the palatability of any crop. When sulfur is shown to be the limiting factor from the test we use, clients who use sulfur on watermelons report a substantial improvement in taste. All fruits are vastly improved in taste and keeping quality when deficient sulfur is supplied, and the nutrient also improves palatability of grasses for animal feed. Sulfur increases protein content and helps control nitrates to a marked extent. If you have problems with nitrates in the feeds, one of the very first things to consider is correcting any sulfur deficiency.

Sulfur deficiency impairs both yield and quality. Inside the plant sulfur forms proteins, helps with enzyme and vitamin development, promotes nodule formation on legumes, aids in seed production and, not least, it is necessary in chlorophyll formation. Elemental sulfur is the most universally available source when sulfur is shown to be needed. Ammonium sulfate also works well, depending on the area. Other sources include copper sulfate, which has 12.8% sulfur. It's an excellent copper source, but at only 10 pounds to the acre, such an application will not supply much sulfur. Iron sulfate has 19 percent sulfur, but at 50 pounds per acre, this computes to only eight or nine pounds of sulfur. Gypsum contains 16% sulfur, which makes it a good source where the minimum calcium requirement has already been met and yet both calcium and sulfur are still needed. Magnesium sulfate is 11+% sulfur, and manganese sulfate contains 15%. Sul-Po-Mag is 22% sulfur and can be of use where sulfur, potassium and magnesium are all needed. Normal superphosphate (0-20-0) has almost 12% sulfur in it. Concentrated superphosphate (0-46-0) hardly has any sulfur—actually 1.4 pounds per 100 pounds of the material.

The last line here is that whether you put sulfur on with superphosphate or anything else, more must be provided than just the amount the plant can take up. Most agronomists will tell you that 10 to 20 pounds of sulfur per acre is enough. If it were possible to get every bit of what is in the soil into the plant, this assessment might possibly be right. The problem is, the roots are not necessarily going to cover the entire area. Therefore it sometimes becomes impossible for the plant to pick up all it needs under such circumstances. Withal, it is now enough to say that we may require 80 pounds of sulfur in the sulfate form to get it into the plant the same as we do with phosphate. Phosphate is not very mobile. Sulfur is. But we require phosphorus—based on a water soluble P_1 test—to the tune of 70 to 80 pounds. Since sulfur moves around in the water, we may get by with 40 to 50 pounds of sulfur in the sulfate form for certain types of crops, but we find that far more is required for others.

If a sulfate sulfur test reveals 200 pounds per acre (considered by some as an excess), that is not necessarily a problem. It depends on what other strengths and weaknesses a particular soil might reveal. Sulfur deficiency symptoms in general are exhibited as a light green or yellow color appearing first on younger leaves. Almost everyone who walks a corn field low in sulfur can identify this symptom. If you don't see it, that can indicate you have an adequate amount of sulfur in the soil. But sulfur can be deficient even in a leaf that appears to be nice and green. An ear leaf too low in sulfur held to the sun will exhibit thin yellow lines. A good tissue analysis will confirm sulfur deficiency.

On furrow irrigated corn, 250 pounds of ammonium sulfate per acre—which is 24% sulfur—means an input of 60 pounds of elemental sulfur in the sulfate form. On some of the best soils in southeast Missouri, sulfur is one of, if not the limiting factor for top yielding corn, even though 60 pounds is applied in the sulfate form as ammonium sulfate at planting. In terms of dryland corn or corn grown under pivot irrigation, farmers may get by with less. But with furrow irrigated corn, we still have to apply ten pounds of elemental sulfur in addition to 60 pounds of sulfate in order to keep sulfur from becoming the limiting factor on yields. Desired sulfur levels depend on how much water each soil receives. Experience with both soil and leaf analysis tells us there is no need to guess.

Two hundred bushels of corn contain 40 pounds of sulfur. If you are going to raise 200 bushels of corn and you have 2.5% organic matter, there is no way you are going to get 40 pounds of sulfur out of most soils. Two hundred-fifty bushels of corn contain 50 pounds of sulfur. On the other hand, if you go backward, 150 bushels of corn will require only 30 pounds of sulfur. If we only have 20 ppm sulfur in a soil, that is just 40 pounds. Technically we would have 10 pounds to spare. But again, the roots can't reach every gram of soil where sulfur might be positioned.

Ten tons of alfalfa contain 55 pounds of sulfur. Soybeans also have their own requirement. I routinely ask my clients with low sulfur levels to start using 10 pounds of sulfur blended and broadcast with other needed fertilizer on soybeans. Most of the time the limiting fertilizer for soybeans, other than lime, is potassium. But when farmers use 10 pounds of sulfur with their potassium input, beans flourish. Yellowing in a soybean plant can denote a sulfur deficiency. If the sulfur inventory falls below 20 ppm, there isn't a chance of making 60 bushel soybeans on most soils. Sulfur can also cause toxicity problems. There is a danger of burning plants if too much dust is in the sulfur and it sticks on the leaves while crops are actively growing.

After attending one of our three-day introductory soil fertility conferences, a former past president of the Missouri Organic Farmers Association decided to have us help him with his soil fertility needs. Even though he felt he had some very good soils already, he wanted to determine more precisely where they stood. For the most part, his soils were in very good shape based on the samples analyzed, but one universal problem was a lack of sulfur. The sulfur was applied in some areas, along with whatever else was shown to be required from the soil tests. Nothing more was heard one way or the other until the next year when he attended another of our soil fertility courses. At that course he explained to everyone present the results where needed sulfur was applied to his fields. He did not apply it everywhere; but where he used it as recommended, he reported that an increase in yield was not the most noticeable difference. One crop on which he already had excellent yields was green beans, and using the sulfur as directed had extended the keeping quality of the green beans once in the cooler. Previously, he told the group, his green beans would be so limp by the afternoon of the first day that it appeared they had been picked for three days. But with the sulfur application made to the soil before planting, they still had a first-day crispness in the cooler even after three days.

Sulfur dust has always been used for insect control. Various companies also make liquid sulfur. These products are still sold and used as pesticides for growing winegrapes, peaches, etc. They can be sprayed on leaves in the proper amounts for disease control. Old timers are quick to remind that a prime remedy for taking care of many problems is sulfur dust. On the other hand, I have clients who use elemental sulfur, some who use ammonium sulfate, and yet they have problems with insects. It should be kept in mind that we are considering two different aspects of the use of sulfur in agriculture here. Spraying sulfur for disease control requires volatilization in order to work. As such, we lose that sulfur to the air. It does not build up soil levels.

At one of our soil fertility training courses we had discussed the need for sulfur and also the fact that too much could deplete other needed nutrients. One peach grower from the area with several large orchards became concerned at the amounts of sulfur he had been applying to his trees and decided to have us soil test his entire acreage. The sulfur he used had been applied directly to the trees for disease control, and when the test results came back, his soils all showed to be extremely deficient in sulfur. Again to do its job the micronized sulfur had to volatilize. It went into the air, not the soil. The same is true for winegrapes. Do not make the mistake that spraying sulfur on the trees or vines provides all the soil needs, too. I can't honestly say that sulfur will do such and such for disease control when applied as a soil nutrient, but I will tell you that if you balance out your soils, sulfur—in combination with the correct equilibrium of the other nutrients—is going to make it easier to handle many problems.

A good friend of mine tells about his experience with an older farmer who lived pretty close to a fish processing plant on the east coast. This was back when nobody wanted all the entrails and waste products of fish processing because of the offensive odors. He spread these materials on his farm and disced them in. All of a sudden an infestation of Japanese beetles appeared in the area. Yet none caused problems on this fellow's farm except in one small area that always produced poorly. His crop was excellent, even though adjacent fields were ruined. There are reasons for such occurrences, and nutrient levels in the soil play a big part.

One of the proofs I use for this is something I learned from the well-known entomologist, Dr. Everett Dietrick. He was one of the first to teach, and then put into practice, integrated pest management. His objective was to watch for problem areas and control them with insects. Dietrick once told an Acres U.S.A. Conference that he did not wait for an infestation to take command of the entire field. He always went to the weak spots immediately. "The insects always come to the weak spots first," he said. If there is a place in the field that doesn't do well and has the worst fertility record, that is where the problem will appear. If you don't have a weak spot, then they are going to come to the edges. If Dietrick couldn't control insects with other insects, he sprayed, but most of the time he didn't have to. This observation has been confirmed time after time. A shortfall or imbalance in fertility draws the insects first. If the fertility of a field is already right, and the weak spots can be corrected, the problem with insects will be even more likely to disappear. Even so, there are steps which farmers can take in the meantime.

There are several ways to determine problems with sulfur in cropping systems. One approach is to look at the leaves and try to differentiate between the various patterns. But generally it is too late for a full remedy once it can be seen in the crop. It is also possible to conduct a measured response test. This is accomplished by using the nutrient in question on a part of the cropping area to find out if there is an actual improvement in yield when applied at a specified rate. So often such tests are begun with good intentions, but the pressures during harvest season push the determination of the end results out of the picture. And in many cases, the full results require 2 or 3 years to completely show up. There is still another possible choice. You can take a plant or leaf test in combination with an accurate soil analysis. This is the approach we try to use for proving the need for sulfur.

In addition to the use of sulfur as a plant nutrient and as a pesticide, it is also used to help with control of excesses such as magnesium or sodium in the soil. Sulfur will not begin to reduce excessive magnesium or sodium until the calcium can be increased and maintained at or above 60% saturation in the soil. Therefore, calcium normally must be increased to slightly above 60% from another calcium source before the sulfur in gypsum can be expected to work.

There are specific situations, though, where gypsum will work when the calcium saturation is still below 60%. Expect more occurrences on lighter soils with a sufficient calcium saturation in the upper half of the 50% range. If the added calcium from one ton or less of gypsum will work out to 64% calcium saturation or higher for that soil, there is no need of using other forms of calcium first. The gypsum will work there just fine without extra calcium carbonate or some other lime source. Because of this type of success on the lighter soils, some consultants mistakenly assume that gypsum will thus work under any circumstances. Split a field! Follow the advice of another advisor on half of it and advice based specifically on the soil test we utilize on the other half for three years and see which approach produces better results.

So-di-um /'sōd-ē-em / *n* [NL, fr. E *soda*] 1 a silver white soft waxy ductile element of the alkali metal group 2 chemical symbol:

| 11 |
| Na |
| 22.98977 |

3 occurs abundantly in nature in compound form 4 very active as a cation 5 a cell regulating element that governs osmotic pressure in cellular tissues and fluids

11
Sodium—What's the Problem?

AS A RULE, THROUGHOUT THE WORLD, unless there is some problem caused by an excess in the soil, farmers and growers take little notice of sodium levels. And even those who do may not understand much more than that generally it becomes a problem due to the amounts in the water and when it gets too high plant growth suffers. Actually some growers need to deal with far more than that when it comes to problems with sodium in the soil. And not only can there be problems with too much sodium, but for certain crops, there can be problems when there is not enough. So it becomes necessary to understand and deal with sodium problems at both ends of the spectrum, when there is too much, and when there is not enough. And for most, the big question is, when sodium is the problem, how can it be corrected.

First it should be understood that sodium problems are not just caused by excessive levels in irrigation water. A soil compaction layer can cause small additions of sodium to accumulate and become a problem when there are only modest amounts in the water being used. When water cannot properly move the sodium through the soil, inordinate amounts begin to accumulate there and can cause problems. In addition to salt pockets and sodium seeps, this can be a problem on farms in the central United States as well as other parts of the world.

Many soil tests do not even consider the amount of sodium present in the soil. And it is not a question of how many pounds per acre that matters most, it is the percent saturation of sodium in that soil as compared to potassium, calcium and magnesium. For soils that contain low or deficient potassium levels, once the percent of sodium saturation exceeds the percent of potassium saturation, plants take up sodium instead of needed potassium. Under such circumstances, and with enough heat and humidity, damage can occur to the plants growing there, or in the worst cases, they may die prematurely.

For some crops, such as cotton or soybeans, the damage may appear to be nematodes. But in fields where this sodium/potassium relationship actually occurs, the application of sufficient potassium to push it just above the sodium percentage has solved what looked like nematodes, but that was not the real problem. Too little potassium for the amount of sodium present was the true problem. There are many situations where nematodes are a problem, and adding potassium has not eliminated that problem. But where testing confirms there is no nematode problem at all, correcting a situation that above ground looks like nematode damage by adding enough potassium to exceed the sodium saturation on the soil test clears it up altogether.

Another problem that can result from too much sodium in the soil also ties in with the percent saturation. When the percentages of sodium and potassium, in any combination, exceed 10%, it will begin to block manganese uptake by the plants. If this situation gets bad enough, it can cause severe problems due to a lack of sufficient manganese uptake. Even when the soil test levels of manganese show to be excellent this will occur, because it is not a nutrient tie-up, it is a blockage of manganese due to such an excess of potassium and/or sodium. Growers who supply potassium through drip irrigation systems should pay special attention to this possibility, especially when sodium is in the water.

On the other hand, there are also problems that can result when there is not enough sodium in the soil. For example, if sodium is less than 0.5% as shown on the specific test we use, barley, sugar beets, table beets, broccoli, cabbage, and cauliflower do not produce as well. In addition, when sodium is too low, its use on crops like apples, winegrapes, tomatoes and potatoes may benefit. By properly correcting soil sodium in such cases it can help provide a positive effect on skin color.

On our soil test report, down the sheet a bit, sodium is expressed as a percentage of cation saturation, and further down in pounds per acre as well. Sodium will accumulate in a soil unless it can pass through with the water. On the test we use, anything above 3% sodium is considered as excessive. Applying anything containing appreciable amounts of sodium can result in unnecessary build-up in a soil. If you have a problem or a potential problem, remember that sodium may come from sources other than the irrigation water. Check your manure and compost, especially in the western states, and consider that there are areas in some states that contain salt pockets in the subsoil.

Often farmers in southeast Missouri will have their fields graded to level them, especially for rice production. In some fields large areas of white-colored material previously unobserved in the sub-soil will now become visible as a result. These areas or pockets represent various forms of sodium. As with any soil that has an excessive sodium level, the very first order of business is to get that soil opened up by correcting the calcium level to 60% saturation or more. Once this calcium saturation has been achieved and there is sufficient calcium to assure it can be maintained at or above the minimum of 60%, begin using sulfur and sulfate fertilizers to deplete any sodium excess.

Two brothers who became clients farmed a 750-acre rented farm. The south field of that farm was 125 acres. One bad area (25 acres in the southwest corner) ran about halfway through the field, then all the way to the north end. They said that when they planted soybeans in the south field the beans in that problem area only grew so tall—somewhere between 6 and 10 inches—and then died. As the beans grew, the outer edges would turn a deep, dark green, then take on a blue green hue. The leaves would get crinkly, and the plants would start dying. Their soil inventory revealed in detail that they had a higher concentration of sodium than calcium. It also revealed the amount needed to properly correct the problem. In this case, four tons of fine-grind calcitic limestone were required to remedy the situation. After the liming was accomplished, yields improved during the next cropping season. By the end of the third year, the sodium was gone and you could not pick out the previous problem area. With maintenance of normal needs through liming, crops have been excellent ever since.

Crops grown in soils with the ideal calcium and magnesium saturations will tolerate much higher saturations of sodium. Any soil that can maintain calcium at 60% or higher—provided the water moves on through—can tolerate the addition of far more sodium without causing a growing problem to the crop. Of all the classic cations, an excess of sodium can generally be most easily removed. The greatest exception is an excess of both sodium and magnesium, which is discussed later in this chapter. Only anions such as nitrates and chlorates will move through the soil more quickly than sodium. But if water moves through the soil in normal amounts from rainfall or irrigation and there is not 60% saturation or more in terms of calcium, sodium will generally continue to increase. This is why in so many cases those who do recognize the problem of too much sodium continue to allow the problem to get worse.

Where excessive amounts of sodium are not presently being accumulated, the worst sodium problem to solve, and the hardest place to grow a crop, is in a soil that also has a magnesium excess. That is, once the calcium saturation has been corrected but there is still an excess of both sodium and magnesium, the person tackling this problem still has a hard job trying to overcome a sodium excess. A soil low in calcium and high in magnesium tends to be so tight, even if no hardpan is present, that water and plant roots have trouble penetrating downward, and especially when sodium is excessive. If sodium is accumulating due to severely tight or hard soils or from compaction problems, it can usually be recognized because a higher concentration of sulfur will be there as well. When soils contain excessive levels of sodium and magnesium, low calcium and high sulfur, be careful. Even with the best of materials applied correctly and using good water, correcting that type soil will be one of the hardest jobs to accomplish. It can be done, but it will normally take longer and require far more investment in time and money than is the case with other types of soil.

If you have a high exchange capacity and it looks like a huge tonnage of lime will be required—above 4 tons per acre—you should not apply more than 4 tons that first year. Wait at least another year and take another soil test. Then consider the calcium still to be released from the previous year (see the material on limestone analysis in the chapter on calcium) and before adding any additional lime that appears to be needed, cut the requirement in half and apply that amount. Test again after another 12 months before considering the addition of any more lime. Be sure you thoroughly understand this before using large amounts of any liming material, because the amount required may not be as great as it first appears. This could result in all those negative consequences from using too much lime as previously described in the chapter on calcium.

Here is what can happen. The added calcium actually causes a decrease in the soil's exchange capacity. I don't know for certain why it does this. I wonder if it has to do with the amount of free cations present. The soil lab determines a soil's exchange capacity, or TEC, by analyzing for the cations (potassium, calcium, magnesium, sodium, etc.) present and available, totaling them up to calculate the exchange capacity. This is sometimes referred to as the *sum of cations* procedure. But when these cations are in the extreme, the colloidal system becomes super-saturated. On a high exchange soil, with a pH above 7.0, more cations can be present than can be held by the colloid. Under such circumstances, if the magnesium, potassium and/or sodium are in excess, liming can still be required to improve the soil. But after the lime is applied the unusually high saturation of the colloidal system is affected again, and consequently we get a downward adjustment in the TEC. Any time more than four tons of limestone are shown to be needed on a high TEC soil, my practice is to cut the amount over and above the first 4-ton application in half and continue from there, still applying no more than four tons in that first year.

Somebody once asked about treating spills or "alkali spots" where the dike breaks around oil wells. There are many such areas in southern Illinois, as well as Kansas, Colorado, Texas and other areas of the west. Usually nothing will grow there, and it is not unusual to measure 20,000 pounds of sodium in the top seven inches of soil. When you have 20,000 pounds of sodium, that extreme excess will tie up a huge load of calcium. I have seen places where it appeared there would never be a response without 12 or 15 tons of high calcium lime. Needless to say the cost of such an input will be hard-pressed to pay for itself on corn and soybean land. Some few farmers have had me evaluate such situations, but never has a farmer decided to spend the money that appeared to be necessary to correct the problem. But if the calcium ever got above 60% base saturation, the sodium would literally move out with the transport of water. In short, it is virtually impossible to hold sodium in a soil with 60% plus calcium and adequate water penetration. Without water penetration, it becomes a case of "back to the soil conditioner." A good soil conditioner can open up the tightest of soils.

As stated earlier with more sodium than potassium, even if everything else is correct, there will be a problem with beans dying when it gets hot and humid. Anything that is a fast growing plant can die under such circumstances. Always keep the potassium saturation above the sodium saturation. For more information on this type of situation, review the material in the chapter on potassium.

With barley and sugar beets, if you have sodium moderately higher than potassium, they can still survive and do well. According to base saturation percentages, sodium should be 0.5% to 3%. Below 0.5—if you want to raise sugar beets or barley—production will be less

Back in the mid-1980s, 200 soil samples were received from one farm in Germany. The owner traveled to Missouri for the initial soil evaluations. One sampled area measured less than 0.5% sodium. I told the owner that he could grow all his other small grains there, but he shouldn't try to grow barley on the field. When he asked why, the explanation was because he had less than 0.5% sodium. If you have less than 0.5% sodium, barley will not do as well. He asked about several fields to check on my evaluation. There were two other fields that did not produce a satisfactory barley crop. Each had less than 0.5% sodium. He told me those were the only three fields on the farm where they had problems with barley yields.

Broccoli, cabbage, cauliflower, and table beets all respond to sodium. None will thrive in soils with less than 0.5% sodium. Some clients who are corn farmers have less than 0.5% sodium on some fields and more than that on others. They tell me that as long as other nutrients are adequate, they raise better corn where the sodium levels are at least above the minimum.

One answer to inadequate sodium might be manure and compost, both can possibly be rich sources. Lots of composts have tremendous amounts of sodium afloat in their digested mass, particularly in the west where the water used to make compost is sodium rich. Measure the sodium levels in manure or compost before applying moderate to large amounts per acre. In fact, a watch has to be put on manures so that soils do not start getting above the 3% level. Still, this is not normally a worry if base saturation is above 60% calcium, and good water penetration is present. But only with a proper soil analysis can you tell for sure.

Now what can be done if you do not have adequate sodium in manures and you have low sodium? A possible choice is to use a material called sodium nitrate or Bulldog Soda. Bulldog Soda is a mined product out of Chile. It is 16% nitrogen. The sodium content is very low. In most soils low in sodium, you can use about 200 or 300 pounds of that material and build sodium up above 0.5%.

On the soils of southern California, testing shows time and again extremely high sodium levels and a resulting high pH, but deficient calcium levels. Gypsum is not the answer if the calcium saturation on the soil tests less than 60% or so. Whether field crops, lawns, or landscaped areas, first correct the calcium levels with needed lime and then use gypsum where possible to loosen the soil up and leach the sodium. Where this is not possible, or progress is seemingly too slow, using a good soil conditioner will eventually get results depending on the severity of the problem.

Sodium has a tremendous impact on pH. A high concentration of sodium can drive the pH extremely high. If you look at pH as the guide, you are going to believe that you don't need any lime unless you correctly measure the calcium present as well. If you don't measure calcium according to base saturation, the real problem will not be recognized and solved. You have to achieve at least 60% base saturation of calcium in order to have that soil open enough so that sodium can move through and out. And until this is accomplished, needed micronutrients are not going to be properly available. In fact, some of the worst levels of trace elements are seen on soils that analyze high in sodium.

In southeast Missouri, a soil that is in the exchange capacities of the mid-20s or less—where we start to see sodium go up above 120 pounds per acre—then we know that water penetration in not at the optimum. This is one of the tools that can be used to tell a farmer he has a hardpan. You can have good water, 68% calcium and 12% magnesium and still have sodium accumulate in the soil if you have created a compaction layer. That is another reason tillage and fertilization go hand-in-hand.

Hands-On Agronomy

Bo-ron / ˈbo(e)r- än, bö(e)r- / *n* [*borax* + *-on* (as in *carbon*)] 1 a trivalent metalloid element found in nature only in combination 2 chemical symbol:

5
B
10.81

3 required for translocation of sugar 4 regulates flowering and fruiting, cell division, salt absorption, hormone movement, pollen germination, carbohydrate metabolism, water use and nitrogen assimilation in plants 5 functions in the synthesis of glycogen and the maintenance of body fat in animal life

Chlo-rine / ˈklō(e)r-ēn, ˈklö(e)r- -en / *n* 1 a halogen element that is isolated as a heavy greenish yellow gas of pungent odor 2 chemical symbol:

3 especially a part of the compound sodium chloride 4 regard essential to the growth of some plants under some conditions 5 an excess of chlorine causes chlorotic spots on tobacco leaves and other plants

Hy-dro-gen / ˈhī-dre-jen / *n* [F *hydrogene,* fr. *hyde-* + *-gene - gen*; fr. the fact that water is generated by its combustion] 1 a nonmetallic element 2 chemical symbol:

$$
\begin{array}{c}
1 \\
\mathbf{H} \\
1.00794
\end{array}
$$

3 the simplest and lightest of elements, colorless, odorless, highly flammable diatomic gas 4 the base for acidity in soil systems

Mo-lyb-de-num / me-ˈlĭb-de-nem / *n* [NL, fr. *molybdena*, a lead ore, molybdenite, molybdenum, fr. L *molybdaena* galena, fr. Gk *molybdaina*, fr. *molybdos* lead] 1 a metallic element that resembles chromium and tungsten in many properties 2 chemical symbol:

3 essential for plants in trace amounts, 0.01 to 10 ppm 4 governs microorganisms needed to set the stage for anion nutrient uptake, and is interrelated as best illustrated in animal health, where an excess makes copper unavailable, depigments hair and accounts for severe scouring 5 deficiency in animals created by excess sulfur, which slows cellulose digestion 6 a deficiency of molybdenum slows conversion of nitrogen to protein

Hands-On Agronomy

12

An Introduction to Micronutrient Needs

WHEN I FIRST BEGAN WORKING WITH SOIL FERTILI-
TY, farmers were being told that they should be concerned only
about the major nutrients (N-P-K) and lime. The trace elements,
or micronutrients, were nothing to be worried about. Most of
the consultants working with soil balancing techniques agreed
with this then, and many still do. They had been taught—and
possibly even experienced—that when the proper amounts of
lime and fertilizer were applied, thus "balancing" the soil's nutrient requirements, the necessary micronutrients would be there
in a form needed for plant utilization.

This explanation is only partially correct. It is true that
micronutrients are most available for plant use when the major

and secondary soil nutrients are properly supplied. A major assumption in such cases is that a sufficient amount of each trace element in an available form is present in the root feeding zone, or even though in the wrong form, it will be released when conditions in the soil achieve equilibrium.

In many of the soils tested by us, even those with a proper balance of the major cations, Ca, Mg, K, and Na, this has not proved to be the case. Therefore the "fertilize with major and secondary nutrients and the traces will come" assumption can cost farmers far more than many agronomists and fertilizer companies ever seem to envision.

If a sign or symptom of a trace element deficiency is strong enough, it is visible to the eye. However, that is too often past the point where the damage can be correctly reversed. The invisible deficiencies, the ones that are truly hurting the crop in some way but can't be seen, are the ones that need to be identified and remedied. This is called "hidden hunger" in the crop, and the soil test is our major approach to initial detections of such problems. Several micronutrients can affect crop yields in this way. For example, the most common crop in which boron figures dramatically is alfalfa. Numerous vegetables also require additional boron. Peanuts and cotton do, as well. The need in such crops is generally understood. But for corn, soybeans and wheat, farmers rarely consider the boron requirement. If it happens to be the weakest link in the chain, repair of its shortfall will furnish quite an increase, as much as 5 – 30 bushels depending on the crop, making boron an excellent example of the principle of hidden hunger for most field crops. Using a soil test is the only safe approach for detection of such problems prior to planting the crop.

The most severe copper deficiencies are expected in high organic matter soils. Yet extremely low organic matter soils can have copper deficiencies that are just as bad. Deficiencies of iron are prevalent in calcareous soil—in other words, soils that are extremely high in calcium. But soil tests show that there are other soils that have iron problems, too. Generally, deficiencies of manganese are on soils where the condition of high pH is a reality, but the problem is also extant in water-logged soils, that is, the extremely heavy clay soggy-type soils.

Zinc is probably the most universally helpful of all the micronutrients audited via soil test. When it is short, it adversely affects moisture absorption in the crop. Pecans and other types of nuts are definitely zinc sensitive. Zinc is well recognized as needed on corn, but when applied as needed, it can also make a real difference on soybeans, too. Our testing has shown situations where every other nutrient level was virtually the same, and the farmer had the minimum recommended level of 6 ppm zinc versus too low on the rest, and the area with the adequate zinc made an extra ten bushels of soybeans to the acre.

Micronutrient needs are expressed as ppm. If you take 999,999 bushels of wheat and mix one bushel of corn in it evenly, that is what we are talking about in terms of understanding parts per million, or ppm. Micronutrients are needed in small but essential quantities because they are the spark plugs or the catalysts for plant processes. They are what get the other nutrients to the right place for maximum production. Without micronutrients there would be no energy transfer or push to get everything going.

Most soils have from 20 pounds to 200 pounds of boron per acre. Most also have from 2 to 400 pounds of copper. In terms of total iron, not the available form, the presence can range anywhere from 10,000 to 200,000 pounds per acre. In other words, an acre of soil that weighs two million pounds will have a high component of iron. Manganese, in a typical soil system, will range anywhere from 100 to 10,000 pounds per acre. The molybdenum payload can range from one to seven pounds per acre. And zinc generally scales in between 20 and 600 pounds per acre.

When you produce 150 bushels of corn, it requires 0.6 pounds per acre of boron. To grow that same 150 bushels of corn, it takes half a pound per acre of copper, but it takes only a tenth of a pound of iron. It takes 0.08 of a pound of manganese to produce that crop; 0.03 of a pound of molybdenum; and 0.15

NUTRIENT	RANGE IN SOILS (total lb/a)	ESTIMATED CROP REMOVAL (lb/a)	
		CORN (150 bu)	COTTON (1,000 lb lint)
Boron	20-200	0.06	0.05
Copper	2-400	0.05	0.03
Iron	10,000-200,000	0.10	0.07
Manganese	100-10,000	0.08	0.03
Molybdenum	1-7	0.03	0.02
Zinc	20.600	0.15	0.06

of a pound of zinc. When we consider the total pounds—and how little seems to be needed for crop uptake—can you see that a person might not tend to worry about trace minerals or micronutrients? The trace elements are already there in large amounts. However, this is talking about total nutrients and not nutrients available for plant use. A soil test usually measures the nutrient load in terms of "available form." This helps explain why soils should have 300 pounds of phosphate showing on a soil test, yet only 85 pounds are needed to raise 150 bushels of corn. Soils have to contain quite a bit more than the growth requirement so that roots can make contact and effect adequate uptake. Roots, after all, do not cover the entire ground-front.

Trace minerals are tiny keys to both crop and feed efficiency. There is increased interest in micronutrient fertilization nowadays because higher crop yields result in greater nutrient removal. Modern fertilizer use has tended to stress and eliminate N, P and K as limiting factors. And newer fertilizer fabrication technology has resulted in higher analysis materials with fewer impurities, including micronutrients. In short, the trade has processed out the micronutrients and sulfur. As a result, earlier sources of micronutrients as impurities are no longer available. This problem is increased by the fact that the humus content of most soils is lower than it used to be.

Hands-On Agronomy

Soil pH is a factor in determining micronutrient availability in the soil. For example, the range for maximum boron availability is between pH 5 and 7. Below pH 7, boron is more available. The maximum range for copper, as with boron, is pH 5 to 7. Once pH gets above that level, copper can be more easily complexed. For iron, the equation says pH 4 to 6.5. Above that, normally plant available iron starts tying up. For manganese, the proper pH range is 5 to 6.5. Molybdenum is most available between pH 7 to 8.5. When the soil pH gets down into the most ideal range for other traces, molybdenum is no longer most available. But molybdenum does make a difference in terms of yield, particularly in soybean production.

The last nutrient that merits attention in terms of pH and availability to plants is zinc. Its maximum availability is pH 5 to 7, exactly as with boron and copper. As a matter of fact, between pH 6 and 6.5, there is maximum availability for boron, copper, iron, manganese and zinc.

But again, this can be true only if there is an adequate amount of each micronutrient in an available form to the plant in the soil so as to supply the need. And each one will be of proper benefit only if—in addition to the ideal pH—the cations affecting the pH are within a proper range, and nitrogen, phosphate, and sulfate are adequate.

Our soil analysis work routinely requires a readout for boron, iron, manganese, copper and zinc. But clients who want molybdenum, chlorides and/or salt concentration tests must specifically request such testing for an additional charge.

Molybdenum is the only micronutrient for which availability increases as the pH goes up. It is especially important to nitrogen fixing bacteria in legumes. In fact, it is important for nitrogen, no matter where. It is associated with nitrogen fixation. If availability on the test we use falls below one ppm, then molybdenum becomes a limiting factor. On citrus trees, if you are below one ppm, the remedy is a 7.5 ounce per acre application of sodium molybdate if no other molybdenum application has been made during the last three years. If one or two applications have been made within the past three years, then only 5 ounces per acre would be recommended. And just that small amount when truly the limiting factor can give an increase of 20 picking boxes of fruit per block of citrus trees.

So the sequence would be 7.5 ounces per acre of sodium molybdate (39-41 percent Mo) if none needed in the last three years and the level is below 1ppm. This would be followed by testing the soil again after twelve months to determine the current molybdenum level. If still below 1 ppm, then apply 5 ounces of sodium molybdate per acre. Test again twelve months later and if still below 1 ppm apply another 5 ounces of sodium molybdate per acre. Then wait three years even if the molybdenum level has not yet reached the desired 1 ppm.

If molybdenum has been applied one time only within the past three years, then consider no more than 5 ounces per acre if needed to reach 1 ppm on the test, and again the next year at 5 ounces per acre if the test still shows less than 1 ppm. Then wait three years before beginning the normal sequence again as given above.

Corn growers often conclude that molybdenum cannot be a limiting factor for their crop. I had a client in southeast Missouri, now retired, who was a seed corn dealer. He had me check molybdenum in several of his fields. Some of the plots were low and some were not. Sodium molybdate can be used to repair a shortfall. The only thing you have to watch out for is the copper level. Molybdenum should not be applied when copper levels are deficient. In such cases, a proper application of both is necessary.

Few growers have done anything with molybdenum. In the entire United States, other than citrus groves and perhaps alfalfa, I know of few growers outside of the ones using our services that are even interested in the possibility of a molybdenum problem. But growers should not just arbitrarily decide the use of molybdenum is necessary. The main reason is that before molybdenum should be applied, every possible soil with a different potential level of fertility in the field should be checked. If certain areas are above 2 ppm, and too much molybdenum is

Only Small Quantities
of Minerals are Needed

In *The Diagnosis of Mineral Deficiencies in Plants*, by T. Wallace, that principle is stated in the following words,

"Since catalysts are not used up in the chemical reactions which they promote, we can understand how it comes about that quite small or even minute quantities of the 'trace elements' iron, manganese, boron, zinc and copper, may nevertheless be essential to the plant's health and growth."

Iron may be used as an example. As the most copiously required trace mineral, an iron level of 80 ppm is nevertheless considered fully adequate in the tissues of many plants. With such an iron content a big hay crop of 5,000 pounds of dry matter per acre would contain less than 8 ounces of iron. If the soil provides half of this, the farmer needs to find ways to provide 4 ounces in his fertilizing program.

In the case of a 120 bushel yield of corn per acre, we are still considering a need for less than one pound of iron. If the soil can provide half of it, the farmer needs to find ways of infusing the other 6 or 8 ounces into his crop; perhaps paying for it by the reduction of his veterinary bills.

—*Lee Fryer & Dick Simmons*
Food Power from the Sea (*1977*)

applied, a toxic situation can occur or may begin to develop. Feeding plants produced on such fields to livestock can result in molybdenum toxicity, which in turn can induce a severe copper deficiency.

Molybdenum is essential for the nitrate reductase enzyme. Some sensitive crops are cauliflower, broccoli, alfalfa and clovers.

If you are growing alfalfa and thinking about using an inoculant on the seed, apply the molybdenum separately to avoid killing bacteria in the inoculant. Common molybdenum sources are molybdic acid and sodium molybdate. The last is 39 to 41% molybdenum. It is water soluble, and the one we recommend for applications on citrus and other crops.

Next let's consider the trace element chlorine. It is a more recent addition to the list of essential micronutrients. Chlorine in the soil, in the form agronomists are talking about, is chloride. It plays a role in photosynthesis. Common deficiency symptoms are leaf tip wilt, leaf chlorosis and necrosis. Some sensitive crops are tomatoes, lettuce, barley, alfalfa, wheat and sugar beets. But there are few known field deficiencies. There is a fellow in Missouri who has a reputation for growing tremendous tomatoes. He told a neighbor that every year when he planted his tomatoes he took a pinch of salt and sprinkled it all around the plant at least six inches from the stem. Without doing a soil analysis, I could not tell whether the chloride or the sodium side is the cause in this case. If you live in a light sandy soil and your sodium is below half a percent, that is going to make a difference. I tried it on my tomatoes, and I can't tell the difference. According to soil tests, I have enough sodium in my soil but chlorides have not been checked. From research that has been done in the South, chloride causes gummosis disease in citrus, the first year in lemons, and after 15 years on grapefruit.

Some of the research on chlorine has been done in North Dakota and Minnesota. And I can relate that from the soils I have seen in North Dakota and Minnesota, most of the heavy black soils are deficient in potassium. If you just look at the measured pounds per acre, they don't seem to be deficient; but if you look at the percentages, they are below 2% potassium. When farmers put potassium on those soils, they get a response. Because the potassium is present in such high amounts in pounds per acre, some have decided it must be the chloride in the 0-0-60 providing the response. But what about those farmers using 0-0-50, potassium sulfate, that has virtually no chloride, and the response is still obtained? So I wonder about that conventional wisdom. Most of the potassium that is applied is potassium chloride, 0-0-60. And when you apply potassium chloride to most of those soils, there will be a response because of the low potassium. But North Dakota and Minnesota authorities decided their soils don't need potassium, they "have enough potassium" already. Now, all of a sudden, agronomists come along saying that chlorides give a response to wheat production and various other crops. What I really wonder is this: Since many researchers do not understand and many even reject base saturation percentages, and they deal with soils that are below 2% potassium saturation, is it actually the potassium that is giving the response while the credit is being handed to chloride? However, it is important to note that using adequate amounts of chlorides in the Northwest has eliminated leaf spot in wheat.

Any time more than 250 ppm of chlorides show up on our test, there is a possible problem. Some concentrations may reach as high as 3000+ ppm when 500 ppm is definitely considered a problem. But by far the biggest part of the problem when such situations occur is when the sodium content is also excessive. Whenever there is 5% to 10% base saturation of sodium, a problem should be expected, and a plan devised to deal with it. It will not be simple to accomplish. Such situations are among the worst in terms of affecting micronutrient availability. Proceeding without a proven soil test and a sensible long-term plan in such cases just provides a path to sure dissatisfaction and possible disaster.

With the material here and the section under potassium sources, the chloride discussion has gone far enough, except to say that soils with high chloride problems can be expected to dissolve with the first movement of water through the soil. We just don't see high chlorides accumulate under normal circumstances without also having compacted soil, especially when the old standby—an adequate calcium level of above 60%— is present.

As noted earlier in this chapter, the range for maximum boron availability is between pH 5 and 7. Below pH 7.0, boron is more available. This does not suggest that a reading above pH 7.0 is to be avoided for the sake of boron or any other trace element. If boron is low and calcium is required, and the calcium would cause the pH to go to 7.5, do not skip the calcium because it might hurt boron availability. Deal with trace element needs once major and secondary elements are properly in place. Always take care of the calcium and let the pH go where it will— and then, if you need to, purchase some extra boron or whatever micronutrient is indicated, and make the appropriate application. This approach will not result in overdoing trace elements by applying amounts indicated for minimum availability even after pH drops back in later years.

Essential Elements in Animal Nutrition with Special Reference to Dairy Cattle

In deficiency diseases caused by the soil, we have to consider factors affecting the chemical nature of our soil, its cultivation, climate, direct conditions such as supplying to our soils chemical fertilizers and so-called "minerals," which should properly be called inorganic nutrients; the extent to which they are absent, or depleted due to cropping and other causes. We should know not only the consequences of their absence, but also the consequences of their optimum presence. The type of crop, the intensity of cropping, and the state of plant growth at which cropping takes place are other factors with which the scientific farmer must be concerned if he wants to correlate animal nutrition with soil conditions.

It is safe to state at the present time that fertile soils should contain at least the following 20 elements: nitrogen, phosphorus, potassium, calcium, magnesium, sulfur, hydrogen, carbon, oxygen, iron, sodium, chlorine, aluminum, silicon, manganese, copper, zinc, boron, iodine, fluorine.

> Until quite recently many scientists believed that only the first ten elements were necessary for growth and the maturing of crops; that only the first three should be considered as fertilizer ingredients; and that the others were supplied by soil, air and water, or were present as natural fillers in manures and fertilizer raw materials.
>
> The modern agronomist, however, takes all these 20 essential elements into consideration, and many so-called "complete" fertilizers contain at least 16 to 18, if not all of the elements mentioned above. Cobalt, essential to animal nutrition, can also most economically be supplied through the soil, even though crops grow without. The same can be said of iodine.
>
> —*J.F. Wischhusen*
> History of Randleigh Farm *(1947)*

What some growers have failed to consider is that a boron application can be toxic to the immediate crop if the proper amount of limestone or another material is not available to supply adequate calcium. You can lose at least two ways when applying soil micronutrients incorrectly. First, application at the wrong time can result in leaching in some instances, whereas others will not become available in time to supply the need if not applied early enough to benefit the crop. Second, some forms of required micronutrients will not raise the levels in the soil as effectively as certain other forms. In the long run, liquid forms are generally more expensive per acre than dry forms, yet do no better job. Of the dry forms, sulfates, usually the more expensive ones are generally the best.

As with nitrate and sulfate fertilizers, the micronutrients borate (boron in the form used by plants) and molybdate (molybdenum for plant use) can leach out of the soil. In the case of borate, the lighter the soil, the harder it is to hold in the soil. Because they will leach, borate and molybdate should be applied in late winter or early spring for crops in general. However, in the case of boron, if the crop is deep-rooted or the need is so great that a split application is essential, the largest amount should be spread nearest the period of greatest growth.

Whenever possible, spread zinc, manganese, copper and iron in the fall. *Always broadcast micronutrients* for best results in terms of soil fertility. Fall applications enable micronutrients to be more available for crop use the following year. When no application is made in the fall, spring-applied materials can still help the crop. Benefits may not be as great, but this is no reason to skip using the needed traces.

Boron is so low in many soils that the token amounts applied will not boost yields. This often causes the farmer who has made such an application to decide he has all he needs. The problem is that for some crops two or three times more is needed than was applied to make the difference in yield. On the other hand, boron (used by itself) can be effective as a weed killer. This means boron can kill a growing crop when used incorrectly. For example, legumes in the seedling stage are very sensitive to too much boron.

To begin a boron program, the amount present in the soil must be accurately measured, and then the levels—if insufficient—must be built up accordingly. Boron is the most unstable of the normally used trace elements and can be leached from the soil. The lighter the soil, the harder it is to maintain an adequate boron level.

Certain cautions must be kept in mind. On corn, for example, if there is not enough phosphate, the boron will be thwarted and a lack of grain-fill can result. Corn requires adequate phosphate and then adequate boron for proper ear fill. If nitrogen rates are high, the need for boron is always enhanced. Excessive amounts of calcium also increase the need for increasing boron levels.

Boron increases nitrogen availability to the plant. It has several other functions in the plant as well, including a role in cell division, pollination, fruit set and seed development. Boron carries the starch from the leaf to the grain or fruit. So when sufficient available boron is lacking, production suffers. Boron also helps in the nodulation of legumes.

Crops require a continuous supply of boron, because once boron is utilized by a plant, it has served its purpose and cannot be used again. Several applications through the season would be ideal where needed if that is possible. Conditions in the soil that contribute to boron deficiency are excessive potassium levels, excessive calcium levels, high soil pH, low organic matter, low moisture and highly leached soils.

The soil should have at least 0.80 ppm boron for general cropping purposes. According to the testing procedures used to determine boron levels, most soils run between 0.40 and 0.60 ppm. Growers should strive to leave some room between what is termed as *excellent* and what is termed as *maximum* levels. Considering boron for most crops, the minimum is 0.80. There are some other qualifications. If the test has a reading above 0.80, then look at everything else before trying to do anything about changing the boron supply. If anything else is low to deficient in that soil and boron isn't short, strive to take care of the other matter before working on boron because it is already above the minimum amount. *Excellent* in terms of boron is anything above 1.5 ppm. Excessive boron is considered anything above 2.0 ppm. This is determined by looking at what is already present in the soil, and it suggests watching any increase in the concentration to that point.

The material used to get to the appropriate boron level is much the same as with other nutrients. Too much of the wrong form of nitrogen can burn the crop. Too much potassium chloride can also burn the crop. Too much boron in the soil causes boron burn or boron toxicity. The maximum amount of boron ever recommended to be applied at any one time is four pounds per acre of actual boron. Just remember some crops will not stand four pounds per acre. If you put four pounds per acre on dry beans, alfalfa or soybeans at planting time, these crops will probably never grow properly if at all. Once a legume reaches the seedling stage, it will take all the boron it can get even to the point of "committing suicide." So two pounds of boron on newly seeded legumes represent the maximum. Four pounds on any crop must be considered maximum. What if you apply four pounds on corn this year and grow soybeans next year? With adequate calcium and an excellent level of boron, you will not have a problem with the soybeans even at the seedling stage of growth. Then once the legume gets out of the seedling stage, you can apply as much as you put on corn (added in small doses) if needed. Alfalfa responds even better to boron than corn.

It takes one pound of boron to raise the level on our test by one-tenth ppm in the soil. If you have 0.7 ppm on our test and want to get to 0.8 ppm, how much boron does it take? Answer: one pound. If you are at 0.5, then three pounds of boron are required to get to a 0.8 reading. Two pounds will take the reading to 0.7. That is enough for soybeans, but not for alfalfa, corn or most other crops. This is an example of failing to reach the minimum plateau for those crops. Not all legumes respond to lower levels of boron. In alfalfa production, 0.8 is not the target; 1.5+ is actually needed for best results.

The most we ever want to raise boron on our test at one time is four-tenths ppm. This translates into not using more than four pounds in any given year. But if an option is available, I try to limit everything to two pounds. On sensitive crops like citrus, this is a must! Therefore, the first application is usually two pounds, and then where needed consider a second application of two pounds or less at the proper time to meet the required amount. There is a valid reason for this. If the person who is spreading boron gets an overlap using four pounds of actual boron per acre, meaning a double spread where it overlaps, that area gets eight pounds of boron. This can create havoc, especially if calcium is low. The lower the calcium saturation, the more likely boron toxicity will occur. So if the soil needs calcium, don't think that you should put on four pounds of boron. The first time you get three days of cool, moist weather—the same kind of weather that calls attention to a phosphate deficiency in corn—an over-application will cause smaller corn plants to turn white. On the fourth consecutive day of cool, damp weather, the white colored stalks of corn will generally begin to slough off and die. Even a smaller concentration of too much in a field can be seen as a salt and pepper effect.

I recall a recommendation made in the fall. The farmer told me that he had not put on lime and was going to follow through the next spring. Though he was cautioned, he forgot that without calcium he should not apply all that boron. The next spring, he didn't get the liming done. Instead of putting on four pounds of actual boron, he applied 4.5 pounds. A few weeks after the corn came up, three to four days of cool, moist, damp weather followed. There were places in the field where the corn actually died.

I have clients who use boron on acres and acres and acres of corn, cotton, rice, wheat and soybeans and seldom run into a problem. And when they do, it is because they have somehow applied more than was recommended. With adequate calcium, boron works the best. If there is not enough calcium, the boron rate should be cut in half unless more can be justified by a current soil test.

Most growers use the terms *borate* and *boron* interchangeably. This causes a lot of confusion. How much borate translates into two pounds of actual boron? Fifteen pounds of sodium tetraborate supplies about two pounds of actual boron. That translates to about 14% boron. When a recommendation is made for *15 pounds of 14.3% boron (sodium tetraborate)*, that means about two pounds of actual boron. When recommending ten pounds of Solubor, which is 21% boron and a material for use in a liquid program, whether organic or conventional, that means two pounds of actual boron. Sodium tetraborate is 14.3% boron, and Solubor is 21% boron.

Borax is 11% boron. It is a good source of boron, but harder to spread evenly when blended with other materials. It is a naturally mined product. Organic growers can use Borax or Solubor. For small gardens, etc., 20 Mule Team Borax from the grocery store works just fine, as long as you apply no more than the correctly recommended amount.

I had a client who used four pounds of boron for two or three years on his corn crop. The operator at a fertilizer plant will generally start blending with the major nutrients and then add enough boron to get the proper numbers. In this case, the amount needed was four pounds of boron per acre, and all the fertilizer people had to do was pour a sack of 14.3% boron into the mixture. The fellow who mixed the product told the customer, "I am sorry, but I have to tell you this. I made a mistake. I put a sack of 14.3% boron in at the first of the mix, and I put another sack in at the end of the mix. You have spread eight pounds of boron per acre on that last load, rather than four." The grower marked the spot where the extra boron had been applied. I should add that this family had worked on our program for ten years. When they needed a nutrient, they put it on. So they had excellent calcium levels. We didn't have a spring with cool, moist conditions for several days in a row. If we had, they might have been in trouble on the corn that received double the boron recommended. As it was, you couldn't pick out where the eight pounds of actual boron had been applied in that field.

One other thing happened on their farm the same year. One of the workers who was driving the fertilizer spreader either forgot to check or wasn't paying attention, and the chain broke. Everything was kicked out right behind the machine. He didn't find this out until he got to the other end of the field. Then he surveyed the situation. The thing we were most concerned about was the amount of boron. We calculated 100 pounds of 14.3% boron per acre was spread between two rows of corn. Of course, they had nitrogen and the other things with it. This meant about 14 pounds of actual boron between two rows. The father had been skeptical about using "all these trace elements" anyway. He was out there that day and said, "Well, I'll watch those two rows and tell you what happens."

Sure enough, when I came back later that year, I said, "Well, have you been down to see how that boron is doing?"

He said, "I drive by there every day. I will tell you right now that the only thing that has happened is that those two rows of corn are greener and taller than all the rest of the field."

In this case, we didn't have the conditions for boron to kill the corn. Excellent growing conditions prevailed. We didn't get that cool, moist weather. If we had, this story probably would have had a far different ending. The point is, just because you happen to get away with a mistake using boron in a certain year, don't think you can continue that way and not have to pay for it when conditions dictate.

The next year the same farmer had a guy running the fertilizer spreader, and he wasn't careful enough. They were applying four pounds of actual boron per acre. This particular field had been in cotton for years but was to be planted in corn. Cotton growers don't always pay as much attention to lime as they should. They hadn't added calcium recently to answer base saturation numbers. That put the readout down to 58% or 59% base saturation. This level still allows for a decent cotton or corn yield if everything else is in place. But in any case, the calcium was low. If the applicator had applied four pounds of boron and gotten an even spread, it would have been fine. In fact, he got a two-row overlap, and in those two rows the corn turned white and some died because we got several cool, moist days in a row.

When talking about spreading one and two pounds of boron, this is not a problem, except perhaps in the case of soybeans or dry beans where a two-pound application represents the maximum rate. For legumes, one pound the first time out and then another pound later on is better, so that an excess due to overlapping is better prevented.

Boron can be tied up by overliming or by extra high potassium levels. If you have extra high potassium levels in a soil, then you are not going to get the same boron efficiency. Boron can leach from the soil the same as sulfate and nitrate. The sandier the soil, the lighter the soil, the lower the organic matter, the more boron it takes to keep a level where it should be.

In terms of leaf deficiencies, boron never shows up as visible to the eye in anything I have seen, except alfalfa and cabbage, so it may be hard to determine what a visual leaf deficiency looks like. By the time it is visible, it is too late for the best response. Test for boron and apply it correctly where it is warranted. Although required in small quantities, where needed it can make a big difference in both quality and yield.

Another aspect of the soil analysis to consider in this chapter in regard to adequate trace element levels has to do with exchangeable hydrogen. On the test we use, exchangeable hydrogen is always determined according to the pH level. Using salt pH will not provide the proper exchangeable hydrogen level on our test, which must be used on soils with a pH lower than 7.0 for establishing the correct cation exchange capacity. Using the water pH method, if the water pH is 7 or higher, the percentage of exchangeable hydrogen will be expressed as zero. So even though there are still hydrogen ions in the soil, above pH 7 there will be no expressed percentage of exchangeable hydrogen. But good crops are still possible.

Perhaps another way to explain this is by considering the amount of air in a flat tire. When a tire loses enough air, the rim touches the surface, and we say the tire is flat. Most of the air that was in the tire before it became flat is still there, but enough was lost so that now the tire doesn't function properly. The same type of example is applicable when we have a pH of 7.0 or higher in a soil. There is still a large amount of free hydrogen in the soil, but we express it as 0% hydrogen because now there is not enough for the soil to function at its best. However you can still raise a good crop there if you supply the proper amount of fertility.

At pH 7, a soil is neutral. The soil is saturated with something other than the ideal number of free hydrogen ions. At pH 6.9, exchangeable hydrogen is always 1.5%. At pH 6.8, exchangeable hydrogen is 3%. Every tenth of a point that a reading drops below 7 will add 1.5% exchangeable hydrogen until you reach a pH of 6. This calibrates how much acidity there is. If you have 10 to 15% hydrogen, that means there is plenty of room for all the other nutrients to find the hydrogen ions attached to the colloid, push them off and take their place on the soil colloids. At 10 to 15%, pH will be between 6 and 6.5. The ideal pH is really 6 to 6.5, but it is only ideal when everything else is in the right equilibrium. Any nutrient required takes precedence over pH. This means you supply the deficient nutrients first, and when you finish balancing the nutrients, the pH will be right.

Then does this mean that a soil with a 6.5 pH is always the ideal in terms of soil fertility and production? No, this is not necessarily the case. I have seen soils that were definitely problem soils in the U.S. and in Australia even though the pH was 6.5. In such cases, the pH was "right," but the soil nutrients were not there in the correct amounts to properly grow a crop. When a soil has the correct pH but a severely incorrect balance of calcium, magnesium, potassium or sodium, the crops will just not grow properly and at times will perform very poorly in those soils.

If you have 10% magnesium and 80% calcium, the only action required is the reduction of calcium by enough to permit potassium its proper base saturation along with adequate micronutrient levels. If there is 76% calcium and 7% magnesium, it is generally best for the long term to start removing calcium down to a 73% level, with a resultant increase in magnesium to 10% base saturation. But for the short term, determine the crop needs for magnesium and supply that using an available form such as magnesium sulfate or potassium-magnesium sulfate (sold in the U.S. as K-Mag or Sul-Po-Mag).

Once 10% magnesium is achieved, in say, a medium to heavy soil and if you have adequate potassium, it is no longer necessary to drive off calcium, provided you have enough iron, manganese, copper and zinc. If any of these traces are missing use adequate amounts of sulfur for the crop to be grown there, but add enough of each of the trace elements to reach the minimum requirements. Once all the other nutrients in the proper amounts are evident, and you have a high calcium reading, calcium merely enables more efficient entry of other nutrients into the plant. Basically, every other nutrient enters in over the back of the calcium ion. So, if high calcium is measured and there is no deficiency of anything else, leave it alone. It always seems to make the uptake of other fertilizer nutrients more efficient when all are shown to be sufficiently present.

For example, if a soil has 80% base saturation calcium, it takes far less nitrogen to grow the same crop. At 80% calcium with all nutrients in a proper balance, a cutback in applied nitrogen is indicated. Especially in this case continued use of excessive rates of nitrogen will cause weakness in the plants. Lodging will result because nitrogen causes accelerated growth and ties up copper. And faulty fertilization, with either a shortfall or a marked imbalance of fertility, may encourage bacterial, insect and fungal attack. Instead of a better crop, simplistic N, P and K fertility management merely becomes an insurance policy for the sale of lots of toxic rescue chemistry.

I have spent most of my lecture time and countless other presentations telling farmers about using the cation exchange capacity and base saturation percentage to determine how much fertilizer including micronutrients to use. The book *Eco-Farm* does an excellent job explaining the subtleties of this Albrecht system, and the volumes, presently eight, of *The Albrecht Papers* flesh out this most precise approach. That is why I was somewhat appalled in years past by the formation of a committee headed by a professor from North Dakota State University. It is a part of an organization called Council for Agricultural Science and Technology (acronym CAST). All the agricultural colleges in the United States belong to it. This professor told a good friend of mine that his job as chairman of this committee for CAST was "to do all I can to discredit the use of exchange capacity and base saturation percentage for determining how much fertilizer to put on a soil." My friend asked, "Why would you want to do that?" The schoolman answered, "Because we are on record that it won't work." My friend asked him if there was any other reason he could give. The professor said, "That is why we are doing it because we say it won't work." The professor felt that measuring pH, phosphate and potassium was enough.

I am not opposed to agricultural education and research at the university level. We need that. But the job should be to educate, teach and demonstrate to the farmers what should be done. Far too many have confused the need to educate with the urge to legislate. In too many states, farmers and those requiring information on soil fertility are being denied the use of materials that in no way damage the environment. No matter how many other states accept or allow their use, that carries no weight. These products have to be "tested and approved" by the appropriate university researchers in that particular state first, all at considerably high costs. Supposedly this is in an effort to "protect" the farmer. Considering what has happened to farmers during the last few decades, it seems doubtful that they need more of this kind of protection.

At one hearing I attended in California in the late 1970s, the chairman of the committee to approve new agriculture products provided an excellent example of the *legislate* instead of educate philosophy. He told how there was a product that farmers had been buying to use on their land. They had it tested, and "it didn't work." They did not say that it was considered harmful. They just couldn't get results. The product was barred from sale there. He went on to say there were still farmers in California who believed it helped them and would buy that product if it hadn't been forced off the market. This is education? No, it is an excellent example of those who should educate but prefer to legislate instead of doing their jobs.

When it comes to what is and isn't profitable in agriculture, the advantage goes to the farmer out in the field overseeing the work and his own profit picture over some "research" directed from behind a desk by someone who probably never in his adult life earned a living from what was produced and sold on a farm. Yet this desk person "knows" what will and will not work on all the farms in the state.

This seems to have been the case with so much of the research in regard to micronutrients. Before micronutrients will work properly, the needed conditions for response must be met. When the soils meet the necessary levels mandated for major and secondary nutrients, micronutrients or trace elements of importance come into focus, but only if there is a deficiency and enough is used to supply the minimum micronutrients needed to provide a response. When the use of the cation balance system is ignored, micronutrient response is sheer guesswork, somewhat like trying to bet on the right number on a roulette wheel—but with thousands of dollars at stake.

To do the best job with regard to supplying plant nutrients requires more than pH, P and K as a soil test. Without the cation exchange capacity and the resulting measurements possible for determining fertilizer needs, the farmer will lose the most valuable tool available for the most profitable and environmentally safe use of fertilizers and soil amendments, including the keys to micronutrient availability and consequent needs.

Cop-per / 'kŏp-ər / *n*, often attrib [ME *coper*, fr. OE; akin to OHG *kupfar* copper; both fr. a prehistoric WGmc-NGmc word borrowed fr. LL *cuprum* copper, fr. L *(aes) Cyprium*, lit., Cyprian metal] 1 reddish ductile metal 2 chemical symbol:

9
Cu
63.546

3 in agriculture, vitally important to root metabolism 4 helps form compounds and proteins, amino acids and many organic compounds 5 a catalyst or part of enzyme systems; helps produce dry matter via growth stimulation, prevents development of chlorosis, rosetting and dieback 6 in animal life, essential for catalytic conversion of iron into red blood cells, and an assist in tissue respiration

I-ron / 'i(-e)rn / *n* [ME, fr. OE *isern, iren;* akin to OHG *isarn* iron] 1 a heavy malleable ductile magnetic silver-white metallic element 2 chemical symbol:

3 in biology, an indispensable carrier of oxygen required in the production of chlorophyll and as an aid in the prevention of chlorosis 4 a difficult nutrient to supply to plants in an available form 5 in human beings and animals, essential for hemoglobin formation because divalent iron occupies a central position in the hemoglobin structure 6 essential in oxygen transfer and cell respiration, and aids in blood cell development, and in the prevention of anemia

Hands-On Agronomy

Man-ga-nese / ˈmăn-gə-ˈnēz, -ˈnēs / *n* [F *manganèse*, fr. It *manganese* magnesia, manganese, fr. ML *magnesia*] 1 a grayish white usually hard and brittle metallic element 2 chemical symbol:

3 resembles iron, albeit diamagnetic 4 aids the oxidase enzyme in carrying oxygen and enters into the oxidation and reduction reactions in plant life required for carbohydrate metabolism and seed formation 5 in animal life, is an essential biocatalyst in normal growth and bone development, maintenance of body weight, and proper functioning of reproductive and mammary glands 6 activates calcium, phosphorus, iron, etc., but may itself undergo fixation by these elements 7 aids in promotion of beneficial intestinal flora

Zinc / 'zĭnk / *n, often attrib* [G *zink*] 1 bluish white crystalline bivalent metallic element 2 chemical symbol:

$$\boxed{\begin{array}{c} 30 \\ \mathbf{Zn} \\ 65.38 \end{array}}$$

3 of low to intermediate hardness, ductile when pure 4 absolutely vital (along with molybdenum) to the life process of soil microorganisms, esp. *Azotobacter*, a non-symbiotic nitrogen-fixing microorganism 5 aids in the promotion of normal growth and tissue respiration in animal life; interrelated with insulin and vitamin B1 deficiencies, important in the development of normal hair coat 6 now regarded as a dietary essential and constituent of carbonic anhydrase

13
Applications of Micronutrients

TRACE MINERAL OR MICRONUTRIENT DEFICIENCIES can exhibit dramatic signs, or they can be invisible on the plant. Major nutrient deficiencies such as nitrogen, phosphorus, potassium or sulfur can generally be recognized and corrected, but trace mineral problems—considering the myths and lack of information extant—are not so easily solved.

So far the lessons should be clear. If you have sufficient amounts of the major and secondary nutrients and a deficiency of a trace mineral, then start taking care of the latter. If you need phosphate or potassium and you have a boron deficiency, take care of the P and K first, because taking care of the boron is not going to work until your major and secondary nutrient levels are relatively well in place. Or if you have a zinc deficiency as well as a big phosphate deficiency, take care of the phosphate deficiency first. But if you barely have enough phosphate and a zinc deficiency, and zinc is the next most limiting nutrient, deal with the zinc deficiency. Just don't overdo it, which due to a lack of proper understanding happens in many fields.

When beginning to consider trace elements, keep this in mind. If you put on "too little," you won't get up to what is considered to be the first plateau. In other words, if you are deficient of a certain micronutrient and you make an application, but you fail to get above the minimum requirement, at times payback for that crop in terms of current yield may be lacking. Grain yield will not always adequately improve until you get above the minimum deficiency level. If you need two pounds of boron and you put on one pound, you might think it will make up half the difference in yield, but it won't do it, even if all the major and secondary nutrients are adequate. If two pounds of boron are required and only one pound can be afforded, it is better to put two pounds on half the field and none on the other half. But never overdo it.

How many field experiments have been used to say micronutrients are not needed simply because the research involved did not properly consider that the soil must have no limiting major or secondary nutrients? And even then potential results will not be achieved if the amounts applied fail to build levels sufficiently enough to reach that critical first plateau.

Micronutrients respond best when calcium is within 60 to 70% and magnesium is within the 10 to 20% saturation. If either one is very deficient, a trace element response should not be expected. If calcium is high and everything else is basically in line, and a deficiency of a particular micronutrient is detected, resolve the deficiency so long as it fits into the fertilizer budget. The important point is to first determine whether there are major or secondary element deficiencies. The information that follows in this chapter applies only to soils already well supplied with lime and primary fertilizer nutrients, therefore it may help to keep the following example in mind.

A few years back a certified organic grower sent in soil samples. The crop was tomatoes and he wanted to maximize tonnage. The soil had a great potential, but the tomatoes needed far more nitrogen than was being applied to achieve the high tonnage. But nitrogen ties up copper, and the soil already had a copper deficiency. In short, without sufficient copper, the tomatoes could not stand the nitrogen required for top yields.

After receiving the soil tests and our recommendations, the client took them to another well-known consultant who worked with many organic growers. This consultant advised that copper levels were so excessive on these samples that adding the amount we recommended would kill the tomato plants. The consultant actually sent a typed evaluation of our tests and recommendations to the grower stating this. The grower, both alarmed and confused by it all, forwarded a copy to me to emphasize his concern of possibly losing his crop.

Naturally the grower did not know what to do now. The other consultant had a very successful business advising a large number of organic growers. And it is true you can kill plants when trace elements are not used correctly. Some of my clients have done it! But time after time it has been due to a mix-up in the application, generally applying more than was recommended—sometimes intentionally so, thinking it will just do more good—but more often just by mistake. Either way it does not work out so well for the grower or his consultant.

But in this case, after a telephone consultation and assurances that the amount of copper was correct and required under the circumstances, the grower decided to make the recommended application. I did advise him to leave a couple of rows without the copper. That way if something else did kill the crop he could be sure it was not the copper.

The copper did not kill any tomatoes. Along with adequate organic nitrogen sources and the other recommended fertilizers it gave a bumper crop. During the harvest season the grower called and stated that normally on this farm in past years he would harvest 10,000 pounds of marketable tomatoes per week. He then said where he had used our recommendations they were harvesting 10,000 pounds a day off the same acreage. The tomatoes were the largest he had ever grown, with no cracking and

A Pinch of Salt Will Do

By topdressing South Australia's "Ninety Mile Desert" with about 60 cents worth of bluestone salts an acre, they have increased productivity more than fourfold. Two healthy breeding ewes can now raise their lambs on an acre of this copper-deficient country which would not support a wether on an acre before it was treated with bluestone. A relatively small outlay has increased the area's income by millions of dollars a year. Similar treatment with bluestone could restore copper-deficient areas all over the world including parts of America.

Scientific evidence suggests strongly that copper deficiency might be a big factor in the steepest decline of sheep numbers in America's history. Experts have blamed economics for this fall, but there is little financial reason why owners should have sold their flocks so suddenly.

As bluestone is a solution of copper sulfate, the easier, more effective use of phenothiazine deprived millions of American sheep of their customary dose of copper. This is important because humans and animals need copper for complete nutrition and health. The amount is so small, however, that even the world's most delicate balances cannot measure it. Chemists report it as only a "trace" because their methods of analysis are not accurate enough to measure the true dose. Hence, metals such as copper, cobalt, molybdenum, manganese and zinc are usually called "trace" minerals in the soil or in humans, animals and plants.

Absence of copper can be detected most easily through the fleece. Black sheep are the best indicators of copper shortage because their wool turns grayish white when they do not get enough of this vital mineral. A smaller dose of copper than is needed to drench for worms will restore the typical black color. Another symptom of copper deficiency is the change in wool fiber from a regular crimp and soft, pleasant feel, to a staple which is almost as straight and harsh as fine steel wire. The trade calls such wool "steely."

"Steely" wool was traced to flocks on certain desert areas which had enough rain to grow good stock feed but failed to yield more than a low unattractive scrub.

After grazing on it for about six months, sheep developed "brittle bones" disease. This meant that their skeletons had deteriorated so much that the slightest knock with a stick or stone would break a rib, leg, or other bone. They recovered quickly when moved to districts with a similar rainfall but different soils.

Nutritionists prescribed calcium and phosphates to cure this obvious deficiency—but without success. Brilliant work by officers of Australia's Commonwealth Scientific and Industrial Research Organization diagnosed the trouble as lack of copper and cobalt.

Farmers should suspect their soils of being copper deficient if their sheep have become less thrifty since their bluestone drench has been replaced by phenothiazine. Cheap, easy application of bluestone is all that is needed to restore copper deficient soils to productivity. It is not too late to apply this new knowledge to help rehabilitate the nation's sheep raising industry. Nor is the task too large when only a part of a farm's soils need to be treated for a start and the amount of "trace" minerals needed is so small.

—*Cohn Webb*
private papers, Acres U.S.A. collection

minimal bruising—even on the hauls of eight hours or so for the fresh market. Without the recommended copper that would not have been the case, as these problems had been present even with the lower yields in prior years.

So if the copper was that sorely needed, why would the other well-known and quite respected organic farming consultant have advised it was going to kill the crop? Mark this well and remember the answer because it causes farmers and growers and consultants big problems when they don't. It is a common mistake that costs growers in terms of both quality and production. This consultant made a big blunder. I did call to point this out in a spirit of doing the right thing—to try and avoid having such mistakes made as often as possible. The consultant assumed the numbers on the test we use were the same as those on the test used there. Obviously they are not even close to the same. And this is the point, in this chapter we will be giving minimum recommended levels for micronutrients as determined by the test procedures we use. This type of testing is more expensive and requires more time than most labs now feel is necessary. They can do it for less expense and in less time if using the newer "modernized" testing methods. But the readings come out differently. In most cases the new numbers to express measured levels are far lower than the ones on our report.

Be careful! Do not try to apply our minimum numbers to another lab's tests. And do not judge the trace elements as too high on our test based on what other tests may recommend. The numbers for the testing they do should be contained in their guidelines. One more thing, the person who claims to understand the soil tests from various labs and what they all show you should do is either a genius, has deceived himself, or is less than truthful. Put them to the test and see which it is because if it is one of the latter two, he is operating at your expense and possibly causing significant losses in terms of quality and yield.

Iron is something to be especially concerned about in high calcium soils. It is necessary for chlorophyll formation and electron transport in enzyme systems. Some sensitive crops and their deficiencies are grain sorghum, citrus and soybeans. The soybean crop is among the most likely to exhibit iron chlorosis. Still, it is possible to have a crop suffering from iron chlorosis without the familiar yellow showing up in the plant. Soybeans, however, represent an easy crop to evaluate, with the nearness of an iron problem generally apparent at once. Go out in your bean field where you suspect iron chlorosis or where your calcium is high. Take some soybean plants when they are about 12 inches tall and pluck all the leaves off, leaving only the stems. Do that on two or three plants and watch how those leaves grow back. If there is a borderline iron deficiency, they will grow back yellow. If the leaves come back green, there is no immediate iron problem.

Common sources of iron include the iron sulfates, available as 19 to 23% iron. If an iron sulfate is to be used, it becomes necessary to consider which one it should be. There is one product called ferric sulfate. It can be used to correct iron problems, albeit only as a soil product, never on the plant. In fact, ferric sulfate (Fe++) can kill growing plants.

There is another iron sulfate called ferrous (Fe+). Consider what color you buy when it comes to the use of ferrous sulfate. Most fertilizer dealers feel it makes no difference, but the black- or rusty yellow-colored product should be avoided. The blue- or white-colored product is always recommended. You can put ferrous sulfate on where plants are growing without a problem, as long as it is not excessively dusty. Dust on the leaves can cause a phytotoxic reaction, turning the leaves black and affecting plant growth. If ferric sulfate is used on grass, it can kill the grass. Ferrous sulfate, on the other hand, avoiding dust on the leaves and applied at normal rates, will do no harm. But a cosmetic caution is in order. Iron sulfates can stain terribly on concrete sidewalks, around the pool or on the driveway. If these areas are wet, wait until they dry before spreading the iron and sweep the areas immediately after application before it gets wet.

Iron chelates can be used as soil amendments or in a foliar application, but they take care of the problem only for the one year. They also cost more than ferrous sulfate, which is roughly 20% iron. There are also naturally chelated irons that are extracts of the corn plant and thus acceptable for organic programs. They can be applied as a foliar or to the soil. It generally costs more than other iron sources. Except in severe cases, growers should not consider just automatically adding iron sulfate to the soil.

In order to build iron in some soils, all you have to do is apply enough sulfur to bring down the calcium level as well as the pH. Soils can have from 20,000 to 200,000 pounds of total iron in the top seven inches, but most of it is in a form that is unavailable to growing plants. A base of 200+ ppm on our test is adequate as long as that exceeds the ppm of manganese, and 300 ppm is considered ideal for citrus trees. Excessive iron seems never to be a problem in terms of production where the calcium base saturation is also correct. Some fields have 3,000 ppm iron and still yield as well as fields that have only 300 ppm iron.

As for deficiencies, it will depend on more than just where your iron level is because iron and manganese work together. Personally, I like to see iron at 200+. Once you get below 100 ppm, there is reason for concern, and if manganese is 75 and iron is 70, that can be trouble. For best results, iron should always be higher than manganese. If manganese is 125, we don't want iron to be 100. In any case, iron levels should be higher than manganese levels, as shown later in this chapter.

Most of the time chlorosis will not reveal symptoms until iron gets down to 75 ppm, or perhaps even 50 ppm. Exceptions are citrus and grain sorghum. Once the iron level dips below 100 in grain sorghum, the possibility of this as a yield limiting factor begins to more clearly reveal itself. This 100 ppm is based on the way our lab runs iron samples. Remember that trace element readouts vary from laboratory to laboratory and provide a wide variety of numbers on a soil test. Evaluations really run the gamut. Some lab numbers run high and some run low. One lab may say 3 ppm is good. Some other lab may say 300 ppm is good. It depends on how they run and interpret the tests. The results seem to be governed by the methods used to make the extraction. The usual procedure for our testing is to put the extracting solution into a test tube with the soil sample. The mixture is shaken for about 30 minutes. Most labs don't shake the sample that long. Accordingly, they develop lower numbers even if they use the same extracts. Is that why one lab talks about 100 ppm for milo, and another lab may suggest 10? The farmer should stay with a lab he can trust and become used to those numbers.

Even so keep the following points in mind for consideration before purchasing and spreading large amounts of iron. Generally, when the iron level is lower than 100 ppm, we consider that to be a "possible" problem. "Possible" because if the roots reach into the subsoil and sufficient iron is there, the plants still may not suffer. Iron levels, more than any other element, will tend to increase in terms of availability with soil depth. This is true for most soils, though it is not true for all of them. So if the subsoil contains adequate iron in an available form, and deep-rooted plants look good, it may be expected that no added iron is necessary.

However, when topsoil and subsoil are both deficient in iron, even if the plants are looking okay, that may or may not indicate there is no need for applying iron. Even then there could still be a possible iron problem in that soil with what is called "hidden hunger." We have had areas where iron showed as deficient and yet the plants looked good. Although the farmers had no sign of yellowing, and felt the crops were doing okay there, they received a significant yield increase on even corn, wheat and soybeans by applying iron. If this could possibly be the situation, perhaps it would be a good time where beans are being grown, to go out and pull off the leaves as described earlier on page 283.

Another indication of a possible iron shortage is likely when the manganese level is higher than the iron level on the test we use. When this is the case on samples we have tested, it causes the iron to oxidize in the leaf. This oxidized iron is not usable by plants. Yet when the leaves are tested, the oxidized iron shows up as still available to the plant. So a leaf test does not pick up this deficiency, even when you can look at the plant and see the yellow (or chlorotic) leaves and recognize that it is a classic iron deficiency. In some cases, when the plants look nice and green, there is still a deficiency, though not severe enough to show visible symptoms. Again there could be sufficient iron in the subsoil to help with or overcome the problem, but without a subsoil analysis the correct answer may not be completely evident.

When iron is deficient in a plant, it may require only one or two applications to make a deeper green color, but it could take several foliar applications to make a difference in terms of improved yield. Too many growers only try one or two applications then quit. This is not a true test to see whether foliar iron will help. Test, and then treat if required. Test again and treat if required. Then test again and treat if required. Keep it up until the need is filled.

Sulfur helps increase iron availability in the soil. So let us say that to this point the low iron on the soil test is being offset by enough available iron from the use of sulfur and the present iron level in the subsoil. Adding lime will always reduce the available iron in that soil. So the lime applied will have an adverse effect on the iron the plants have there to use at present. This can result in iron deficiency in any one of the next three years after lime is applied, because it takes that long to realize the full effects of lime after it is applied.

When the soil test shows deficient iron and the availability of iron from the subsoil is unknown, and the manganese level is higher than the iron level, or lime has been applied that will adversely affect the available iron levels, adding iron to the soil will be recommended. In such cases, conduct a test on a smaller area before spending large amounts to treat entire fields. Only then should growers consider applying amounts that the budget would allow.

Once iron is shown to be needed, if applying all that is required is not possible, apply a sufficient amount to less acreage rather than using too little on the entire area that needs the iron. Always use good common sense when it comes to the application and use of iron. But if you need iron, it can make quite a difference in color, quality and yield.

The reducing action of manures decomposing in the soil aids in making available iron and manganese. These are present in all soils, but are sometimes less available under excessive oxidizing conditions. Manure in effect supplies nitrogen and drives out calcium, thereby lowering pH. Compost may or may not do the same, depending on its contents. When you have an extra high calcium level and therefore an extra high pH in the soil, manure or compost may help make iron and manganese more available.

Manganese, not to be confused with magnesium, helps crops in several ways. It accelerates germination and hastens fruiting and ripening of crops. It is important in the assimilation of nitrates, and is essential for the assimilation of carbon dioxide in photosynthesis. In combination with potassium and copper, it provides stalk strength to the crop. Manganese is an essential part of the enzyme system in plants and, in particular, activates fat forming enzymes. It is also directly involved in the uptake of iron, carotene and ascorbic acid by plants. Furthermore, it is directly related to the uptake of glutathione in plants. Stressed plants produce more of this substance than those doing well, and therefore attract insects. Insects eat the plants, gorging themselves in order to get the glutathione.

Soils most likely to show a manganese deficiency are light, sandy soils, water-logged soils and previously wet areas that have been drained, heavy cuts on graded fields, deeply eroded areas and alkaline soils.

The first plateau for manganese is 40 ppm. Excessive is considered to be above 250+ ppm. The textbooks will tell you that 100 ppm manganese is good and that 200 ppm is toxic. I haven't been able to confirm that. Perhaps this is based on the way their tests were conducted and reported.

For general crop purposes, the minimum amount of manganese that should appear on our test results is 40 ppm. Depending on test methods, other lab minimum levels could be quite different. However, as other limiting factors are eliminated, manganese levels should at least be maintained above 80+ ppm, with a beginning excellent level being 125+ ppm. In fact, when all other nutrients are properly supplied, the best wheat yields are attained at even higher levels of manganese.

A Nutritional Cure for Brucellosis

We fed manganese-iodide in approximately the same proportion as potassium-iodide with results that seemed almost incredible. In fact the herd to which this was fed was almost wholly infected with brucellosis and none of the cows had been able to deliver a calf—all of them aborted. To our surprise, after the feeding of manganese-iodide, many of the cows delivered living calves. To assure ourselves that this was not a coincidence, we tried the manganese-iodide in the feed of a second herd. All but three out of the 24 cows delivered a calf.

Whether or not manganese is an insufficient mineral we do not know, however, we proceeded to feed this to still another herd which was infected with brucellosis. We administered at least 10 grains of manganese sulfate, disregarding the iodine, and only one cow aborted.

Because of past experience in combining manganese-iodide with chloride of cobalt, we next added chloride of cobalt to the iron sulfate and manganese-iodide in the feed of certain cows which were obstinate cases and where an abortion seemed inevitable. To our great satisfaction the abortions were avoided and the animals delivered normal calves.

To get satisfactory results in the treatment of brucellosis, we tried an experiment. We took an infected cow and placed it beside a clean cow which was not infected and kept the two together in the same stall for a period of one year. At the end of the year, we found the infected cow still infected and the clean cow still clean. Our veterinarian concluded that the clean cow might be carrying some infection which would be a counteraction to the brucellosis germ, and "since he was not satisfied that the test was conclusive, he would not permit infected animals to be introduced into a herd of non-infected animals.

His precaution has proved wise for since the event of testing for brucellosis in cows, whole herds have been cleaned up by the isolation method, and now herds are being sold with a guarantee that they are clean, and not infected with brucellosis.

Our conclusion is that iodine, manganese and cobalt are important elements in the feeding of cattle to eradicate brucellosis and should be given to high-producing cows in their feed rations.

—*Oscar Erf*
quoted in The History of Randleigh Farm *(1947)*

In Germany, the highest wheat yielding soils on the farms that I work with have the highest manganese levels. Some will run as high as 250 ppm. A top yielding field composed of light sand set a record for that type of soil in Lower Saxony. When I started working there, it was a problem field, yielding 80 to 90 bushels of wheat per acre because it had been over-fertilized and overlimed. In the fourth year after working with it, the wheat yield went to 131 bushels per acre. The manganese level in that wheat field was 240+ ppm, with all other nutrients at good to excellent.

The elements manganese and magnesium are often confused because they sound so similar. Magnesium is a secondary element generally supplied by dolomite limestone, magnesium sulfate, or other forms of fertilizers. Even manganese and magnesium deficiency symptoms are somewhat similar. In both cases the leaves of many plants turn yellow or white except for the veins, which remain dark green. But the difference between them is that a manganese deficiency shows up first in new leaves at the top of the plant, whereas magnesium deficiency shows up first in the oldest leaves at the bottom of the plant.

Manganese plays a major role in photosynthesis as well as chlorophyll synthesis and enzyme system construction and operation. Some manganese sensitive crops are soybeans and dry beans, oats, sugar beets, table beets, lettuce and citrus fruit. One of the fastest responses to manganese is on beans. In those heavy, black, soggy-type soils in northwestern Ohio where the manganese is deficient some farmers spray a foliar manganese. When it is time to quit and go to lunch, the grower could drive the tractor to the house and not mark anything because, after lunch, those beans are already green to the row where he stopped spraying. The crop assimilates the nutrient that fast. But too often that is not enough to affect yields. It may require 2 or 3 more foliar applications to do that.

Manganese-deficient soybeans have a coloration best described as very yellow. Once you drop below 40 ppm manganese, soybeans suffer, more so than most other crops. But growers should be just as concerned about wheat. Manganese has shown to be needed on our tests and subsequently applied on fields of soybeans and wheat in various areas. Manganese deficiency in corn really presents no signs until it drops below 30 ppm. Below 30 it actually stunts the growth of corn. It shortens internodes on the stalk. But it will slow emergence of corn and most other crops even if above 30 ppm.

In terms of the amount needed and how it affects all crops, manganese is the most important of all the micronutrients. However, on many fields where needed, it is not recognized as being necessary due to the latent deficiency (hidden hunger), that is low enough to affect yield, but not enough to show up in the leaves of the crop.

A soil analysis should always be conducted to determine present levels before any manganese is applied. This is especially true since manganese toxicity is possible in soils with a pH of 5.5 or less, depending on the levels available in any particular soil. Raising the pH from 5.5 to 6.5 decreases the amount of manganese available in the soil solution by 100 times.

Since manganese availability in many soils begins to reach critically low levels as pH rises above 6.5, the first rules to consider in order to provide adequate levels for a crop are, "Know how much is present and be careful not to overlime your fields."

Hands-On Agronomy

Overuse of potassium or magnesium fertilizers can also reduce manganese availability because both of these nutrients increase soil pH too. Regardless of the pH level, unusually high potassium or sodium levels (in combination totaling 10% or more of a soil's base saturation) mean that manganese uptake will be blocked out of the plant, no matter what the soil test may show. In this case manganese is not tied up in the soil, it is still available, but the excessive saturation of potassium and/or sodium is so high that the manganese cannot be properly taken up by the crop. This problem occurs most often on lighter soils, and is especially troublesome for cotton, wheat, soybeans, peas, oats, tomatoes, citrus, walnuts and grapes.

In addition, low sulfur levels can cause less manganese to be available to the crop. Also, very high organic matter (6% or above) and very low organic matter (less than 2½%) can restrict manganese availability. Sufficient moisture, warm soil temperatures and adequate aeration are important factors which help provide an ample supply of manganese.

Sources of manganese include manganese sulfate for soil and foliar applications and manganese chelate for foliar use as well.

One common source for manganese, and the one I rely on most, is manganese sulfate. In this form, it is most economically priced and the easiest with which to build soil levels. It is generally styled 23 to 32% manganese sulfate.

Despite many claims to the contrary, our best results for building manganese levels in the soil have been from the use of manganese sulfate at broadcast rates. When lime is applied the same year, a second application may be needed before levels show an increase, since liming tends to reduce availability of manganese. It is also effective as a foliar application, though chelates and other forms can also be used effectively at the recommended rates as a foliar.

The only time manganese oxide might be considered for building soil levels is when it is possible to absolutely pulverize the product into a powder and then build it back to a prill or a pellet. If it is pulverized first and then built back, it may be possible to get a breakdown as good as with manganese sulfate. But if it isn't pulverized, it will simply rest there and fail to build up the desired nutrient levels.

Manganese chelate is something altogether different. Some farmers spray it on their soybeans. They have been told that the use of manganese sulfate is no good for the purpose of building manganese levels in the soil. A more valid approach, perhaps, is to call around to see what kind of cost comparisons are available. If we have a soil with 36 ppm manganese and put on 25 pounds of manganese sulfate, most soils will be taken care of in regard to that manganese deficiency with one application of 25 pounds per acre. As far as manganese chelate is concerned, it comes down to taking the amount of manganese usually fed into the leaf and supplying it as a foliar. That equivalent feeds the plant but will not influence soil levels. This means the procedure has to be done every year, year in and year out. In order to get enough foliar manganese chelate on a soybean crop to be equivalent to the reaction from 25 pounds of manganese sulfate, it costs about the same. With the manganese chelate, this cost is repeated every year. Manganese sulfate, on the other hand, builds up soil levels. A caveat has to be added—*most of the time this is a true statement.* Certain soils can absorb manganese at a 25-pound-per-acre rate and only improve the level by a little bit, if at all, from the first application. Applied a second time, the recorded level will generally go up a bit more. And applied a third time, it will increase again, generally by the amount it should have after the first application. But there are some soils for which we really don't solve the manganese problem for several years. The level may be improved temporarily, and then drop back down. Just keep checking the levels in the soil. For most soils, however, the manganese problem is solved with the first application, and manganese sulfate is the most economical source to apply.

Why won't the chelates do just as well? Actually, the manganese chelate contains a very minute amount of manganese, essentially the same payload the plant roots would forage from the soil.

Regional Variations in the Mineral Composition of Vegetables

Samples of cabbage, lettuce, snapbeans, spinach and tomatoes were obtained from commercial fields of these crops in Georgia, South Carolina, Virginia, Maryland, New Jersey, New York (Long Island), Ohio, Indiana, Illinois, and Colorado. The total number of samples examined was 204.

The collecting had to be done during the mid-summer months, and this made it impossible to obtain samples of all five crops from all ten states. Fortunately, samples of snapbeans and tomatoes were secured from every state. This report, therefore, deals primarily with the findings on these two crops. Bountiful snapbeans and Rutgers tomatoes were chosen for collecting, and most of the samples belonged to these two varieties. Insofar as possible, the cabbage, lettuce, and spinach samples were confined to the Golden Acre, Grand Rapids, and Savoy varieties, respectively.

All samples were collected at the stage of growth when they were being harvested for market. Field collection was followed by as rapid transportation to the laboratory as possible. Only the edible portions were prepared for analysis, the outer leaves of cabbage and lettuce being discarded. All samples were rinsed in cold distilled water. The tomatoes were rubbed also with a clean cloth. The samples were dried in a hot-air convection oven at temperatures ranging between 70° and 80° C. Samples of the vegetables were wet-ashed with a mixture of nitric and perchloric acids and made up to volume. Aliquots were then analyzed for the major nutrient elements by standard procedures, including the use of the flame photometer for determining calcium, potassium and sodium. Another sample was dry-ashed at between 600° and 700° C, and analyzed for the minor mineral nutrient elements by the use of a spectrograph.

The soils involved in the eastern coastal plain states were of the Tifton, Bladen, Orangeburg, Portsmouth, Norfolk and Sassafras series. These belong to the podzolic group, including both the red-yellow and the gray-brown zones. They have all been developed from coastal plain materials and have been thoroughly leached, they have relatively low exchange capacities, and they contain only very limited supplies of mineral nutrients.

The soils involved in the east north central states were of the Wooster, Miami, Crosby, Brookston, Clarion and Webster series. The first four are members belonging to the gray-brown podzolic group, which have been developed on glacial drift, some of which was of a calcareous nature. Those of the last two series are prairie soils, which have been developed from calcareous glacial drift.

The Colorado vegetables were obtained from areas where the Laurel, Gilchrist and Berthan series predominate. These soils belong to the brown and planosol groups, and are under irrigation farming. They are high in calcium carbonate and in available mineral nutrients.

Fertilizing and liming practices influence the mineral composition of plants. Consequently it seemed desirable to make a survey of these practices as employed on the fields from which the samples were selected. The data from this survey are summarized in the table. It is important to note the relatively high rates at which fertilizer is applied in the coastal plain states as compared to the rates employed farther west. In the east north central states less dependence is placed on fertilizers and greater use is made of clover sods and manure. Only relatively small amounts of fertilizer are used in Colorado.

> The rate of use of lime increases from Georgia north-
> ward to New Jersey. It varies considerably from farm to
> farm in the east north central states. No lime was used on
> the Colorado farms.
>
> Data on the ash and mineral cation content of 46
> samples of snapbeans and 67 samples of tomatoes are
> shown, state by state, in the table on page 297.
>
> —*Firman E. Bear*
> The Land News [Friends of the Land] *(1949)*

This small amount from chelate is not sufficient enough to increase the overall availability of manganese in the soil. With the chelate, you are using a small amount of manganese to get it into the plant. Our objective in taking the soil route is to build levels to a point where the farmer doesn't have to keep spending money to correct manganese deficient soil and crops year after year.

Growing rice tends to increase manganese levels in the soil over time. Another effective means of increasing manganese availability is the use of ammonium sulfate or ammonium nitrate, especially on alkaline soils. So if soil pH is above 6.5, these materials provide a special advantage for soils that are below the desired level of manganese.

Manganese availability is most affected after you get above a pH of 7. It is also affected when you have a pH even below 7 in heavy, soggy soils. Just be sure your soils have at least 40 ppm manganese when our tests indicate that micronutrients have become the limiting factor for soil fertility levels.

Following just after manganese on our test is the reported copper level. When it comes right down to it, information on whether or not a farmer should be trying to increase the copper level in his soils can become very confusing. For example, one Midwestern university extension publication from the 1970s reads, "The amount of copper available for plant growth is not adequately known since a reliable soil test for copper does not exist." Then the author goes on to recommend how much copper to use on particular crops anyway. Even though he doesn't understand the test, he knows what you need! When it comes to micronutrient use, much the same thing still goes on today.

Copper is a micronutrient, needed in small amounts when compared to N, P and K, sulfur or limestone. And all of these nutrients are needed in adequate amounts before trying to increase production capabilities with trace elements such as copper.

Severe copper deficiencies are most common on boggy-type soils such as peat, muck or those unusually high in organic matter. A soil humus level above 7½% ties up available copper. Very sandy soils are also more likely to be copper deficient. But slight (latent) deficiencies—"hidden hunger"—are prevalent for some high yielding crops even on good mineralized soils. Such problems can occur due to heavy applications of nitrogen or high amounts of phosphate in the soil. Either of these can reduce copper availability. High soil pH levels (above 7.0 on our test) and drought conditions intensify any copper problems. Also, excessive zinc levels can lead to serious copper deficiencies in the crop. When neglected, copper can become the limiting factor in yield, especially in small grains, particularly wheat, but can also limit cotton, grasses, fruit trees and certain vegetables such as onions, spinach and members of the cabbage family, including rapeseed.

Copper is essential to chlorophyll formation in plants. It is also important in the reproductive stage of development, meaning better seed production. Copper helps increase the sugar content of fruits and vegetables. It contributes to both better color and flavor, and helps increase storage and shipping qualities. Copper will increase stalk strength in combination with adequate potassium and manganese, which enables crops to withstand higher rates of nitrogen without lodging problems. And in this regard, adequate copper seems to increase the uptake efficiency of plants receiving ammonium forms of nitrogen. This can be especially important to those crops receiving late

Hands-On Agronomy

Average ash and nutrient-cation content of snapbeans and tomatoes and highest and lowest individual values* for these and 3 other vegetables

Ash in percentages and cations in milliequivalents per 100 grams dry matter

SNAPBEANS

STATE	Ash	Ca	Mg	K	Na	TOTAL CATIONS
Georgia	6.50	14.5	38.3	51.7	1.3	105.8
S. Carolina	6.26	23.0	32.9	44.8	2.2	101.9
Virginia	5.98	17.0	25.5	50.9	1.7	95.1
Maryland	6.49	20.4	36.2	56.0	0.8	113.5
New Jersey	6.62	24.0	43.6	48.8	3.9	120.3
New York	6.34	25.5	39.5	64.5	3.0	132.5
Ohio	8.53	30.5	45.2	71.1	1.7	149.1
Indiana	6.59	30.5	46.0	67.5	1.3	145.3
Illinois	7.73	26.5	43.6	70.6	1.3	142.0
Colorado	7.68	29.0	48.5	56.5	0.4	134.4
SNAPBEANS						
Highest	10.45	40.5	60.0	99.7	8.6	
Lowest	4.04	15.5	14.8	29.1	0.0	
CABBAGE						
Highest	10.38	60.0	43.6	148.3	20.4	
Lowest	6.12	17.5	15.6	53.7	0.8	
LETTUCE						
Highest	24.28	71.0	49.3	176.5	12.2	
Lowest	7.01	16.0	13.1	53.7	0.0	

TOMATOES

STATE	Ash	Ca	Mg	K	Na	TOTAL CATIONS
Georgia	7.78	6.0	32.9	85.7	3.0	127.6
S. Carolina	8.20	7.5	30.4	85.7	3.5	127.1
Virginia	8.44	7.0	33.7	97.2	2.2	140.1
Maryland	7.00	14.0	14.8	88.2	0.4	117.4
New Jersey	8.14	13.0	21.4	83.1	2.2	119.7
New York	8.95	14.5	17.3	107.4	1.3	140.5
Ohio	9.10	13.5	26.3	101.8	1.3	142.6
Indiana	9.18	15.0	28.0	101.8	2.2	147.0
Illinois	8.59	13.8	28.0	96.0	1.3	139.1
Colorado	11.54	15.0	33.7	111.0	0.8	160.5
TOMATOES						
Highest	14.20	23.0	59.2	148.3	6.5	
Lowest	6.07	4.5	4.5	58.8	0.0	
SPINACH						
Highest	28.56	96.0	203.9	257.0	69.5	
Lowest	12.38	47.5	46.9	84.6	0.8	

*No two of these extreme values are for the same sample. Thus, for snapbeans the highest Ca, Mg, K and Na values were found in Colorado, Indiana, and New York, respectively.

applications of ammonia nitrogen such as wheat or medium-to full-season corn. It is also important where manure or compost is used because ammonia can be directly used in the production of amino acids at late stages of growth and copper is involved in building and converting the amino acids to protein.

Copper rarely ever occurs in significant enough quantities to be increased in the soil or plant by amounts contained in the usual mineral fertilizers. But sufficient applications of the proper materials can build up the levels in the soil for longer periods of time than is possible for most other micro-nutrients. Copper sulfate is the most effective form to use in building copper levels in the soil. It acts rapidly when applied to the soil, but such small amounts are required that it must be uniformly mixed or blended with other fertilizers in order to be spread properly.

Copper chelate, 2% to 7½%, is an effective foliar source. However, applications as a foliar feed source supply only the present crop and in only one year will have no significant effect on measurable copper levels for future crops to be grown there. But when copper is applied consistently over the years, it is possible to build levels, even to an excess.

The critical ranges for copper are these. Anything below 2 ppm copper means deficiency. Five ppm is excellent, but 10+ ppm is still not considered as excessive. Above 10 ppm, plenty of phosphates are mandated because copper may tie up phosphate just as phosphate can tie up copper. Without excellent phosphate availability, it is better to stay between 5 and 10 ppm, and above 2 ppm. Don't even start thinking about getting to 5 ppm until everything else has been put into proper equilibrium, at which point it is time to reevaluate how much money can be spent. Always soil test before adding copper to the soil. Continuing applications beyond the point needed for top production can lead to toxicity problems. Excessive levels can affect phosphate, zinc and iron uptake.

When it comes to copper, remember what happens when you put on extra nitrogen. Too much nitrogen stops the uptake of copper. Overuse of nitrogen can mean a copper deficiency on soils that appear to have all they need.

Hands-On Agronomy

Copper, per pound, is the most expensive of all the nutrient elements required for general crop production. It is also the most stable element. Once the copper level gets built up, it does not have to be built up again for long periods of time.

If you put on 25 pounds of 28% manganese sulfate, we generally expect that this is going to raise the manganese by about 3.5 ppm (i.e. -7 pounds) per acre. When we apply copper as ten pounds of 23% copper sulfate, it will raise the copper level in a year's time by 0.6 ppm. Five pounds of copper sulfate will raise the level by 0.3 ppm. In other words, if you have 1.4 ppm and you want to get to 2 ppm, five pounds of copper sulfate will carry the soil system to only 1.7 ppm that first year, still short for wheat and other similar crops.

Except in the case of wheat and other small grains, if the soil test indicates that you need ten pounds of copper sulfate but that amount represents a cost that is too high, you could consider putting on two pounds for the next five years instead of ten pounds all at once. You can build copper levels this way because that nutrient is so stable in the soil. Almost every soil analyzed is deficient in copper. The few exceptions are where there is naturally occurring copper in the soil or where manure has been used, or along rivers where soil has been moved in by constant flooding, and where alluvial deposits keep the soil built up. The other place where we don't have copper deficiencies is where large amounts of pesticides containing copper have been used in the past, and where turkey litter is commonly used.

When crops on soils with adequate fertility that test low in copper fail to respond to copper applications, a molybdenum test should be considered. Both need to be present in adequate amounts, since either one can influence the amount a crop can take up of the other one.

A farmer from Iowa I had worked with for eight years called me one day. He said he had a problem with some of his corn going down. He wanted me to look at the soil test. He had 80 acres split into four 20s, and one had a 1.5 copper, his lowest level. I told him that his copper was 1.5 ppm and he was going to have the weakest stalks there. It was true. He said, "Well, since that is true, what about the next field?" We went through all the data until he hit 2 ppm. In each case he lost corn from lodging, but the lower the copper level below 2 ppm, the worse the corn was lodged.

Copper gives resilience to a plant. The other key to flavor after sulfur is copper. Copper doesn't move in the soil. If you see a copper deficiency at all, it is like sulfur. It shows the deficiency in the youngest growth first. Adequate nitrogen means you get better copper uptake. Too much nitrogen means you actually decrease the availability of copper to the plant. Wheat is a crop that responds well to copper. If the other needed nutrients are adequate, but you are below 2 ppm copper and you put enough copper on your wheat to get above 2 ppm, it will produce an extra five bushels (300 pounds/acre) of wheat.

I was asked to make a consulting trip to Germany in 1985. The client who asked me there had arranged for speaking engagements to several groups of farmers. He told me to tell them just what I had done on his farms. In Germany, they use the taller varieties of wheat, but they also use growth regulators to keep plants short. When the subject turned to copper, I mentioned that if the soil had below 2 ppm and copper was put on, it would increase yields by five bushels per acre. I also told them that every soil I had checked in Germany was below that level. One man raised his hand, stood up and spoke for two or three minutes. The interpreter leaned over and said, "This is the man who is in charge of fertility for the university in this area. He is telling the farmers why they don't need to really worry about the copper that you said should be put on." When he had finished, a doctor of fertility research rose and reported a ten-year study (unknown to me) just completed which had shown exactly the same results I had mentioned on wheat production.

Copper sulfate, 22.5 or 23%, is water soluble and can be applied to soil or as a foliar. A word of caution here. When copper is mixed in solution with other elements it may show as compatible in the mix, but use it up. Do not let it set in your

ZINC PLAYS A ROLE IN ENZYME SYSTEMS, GROWTH REGULATORS & PROTEIN SYNTHESIS
SOME SENSITIVE CROPS & THEIR DEFICIENCY SYMPTOMS ARE:

SENSITIVE CROP(S)	DEFICIENCY SYMPTOMS
Corn, Sorghum	Interveinal chlorosis, shortened internodes, crinkled leaves
Soybeans, Dry beans	Interveinal chlorosis, severe stunting
Pecans	"Little leaf," die-back, rosetted leaves
Rice	Leaf lesions, leaf bronzing, shortened internodes
Citrus	Creamy, yellow chlorosis, die-back

spray tank, pumps or hoses overnight. It can harden to the point that the entire spraying appratus has to be scrapped. I won't bother with other copper sources if I can get copper sulfate because I know it works, and I know how much can be applied safely. A ten-pound application of copper sulfate—after 12 months time—will raise the copper level by 0.6 ppm on the specific test we use. A copper level is the easiest to build and maintain, and zinc is next in the pecking order. Both have staying power in the soil.

Zinc aids in the absorption of moisture. Along with potassium, think of zinc in critical moisture situations. It also helps transform carbohydrates. It regulates plant sugar use. Zinc plays a role in enzyme system functioning, as well as with the growth regulators normally present in the plant and protein synthesis.

SOME COMMON ZINC SOURCES:

SOURCE	Zn PERCENT
Zinc sulfates (hydrated)	23-35
Zinc oxide	78
Basic zinc sulfate	55
Zinc carbonate	52
Zinc sulfide	67
Zinc frits	Variable
Zinc phosphate	51
Zinc chelates	9-14
Other organics	5-10

Consider zinc needs, especially in sensitive crops such as corn and grain sorghum, also soybeans and dry beans. As far as zinc levels are concerned, the minimum is 6 ppm. Below that, enough should be applied the first year to get up above the 6 ppm figure. There has never been a soil—in my experience at least—that required more than 30 pounds of zinc sulfate to completely take care of the worst zinc deficiency, provided limestone didn't have to be applied at the same time. If lime is applied, the lime won't drive out the zinc, but it will affect zinc availability. If you need zinc and lime and put on the lime but don't put on the zinc, expect your zinc level to get worse. Zinc probably gives a response more often than any other micronutrient when it is applied for crop production. I see many soils that need zinc. All can be taken care of, generally with excellent response. Only a few crops do not respond well to zinc when only slightly deficient, one of them being wheat. Again, for zinc, 6 ppm is the minimum. Excellent means at least 10 ppm, and an excess is 35+ ppm.

A classic sign of zinc deficiency in corn is the whitish stripe in the leaf color, which looks much like a magnesium deficiency. In the field, often I can't tell whether it is a zinc deficiency or a

Hands-On Agronomy

magnesium deficiency. The difference between zinc and magnesium deficiencies should be that zinc will be white and magnesium will be white on top with a purplish color on the bottom.

High phosphorous, high calcium or high potassium levels can induce zinc deficiencies as does the overuse of nitrogen. Also, as the pH goes up from 6, when a soil has good zinc levels, availability begins to decrease. It can go as high as pH 7 before it decreases good zinc availability to the point that it becomes a problem. Heavy cuts, such as when the field has been graded or the topsoil has been taken away, or when eroded soil allows subsoils to appear, strong zinc deficiencies become evident.

Zinc is not easy to leach away. It is held well on clay and humus. Once zinc levels are improved, it is relatively easy to keep them up. When zinc sulfate is applied on the tests we have, an exact relationship between the amount of zinc applied and the increase shown on the soil test can be expected. Using 36% zinc sulfate at an application of 10 pounds per acre will exhibit a 3.6 pound increase of zinc on the test. The correlation is classic. Putting on ten pounds of 36% zinc sulfate means putting on 3.6 pounds of zinc per acre. A soil test—when the zinc is finished breaking down—should show an increase of 3.6 pounds of zinc. That translates into 1.8 ppm, meaning every 10 pounds of zinc sulfate applied will raise the zinc level by 1.8 ppm. There is one other thing to be remembered about pure zinc sulfate. Put on ten pounds of zinc sulfate today, then come back next year and pull a soil test on the same day. That zinc is only going to be halfway to its final level. You are only going to see a 0.9 ppm increase in the soil. When you put on sufficient zinc it will not reach the desired level for two years, but will supply enough zinc for the crops grown for both years.

Some firms say they have a 36% zinc product, it being a 36% oxysulfate. It is cheaper at the counter, but it does not always build zinc levels. There are some zinc oxide products that have been pulverized and then prilled which have also proved effective for increasing the levels in the soil. Apply ten pounds, the same as with 36% zinc sulfate, and see if next year the deficiency is still there. Pure zinc sulfate is the sure choice.

With the exception of boron, on most soils the technology exists in order to build the levels of trace elements to a point that it is not an annual expense, but basically an initial expenditure. Then afterwards, it is a matter of testing and fertilizing as needed over the years to keep the levels up. Many farmers, ranchers and growers initially resist the addition of trace elements to increase fertility levels, objecting to the added expense. But when you consider the years spent taking from the soil without adding the traces back, replenishing should be expected. And supplying those micronutrients have helped increase corn yields by 20-30 bushels, and wheat from 5-25 bushels per acre. Micronutrients, when applied in the right form, to build up the levels in the soil will help quality and crop yields accordingly.

Some farmers who have livestock have always felt they shouldn't have to be concerned with trace elements because their manure or compost would take care of it. I work with many farmers who use manures and compost, and this is rarely the case. Think about it. When a soil is deficient in copper and adequate copper is not being supplemented, how can enough be in the manure? Manure is generally low in sulfur, boron and copper—the nutrients most often lacking in our soils used for growing the crops. Keep in mind, when manure is applied, you can influence the soil nutrient level to only the extent of what is there in the first place. Nevertheless, manure is certainly helpful and in certain soils even sufficient to keep the trace elements that are present in a soil most available for plant use, while at the same time helping to recycle those that are picked up in the feed. And therefore, as the use of manures in an area declines, the need for trace elements will increase.

Most soils we analyze just do not have an adequate supply of trace elements to assure that the crop will do its best. So keep in mind that just because there are enough of the major elements for the crop, does not assure that trace element levels will also be adequate.

Hands-On Agronomy

Under the present economic circumstances, every farmer needs to have the confidence that he is on a solid footing, and doing all he can to supply his crops the fertility needed from start to finish. The misconceptions and misunderstandings about soil fertility make this even harder to accomplish. The more farmers or those involved in a soil fertility program understand the reasons behind micronutrient recommendations, the more confidence there will be in those recommendations and the decisions made on how to use them. The lack of any nutrient, whether needed in major, secondary or trace amounts, hurts the soil and all that must live from it.

For further study concerning micronutrients and what they do I would recommend six references that have proven very helpful to substantiate the value of our program over the years:

Bennett, William F., Nutrient Deficiencies and Toxicities in Crop Plants, APS Press, St. Paul, Minnesota.

Bergmann, Werner, Nutritional Disorders of Plants, Gustav Fischer Verlag Jena.

Marschner, Horst, Mineral Nutrition of Higher Plants, 2nd Ed., Academic Press, Harcourt Brace & Company.

Mittleider, Jacob R., The Garden Doctor, Volumes I, II and III, Autumn House Publishing Company, Hagerstown, Maryland.

Datnoff, Elmer and Huber, Mineral Nutrition and Plant Disease, APS, St. Paul, Minnesota.

Schutte, Karl H. and Myers, John A., Metabolic Aspects of Health, Discovery Press, Kentfield, California.

14

Plant Tissue
Analysis & Fertility

FROM WHAT IS EXTANT IN THE LITERATURE and given as accurate information in many articles and textbooks, it seems necessary that this chapter should begin with a very important point. There are many in agriculture that will strongly disagree, but read the rest of this chapter and the reasons given for the statement, before you make a decision contrary to what is about to be said. Always (and because of its permanence, you will rarely see that word used in this book—yet I repeat for emphasis as above) *always* use a plant analysis to understand the nutrient needs and correct them in the plants themselves, but *never* (same comment as for "always") to determine what should be done to the soil in which those plants are growing.

Earlier in the book using a leaf analysis was mentioned for determining sulfur needs of corn. But, just as with soil testing, many farmers, fertilizer dealers and consultants do not trust a plant or leaf analysis, and not necessarily without justification.

For determining what has been done, or what should be done, some tests seem to be worth about as much as the paper on which they are printed.

A plant tissue analysis that provides the grower with understandable and usable information can be an excellent tool. However, like soil testing, most of these tests differ in terms of how analyzed results are reported and evaluated. They only become useful tools for those who can accurately correlate what the numbers indicate as specifically needed for the plants being tested. A plant or leaf tissue test should reveal what needs to be supplied to the plant *right now*. However, that same leaf blade or plant analysis should be used to reveal more than just what is lacking in the plant. It should also show anything that is too excessive and what is present for use in the correct amount by the crop being grown there as well. The test we use measures, calculates and reports results and requirements in such a way that when correlated with the soil tests from the same location, all three of these considerations can normally be answered for the particular crop. With just a little coaching the results and recommendations will become clear and for the experienced grower moderately easy to understand. Because both deficiencies and excesses can be measured, some clients use the leaf tissue analysis in combination with a soil test where they are growing their very best crop or crops just to determine if there may be some nutrient that could be applied, or reduced, to "fine tune" their fertility program.

For those interested in using plant or leaf analysis and would like a place to begin, perhaps a good starting point would be to put the particular leaf analysis of your choice to the test. Select leaves from a poor-growing area of a field for one sample and leaves from a good-growing area for a second sample. Mark the samples so as not to give a hint about which is which, but keep a record so that you know. Send them in and ask the consultant to identify which sample has the problem and why, and what specifically should be done to the problem area to bring it into line with the better one. If you decide to do this with our company, first read the rest of this chapter because more is required from clients than taking and sending just any type of leaf sample to determine the problems and provide correct recommendations as to what should be done about them. If the test is not done correctly, it is only a waste of time and money.

Again, growers should consider a plant or tissue analysis for use in understanding nutrient levels and how to correct them in the plants themselves. But do not use a plant or leaf analysis when trying to determine what should be done to the soil in which those plants are growing. It is true there are times when needed corrections cannot be made quickly enough via the soil. In such instances, nutrients required for immediate growth and production should be provided via the leaf. Use a leaf or plant analysis to determine what to supply as a fast acting or foliar application, and a soil test to determine what materials should be applied to the soil in order to build fertility levels there. *This is extremely important.* Don't look at a plant analysis to determine long-term fertilizer needs. Look at the fertility levels in the soil for that, and then consider a plant analysis for verification purposes, or to help with decisions as to what—if any—foliar or fast-acting plant feeder materials could be helpful.

Although foliar materials can be utilized rather quickly, applying only one application may not be enough to completely solve a nutrient deficiency problem. However, the recommended amounts are all that is advisable to use at any one time. Using the specified amount avoids possible phyto-toxic reactions and/or blaming a foliar material if something else should happen to make the plant or crop fail. Assuming that one application of any lacking nutrient will be sufficient to make a useful difference in the plants tested is oftentimes an incorrect assumption. Because the plant may utilize all it can receive at once in a very short period of time, to do the job completely a follow-up leaf analysis should be considered after each treatment until all deficiencies are shown to be resolved. For example, on tree crops such as almonds, apples, etc., a leaf test is recommended at the first of each month in May, June, July, and August, unless prior testing has confirmed that the deficient materials have been properly supplied.

However, using a leaf analysis to decide how to fertilize the soil can be a serious mistake. For example, when a soil has too little magnesium, the plants growing there will also have too little magnesium as shown by a plant or leaf analysis. But in many crops, including strawberries, corn, soybeans and alfalfa, just to name a few that stand out in this regard, we often see a lack of magnesium in the plants when the soil tests correctly show that the level in the soil is far too high.

Too much magnesium in the soil does not assure plants growing there will receive enough. You can have too much magnesium in the soil and still show an actual deficiency in a grapevine or a grass plant. This happens even though you can measure three times more available soil magnesium there than the crop needs. It would be correct to supply additional magnesium as a foliar treatment, perhaps even several times, but incorrect to assume from a leaf analysis that every soil where plants are shown to be short of magnesium needs more magnesium applied to the soil in order to eliminate future deficiencies. In cases where the magnesium level is already too high in the soil adding more to increase soil magnesium levels will only make the problem of too little in the plant last that much longer.

If the magnesium level in the soil tests low, it would be correct to add the proper amount of magnesium. But if the soil level is already too high, adding more magnesium to that soil can be an expensive mistake that will only make matters worse. Only a soil analysis that measures the saturation of magnesium for each sample will give the true answer as to whether that soil needs more magnesium. If the magnesium level is where it should be, between the required 10%-12% on clay and 12%-20% on sand, the crop should not come up deficient. But if you get magnesium in the soil above the required level, you could still have deficiencies in the plant. This situation holds true for such diverse crops as cotton and strawberries. Magnesium is only one example of several that could be used to demonstrate why a leaf analysis does not replace a soil analysis, or vice versa. Both have their place, but serve different purposes.

Manganese can present the same type of problem as magnesium. There can be too much in the soil, and the plant will not be able to get enough. Eyeball appraisal can sometimes detect the dramatic deficiencies, yet at times the truth escapes notice and what is called "hidden hunger" requires verification by some other testing method. Leaf analysis is an excellent tool to choose in such cases.

There is yet another consideration when it comes to using a soil test and not a leaf test to determine a problem. When the level of manganese exceeds the level of iron on our test, the plant will begin to show yellowing or iron chlorosis. Even though the plants show a definite iron deficiency, a leaf test will show no iron problem there. When the manganese level exceeds the iron level on the specific test we use, it oxidizes iron in the leaf making it unavailable to the plant. But when the leaf is analyzed, the oxidized iron is released and shows as if it had been available to the plant all along. If you only use a tissue or plant analysis, this problem will never be identified. Only by measuring these levels properly on a soil test will the problem be identified and solved.

The following example will illustrate how to use both soil and plant testing. I have a client in California who received a call from a company in the process of completing a million-dollar landscape project for a home. Two and a half months after laying new sod, the grass was dying on a third of the lawn. The landscape architect called my client and asked for help. He looked at the problem and called me. We had the company pull soil samples and take leaf samples on the part of the lawn turning brown as well as from areas still okay by comparison. The company had leveled the surface and removed the topsoil from the problem area. No one bothered to put any of the topsoil back before laying the sod. In the area where they were down to subsoil the grass died because of the imbalance in and lack of needed nutrients. This dying area of grass became a perfect indicator of what happens when calcium levels are lower than magnesium in the soil. A soil analysis promptly identified the problem and suggested the long term solutions. But we needed the analysis of the grass leaves to indicate what to do in the short term. According to the tissue test done, it was recommended that a mixture of foliar calcium and the deficient trace elements be applied to the dying grass. In a week and a half that brown grass was green again. Then instructions for the long term treatments were put into effect as indicated by soil tests. Six months later my wife, Linda, and I visited the site. There was no evidence of any problem area at all. It would have likely been impossible to save that grass by relying on either a soil or plant analysis alone. By determining what was immediately needed via leaf analysis and supplying each of the individual nutrients as a foliar, it was possible to accomplish a "green up," as it were. But only through supplying what the soil analysis indicated were we able to eliminate continuous use of foliars to maintain the color in the grass. When you have specific problems, keep in mind that soil tests are the foundation on which plant analysis helps the grower build. Trying to skimp by with only a plant analysis can prove very costly. On the other hand, using plant analysis to detect a need or the correction of a need is extremely helpful, especially in a world confused about sulfur and micronutrient use.

Southeast Missouri produces several thousand acres of potatoes for the chip trade. One grower hired me to help him with his 1,200 acres of potatoes. Soil tests were taken on all the different farms he had in potato production. One of those farms exhibited calcium levels in the 65 to 68% range. He raised the best yield of potatoes on that farm. All of his other potato farms proved to be deficient in calcium. If you are deficient in calcium and want to grow potatoes and it is February with planting to begin in March, you had better not apply large amounts of limestone even if you expect it to break down in time. Such a procedure can sometimes increase scab problems in the potatoes before the year is over. To be safe, you should put lime on potato ground at least 12 months before planting the potatoes.

Following the calcium deficiencies, the next observation on the potato program's soil audits revealed copper deficiencies almost everywhere. Every soil also exhibited a boron deficiency based on analysis of this light, sandy type soil. The grower asked me to send leaf samples to a lab known for its competence in potato acreage analysis. The lab that I used had not done many potato plant analyses, but I recalled an agronomist out of Texas who told me about another lab that did a great job on leaf analysis for potatoes. The month before there had been an article in a potato grower magazine about this particular laboratory and how well the lab did with potatoes. Although I was not aware of the article, the client was. When told that the leaf samples would be sent to the laboratory featured in the article, the client was overjoyed. Over time the fellow in this lab became a good friend as well as a very close advisor. After the soil read-outs came back and all the fertilizer was down, just about the time the potatoes were blooming, leaf and petiole samples for analysis were gathered and sent to the lab.

The very first field planted was right at the seed potato house. The day they started planting, a potato company field-man came up from Florida. Something was said about putting on ten pounds of copper. What was really meant was ten pounds of copper sulfate. The agent from Florida said it would kill the potatoes. They started planting, and left a message for me to call. By the time I called, the first field was planted. The grower explained, "They said it was going to kill the potatoes, so we didn't use any copper. Are you sure the copper won't hurt anything?" Now, I wouldn't tell him how to grow potatoes without checking with another grower who had extensive experience with copper and growing potatoes in sand. The grower I called just happened to be a consultant who lived in Florida and who used the very same analysis I was using for potato production. Though I had called him already, I called again. He said they used ten pounds of copper sulfate every year on potatoes that

SAMPLE REPORT: LEAF ANALYSIS (GOOD)

Kinsey Agricultural Services, Inc.
297 County Highway 357 - Charleston, MO 63834
Phone 573-683-3880 Fax 573-683-6227 e-mail neal@kinseyag.com

LAB NUMBER: 001

SAMPLE NUMBER: OGF1

CROP: OLEANDER GOOD
FIELD: OLEANDER GOOD

DATE OF REPORT:

ANALYZED RESULTS

N	S	P	K	Mg	Ca	Na	NO3-N	Fe	Al	Mn	B	C	Zn
			(%)							(PPM)			
1.3	0.23	0.37	1.04	0.54	2.49	0.062	1443	134	156	53	67	21	39

OPTIMAL RANGES

N	S	P	K	Mg	Ca	Na	NO3-N	Fe	Al	Mn	B	C	Zn
2-	0.15-	0.2-	1.5-	0.3-	0.5-	< 0.1		50-	<250	30-	30-	6-	30-
4.5	0.40	0.6	3.5	1	2.5			200		80	50	40	75

NUTRIENT LEVEL	MINERAL NAME	NUTRIENT INDEX
LOW	NITROGEN (N)	-30
	POTASSIUM (K)	-20
	ZINC (Zn)	-11
	SULFUR (S)	-5
	MAGNESIUM (Mg)	-5
	PHOSPHORUS (P)	-2
	COPPER (Cu)	-1
OPTIMUM	MANGANESE (Mn)	0
	IRON (Fe)	4
	CALCIUM (Ca)	21
HIGH	BORON (B)	56
VERY HIGH		

* Element not evaluated due to excess level

OTHER ELEMENTS TESTED
Mo   2.79   PPM

Hands-On Agronomy

SAMPLE REPORT: LEAF ANALYSIS (BAD)

Kinsey Agricultural Services, Inc.

297 County Highway 357 - Charleston, MO 63834
Phone 573-683-3880 Fax 573-683-6227 e-mail neal@kinseyag.com

LAB NUMBER: 002

SAMPLE NUMBER: OBF1

CROP: OLEANDER BAD
FIELD: OLEANDER BAD   DATE OF REPORT:

ANALYZED RESULTS

N	S	P	K	Mg	Ca	Na	NO3-N	Fe	Al	Mn	B	C	Zn
			(%)							(PPM)			
1.4	0.24	0.37	1.01	0.51	2.35	0.054	1875	136	162	79	90	15	41

OPTIMAL RANGES

2-4.5	0.15-0.40	0.2-0.6	1.5-3.5	0.3-1	0.5-2.5	< 0.1		50-200	<250	30-80	30-50	6-40	30-75

NUTRIENT LEVEL	MINERAL NAME	NUTRIENT INDEX
VERY LOW		
	POTASSIUM (K)	-34
	NITROGEN (N)	-33
LOW	ZINC (Zn)	-15
	COPPER (Cu)	-14
	MAGNESIUM (Mg)	-12
	SULFUR (S)	-9
	PHOSPHORUS (P)	-7
	IRON (Fe)	-1
OPTIMUM	CALCIUM (Ca)	13
	MANGANESE (Mn)	15
VERY HIGH	BORON (B)	95
EXCESSIVE		

* Element not evaluated due to excess level

OTHER ELEMENTS TESTED
Mo   1.65   PPM

needed the copper, and "it won't kill them." I called my client back and told him that, and he said that he would compromise on the next field and just apply five pounds. By the time he got to the farm after that one, he decided to go ahead and apply the full ten pounds of copper sulfate. When leaf analysis reports came back, the results spoke in loud overtones. In the first field where planting was started without adding the needed copper, copper was the limiting element. Right behind it was calcium. On the other field where they had applied five pounds of copper sulfate, calcium was the limiting factor with copper trailing close behind it. On the next farms where the ten pounds of copper sulfate had been applied, there was no deficiency of copper at all. While copper was certainly not a limiting factor on these particular farms, calcium continued to show most deficient. We finally came to the samples from the farm that already produced great potatoes. Here the calcium levels were in the right order with a base saturation of 65 to 68% calcium. Every field had exhibited calcium as a limiting factor on yield until we got to this farm. Calcium didn't show up here as a limiting factor at all. Neither did boron because it had been applied as directed based on deficiencies evident in the potatoes from prior years.

If the soil test calls for a nutrient, and you fail to put it on, the shortfall will be exhibited by use of an accurate tissue analysis. I have continued to use tissue analysis to verify various soil readouts, and the procedure has worked very well.

Soil tests allow for application prior to planting, and a plant analysis can be a good diagnostic tool for the current season. Neither method should be considered as foolproof. Using either can help, but using both is the best combination for top results.

Consider that the soil analysis is a tool to confirm what nutrients are present as available to the plant from the soil and also shows any needed corrections that should be made to the soil itself over the next year. The soil requires that long to "process" the nutrients and have them show up as supplied, based on that soil's nutrient "holding capacity" or TEC. Always use a soil test to determine what materials should be applied to the soil.

The results of an actual leaf analysis from good and bad plants are provided here (pp. 314-315) to help show how they can be utilized. A leaf or plant analysis shows what is lacking in the plant, and should show what is there in too large an amount as well. (Hence the pluses for too much and the minuses for too little—along the right-hand side of the plant analysis pages.)

On the soil tests for the bad vs. the good plants, potassium shows to be a problem for the bad one. Although the potassium is actually higher in the bad soil, the plant is having a problem getting it because the sodium is being incorporated into the cell walls instead of the potassium (this occurs when the %Na exceeds %K in the soil). When it gets hot and humid, which can even happen in a dry climate if irrigated well, the sodium allows excess water to be taken into the cell and eventually causes the cell wall to break down killing the plants one cell at a time. So when the plant test shows potassium as the most limiting factor that is exactly what we would expect. Notice that the sodium is actually lower in the problem plant, but this does not show where the plant has utilized it. From the soil test having a higher Na% than K%, we know that too much sodium has replaced potassium in the cell walls. This replacement is not the case in the good plants because plants will predominantly utilize which-ever of the two has the highest percentage of saturation in the soil to build the cell walls. The potassium is a major limiting fac-tor in both the good and the bad plants, but it is not as great a problem in the good leaves because the sodium percentage does not exceed the potassium percentage in the soil.

Nitrogen is the second most limiting element in the problem plants, and most needed of all nutrients in the good plants. But this is obviously not the big problem because there is less in the good leaf sample than the bad one. Zinc is next most limiting in both cases—good and bad. On the good one, it is not because the soil is lacking zinc, but because the phosphorus is too high. High phosphate blocks zinc uptake into the plant. This then causes a need for more water in the soil to correctly supply the plants because zinc aids the plant in optimizing moisture uptake.

So the resulting lack of zinc and excessive phosphate in the soil increases the need for additional moisture to accomplish the same amount of growth.

Note that the zinc level is what we would call O.K. on the problem soil, but this is only true when the phosphate is in the same category. On the Olsen phosphate test 125 lbs./acre of P_2O_5 is considered excellent. An excellent P_2O_5 with an O.K. level of zinc means not enough zinc to properly do what the plant needs done. That is why we always emphasize that building both P_2O_5 and Zn at the same time in the soil itself is so important. Using a 7% zinc chelate as a foliar at 12 oz./acre on both the good and the bad plants will begin to help solve this problem. Perhaps only once will do the job on the bad area, but likely more will be required to completely correct the problem on the "good" area because of the excessive P_2O_5 there.

Copper is the next most limiting factor on the bad area, and it is below the 2 ppm minimum on the soil test. It is much better in the good plants although only barely above the minimum of 2 ppm. Some will claim this is just happenstance, but you can see with testing and building the copper in the soil over time that it is not. Using 4 oz./acre of a 2% copper chelate as a foliar is recommended for the bad plants.

Sulfur shows to be the next most limiting factor on the good plants. (We normally concentrate only on the top four most limiting nutrients at a time.) The optimal range for sulfur is 0.15 to 0.40, and we have 0.23, which means sulfur is still being utilized basically as well on the good as on the bad area. As it stands now, once we supply the most needed nutrients for both areas, using sulfur will still keep the good ones ahead of the bad ones in terms of growth and appearance.

Also, note how much higher the molybdenum is in the good plants, which was not requested to be run as part of the soil test. Using $7^1/_2$ oz. per acre of sodium molybdate on the problem area just one time should be extremely helpful if none has been used in the last 3 years.

Hands-On Agronomy

Test the soil and plants again before using more of the required materials. After this initial application wait until testing shows a definite need to use any foliar at all on the good area.

With these points in mind, there is one other aspect of leaf, plant or tissue analysis that is a critical consideration. The analysis and recommendations can only be correct if the sample is taken correctly.

First, be sure to select clean specimens to send for analysis. If that is not possible, lightly rinse off the plants or leaves using distilled water. Water from the well or tap can contain nutrients that will affect the analysis. It does not require much soil residue to throw off the analysis. Soil splashed on plants from rainfall or overhead irrigation, or extremely dusty conditions that cause it to settle on the leaves are some good examples. If you fail to send clean plants, it is usually easy to recognize on the test because the iron, aluminum and manganese will be extremely elevated, making it appear that all are at seriously high or toxic levels.

Next use clean bags to place the leaves or plant tissue inside. Paper bags are best. And if plastic must be used, then punch holes in the side to help avoid moisture accumulation and a possible moldy sample that arrives to be analyzed.

The plant parts to sample and send in for analysis will depend on the circumstances. When plants are small, the entire above-ground portion can be sampled and sent. In some cases a particular plant or leaf sampling method may have been used for years and changing may mean a loss of correlation with data from the past. If no guidelines are provided, then taking enough of the youngest completely mature leaves for doing the analysis works well. For cotton, take the leaf opposite the bole. On fruit trees, take the leaf from a fruiting branch and avoid the leaves from non-fruiting branches. If in doubt, call our office first to see if there are any special instructions for the particular crop. Petioles can be analyzed if requested, but it is strongly recommended that if one or the other is to be used, the plant or leaf analysis would be considered the better of the two. Drying the leaves first is no problem, so long as contamination can be avoided in doing so.

Due to regulations in place, any tissue or plant samples sent from other countries must be dried and cut into small pieces before they will be cleared for testing in the U.S. by the Customs authorities. This virtually eliminates any quick solution to growing problems of plants outside the U.S. Be sure to check for any further special instructions before sending plants or plant tissue to be tested.

Overall, plant or plant tissue analysis can be a helpful tool and help solve immediate nutrition problems and needs for growing plants. Such tests are also very helpful at evaluating whether insufficient or excessive amounts of a particular nutrient are present at any given time in the crop. If you have a good testing program that works well for you, stay with it. But if your program does not include crop monitoring through use of timely leaf analysis, it may be useful to consider leaf analysis in addition to the use of soil testing.

My-cor-rhi-za / ˈmī-ke-ˈrī-ze / *n* [NL, fr. *myc* + Gk *rhiza* root] 1 the symbiotic association of the mycelium of fungus with plant roots 2 an underground living complex that decomposes organic materials, making soils fertile by entering into symbiotic relationships with roots of higher plants to supply them with critically needed compounds

15

The Grower's Purpose

EVERY CONSULTANT SHOULD STRIVE TO TEACH that a farmer needs a complete fertility program, not just for the crop, but for the benefit of everything concerned—the farmer or grower and his posterity, as well as the soil chemistry, physics and biology of the land. It is not merely a matter of selling the idea of a soil test. Although a good, dependable soil test is mandatory, there has to be a program to accomplish what will profitably work for all concerned. As part of our service we strive to teach the fact that the products applied must fit into the plan. It is our policy never to tout a specific product and then try to build a program around it. It is our purpose to try and determine where you are and then recommend the products that are most readily available and will accomplish this goal most economically. If that does not happen, everyone loses. Both ends of the equation need to encompass ways and means available to accomplish the grower's purpose.

Let's say you have a farm and you would like to produce in the most economical way, but you can't use manure. Or, if you have manure and can spread it, then we at least need to know what type of manure it is and what it contains by analysis. Once that information is available, we are ready to face reality. At that point our job is to help the grower understand and utilize the materials required. Our company is not in the fertilizer business—we sell a service as soil fertility specialists, and the farmer or grower, not us, chooses the supplier, and, in the end, the products he decides to use.

So far, in the establishment of a needed program, we have looked at the structure of the soil, its composition—minerals, humus, air and water. We have looked at these in terms of chemistry and we have looked at them in terms of physics. But chemistry and physics can supply only two-thirds of the answer. For the full answer, we must also look at the biological side of the soil. In most instances, the biological side of the grower's equation gets slighted. For reasons that escape me, farmers are not quite as interested in biology, although that seems to be changing somewhat in recent years. Yet many do not realize they have to have 25% air and 25% water in the soil system. Why is that? Microbes require that balance of air and water to live and properly do their job. Sandy soils generally have too much air and not enough moisture.

In a heavy clay soil, the mix goes the other way. We get more water saturation and not enough air space. There is less pore space because colloids stick closer together. So the biology of the soil needs the exact physical and chemical mix detailed here to function as it should. Examine soils and you will conclude that every time the texture changes, so does the soil's ability to absorb moisture and deliver nutrients. Topsoil has to be completely saturated before water will penetrate into the next layer. When soils are worked, a chisel plow or offset disc is normally to be preferred over a moldboard plow. Unlike a moldboard plow, either implement will help keep nutrients and residues near the top where they can accomplish the most benefit. By way of contrast, a moldboard plow turns over the soil, creating a new and generally hostile environment for the microbes present.

William A. Albrecht always stressed that if you want to do it right, look at nature and determine the proper pattern, then try to get as close to nature as possible.

Even a disc or a chisel plow keeps coarser particles on top, with the finer particles sifting downward. This can actually create a silt layer in the soil when worked at the same depth all the time. What difference does it make? You have to keep the soil open so that there are avenues for the water to travel through. Say that the first two-inch layer has more sand. It has to become saturated before water will penetrate the next layer. Then that layer has to be saturated before it allows water to move into the next layer. The soil system works best with coarse particles on top, with medium and fine particles below.

When Mount St. Helens erupted in Washington state, I was in touch with a good friend who worked as a consultant in the area. A lot of farms had an inch of volcanic ash deposited on top of the soil. That ash was a finer textured material than the soil itself. He analyzed the ash for its nutrient content. He also wanted to see what the fines were, what the medium sizes were, and the character of the heavier soils. That volcanic ash matched out to a silty type soil.

The topsoil where he was working was a sandy type soil. The farmer who used a moldboard plow to turn under the ash created a new water barrier. If you have coarse sand on top, and then you put a silt layer down, all that sand has to get completely saturated with water before it will move into the silt layer. Then—if you have enough moisture—if you can keep it coming in, it will finally penetrate the silt layer and move down below it. When the plant wants to pull moisture back up, the task becomes nearly impossible if water didn't get past the silt layer. It has to complete the saturation process before water can wick back into the top. Farmers who knew enough to mix the volcanic dust into the top six inches of soil didn't have the problem created by those using a moldboard plow.

Any time you get a different consistency in terms of texture, you are impeding water movement. You can get some sediments near the surface if the soil is not kept open. The first key to keeping pore space open is to keep a proper calcium saturation. The second key to keeping it open is to minimize compaction. And a third key is to offset compaction if indeed it occurs. A water penetration problem is also a root penetration problem. When you begin to see a uniform brown color throughout the topsoil layer, you can know that something is working in the right direction. When the lower portion is gray or yellow in appearance, it indicates that soil will need extra help. A soil conditioner works well in this regard. Just keep the top 6.75 inches open and we have effectively canceled out the need to worry in terms of initial water penetration. But when the top is skinned off down to a subsoil level, then new problems arrive. Roots will not penetrate properly unless hardpans are eliminated.

Basically, the farm publications do not deal in soil biology. Perhaps the reason is nobody is making enough money on microbes to be able to pay for the advertising or to pay the people to do the articles. It seems the big money is still in selling herbicides and pesticides, which rate so much advertising space. Of course there are those professionals who say that farmers still aren't using enough phosphate and potassium, so there is no need to worry about all these other things, like soil biology.

Most of the people in mainline companies imply that using natural systems is old fashioned. They feel it won't work in today's agriculture. They say you can't use natural systems because it would be tantamount to going back to the mule and the garden plow, and neither enables mega-farm management. Well, I am not just talking about that kind of a natural system—I stress natural systems that *work* in a modern operation. You have to look at the natural cycles in nature to use the biology of the soil properly.

There are cycles in nature and one of them is the nitrogen cycle. Rain will provide a certain amount of nitrogen from the air, reportedly 4 to 5%. This blessing is available in a form the plant can use. Of course, manures go into the soil and confer nitrogen on the nutrient complex. Nitrogen can be fixed in the soil biologically by *Rhizobium* bacteria. There are other forms of microbes and soil life that fix nitrogen, including the algae. We can harvest nitrogen from both plants and animals and recycle it as much as possible. In the soil, there are systems that bring nitrogen back out. Chemically, it goes from ammonia to nitrite to nitrate. Nitrogen is used in forming proteins. It escapes the soil as nitrogen oxide in a gaseous form. If bacteria fail to break it down again, it may re-enter the atmosphere. Nature's cycles—carbon and nitrogen—are more wondrous than anything man can account for.

Academia can take 180 bushels of corn and show the amount of nutrients used by the crop according to the number of growth days. According to these data, 19 pounds of nitrogen are taken in by the corn during the first 25 days. We also hear it stressed about having phosphate on the soil for seed production, or the need to have phosphate early for corn. In the first 25 days, a 180-bushel corn crop takes four pounds of P_2O_5 out of the soil. In the first 25 days, it also takes 22 pounds of potassium. But what do we hear stressed when we talk about raising a 180-bushel corn crop? The term is nitrogen, nitrogen, nitrogen. Yet it takes only 19 pounds of nitrogen for the first 25 days of that above-mentioned corn crop. But it takes 22 pounds of potassium in the same first 25 days for the same production record. The same corn crop takes more potassium than nitrogen during the first 25 days. At 50 days, the calculated intake is 103 pounds of nitrogen and 126 pounds of potassium. Yet we will come in and put on 200 pounds of nitrogen and, say, 90 pounds of potassium or less is enough. How can we do that? If you have good potassium levels in the soil, it works well. On the 75th day of 125 day corn, 198 pounds of potassium will have been taken up, as will 178 pounds of nitrogen. At 100 days, the numbers are 226 pounds of nitrogen and 234 pounds of potassium. At 125 days, nitrogen and potash basically balance out, 240 for nitrogen and 240 for potash.

Versatility & Industry in the Soil

Every saltspoonful of soil on this planet contains at least two billion microbes. [A recent survey showed that there are more bacteria on and in every person's body than there are human beings on earth.] That is an incomparably larger population than those of the few microbial species we believe to be nuisances. Just as the astronomical hordes of bacteria covering our persons have no ill effects, and indeed are useful to us, so the microbial community in the soil is exquisitely well adjusted for coexistence with the plants, and animals, that it supports.

One of the key functions of soil microorganisms is to break down dead plant and animal tissues and return their nutrient chemicals to the soil. Yet in high summer a field of, say, turnips or potatoes can grow vigorously in intimate contact with billions of creatures specifically capable of destroying these vegetables. Only if and when the tissue has died can the scavenger organisms operate, and then they do so swiftly and efficiently. As with our skin inhabitants, there is a disturbing lesson here for those who believe in shattering the natural balance of the microbial world by chemical overkill.

—Bernard Dixon
Magnificent Microbes *(1976)*

Any time you overuse ammonia nitrogen, you cut off a portion of the potassium uptake. It is absolutely necessary to leave plenty of room for potassium because corn is going to take more potassium than nitrogen until the last 25 days in the growth cycle.

On soybeans at 40 days, a 50-bushel crop takes 7.6 pounds of nitrogen and 6.1 pounds of potassium. It takes more nitrogen in this case, but remember, microbes are supplying 50 to 70% of the nitrogen requirement. If we look at what has to come from the soil, even if it is half, we are talking about 3.8 pounds of nitrogen versus 6.1 potash. Nitrogen gets well ahead of potash, but when you look at a 50-bushel bean crop, you need 257 pounds of nitrogen and 187 pounds of potash. But of that 257 pounds of nitrogen, at least 50% of it probably came from the soil.

Now consider a 135-bushel per acre grain sorghum crop. The first 20 days take nine pounds of nitrogen, and 18 pounds of potassium. After 40 days, grain sorghum will have taken in 70 pounds of nitrogen and 121 pounds of potassium. After 60 days, the numbers say 130 pounds of nitrogen and 206 pounds of potassium. At 85 days, it is 157 versus 245—almost 100 pounds more potassium than nitrogen. At 95 days, the numbers are 185 pounds of nitrogen and 258 pounds of potassium. It becomes obvious that potassium significantly contributes to a grain sorghum yield in terms of pounds per acre. But how many poor yields of grain sorghum are blamed on potassium deficiency?

Calcium and phosphorus requirements in alfalfa production should be strongly considered. Potassium also has to be stressed, but in first cut alfalfa, yielding 2.35 tons, there will be 136 pounds of nitrogen, 50 to 70% of which came from the air. There will be 31 pounds of phosphates, 124 pounds of potassium and 50 pounds of calcium. A second cutting at 2.1 tons means 11 pounds of nitrogen, 24 pounds of phosphate and 107 pounds of potassium.

In the third cutting, 2.03 tons, and in a fourth cutting, 1.5 tons—now an eight ton total from four cuttings—the breakdown is 415 pounds of nitrogen, at least half of which came from the *Rhizobium* symbiont, 94 pounds of phosphorus, 401 pounds of potassium, 151 pounds of calcium, 36 pounds of magnesium and 26 pounds of sulfur. Convert sulfur to sulfate—26 times three—it turns out to be 78 pounds of sulfate sulfur versus 94 pounds of phosphate phosphorus. Sulfate is needed almost in as large an amount as is phosphate, even on alfalfa.

We apply phosphorus all the time, and it doesn't normally leach out. But do we really need to be concerned about the sulfur? We most certainly do. The crops need it.

Corn is one of our highest yielding plants, yet it is only 2% efficient in utilizing sunlight at 150 bushels per acre. Theoretically, corn should be able to produce 400 bushels per acre. As far as using the microbial activity in the soil, clovers, soybeans and alfalfa require different types of bacteria, and they have to be the correct *Rhizobium* species in order to do their best.

Microbes in a healthy acre of soil will weigh as much as an average sized cow. The soil is alive and it has to be alive in order to get efficiency from fertilizer inputs. If that soil is not fully active, there will be less efficiency from the fertilizers applied.

We all hear nitrate nitrogen is what the plant uses. Well, if we didn't have the microbes there to convert it, it would never achieve the right form. We add P_2O_5 phosphate to the soil. Microbes convert it and combine it with hydrogen before the plant can use it as a food source. If we put phosphate on and in the soil and have no microbial conversion, the plant will starve.

William A. Albrecht fairly chafed at the statement that humus isn't necessary. He said, "People who say that don't know what they are talking about!" However, to say that you have to have a huge amount of humus is also mistaken. If you take all the humus out of a soil and try to grow a plant, nothing will happen. But put the smallest amount of humus back into that soil, and plants will start to grow again. I have never seen a soil test that didn't show at least some humus. Admittedly, some soils are very low in humus, but I haven't seen one for which we couldn't measure and find some humus.

From experience, there is a real possibility that you can actually overdo the microbial activity in the soil just as much as you can overdo anything else. One of the most talked-about life forms in the world is called fungi. Fungi tolerate acid soils below pH 6. Bacteria, on the other hand, survive well above pH 7. But both do well on a soil that has balanced nutrients and the resulting pH of around 6.3 to 6.5.

One microbial life form that can be observed often, especially by farmers who grow corn, is actinomycetes. These are intermediate between bacteria and fungi. When you work the soil and detect that good fresh soil smell, actinomycetes are at work. In spring you can dig out a piece of cornstalk that lies buried and you see a kind of white mold. That, by scientific name, is actinomyces.

Another microbial life form people do not talk about very much is algae. Some algae can fix nitrogen and some of them carry on a brand of photosynthesis. Microbial animal life in the soil includes protozoa and nematodes. Nematodes are eel-like in shape. They can be serious parasites, but it must be remembered that there are hundreds and hundreds of types of nematodes. Very few of them present problems. Most nematodes in the soil are beneficial. There is an analysis for nematodes. It involves a microscopic count of all the various types. If the soil chemistry is not balanced, a nematode that is actually beneficial to the soil may become parasitic. It can take from the plant what it actually should be getting from the soil. Nematodes are generally not the problem in heavy soils that they are in light, sandy soils.

At least 70% of the aerobic bacteria, the ones that need oxygen, work in the top two inches of a soil. And 70% of the humus in a soil is formed in the top two inches. That should tell us something. It takes aerobic bacteria to account for humus formation. All humus is formed in the top five inches or so of a soil system. This is basically as deep as the fencepost rots. Below that, there is insufficient oxygen. Where oxygen is lacking, anaerobic bacteria predominate. They get their oxygen by breaking down residues. When microbes must break down other materials to obtain oxygen, you don't get the right carbon-nitrogen ratio, and you don't get humus build-up. So if you take your residues and crops that are grown on top and turn them down eight or nine inches, you have canceled out the overall ability of microorganisms to make or maintain humus levels.

It takes an average of one pound of nitrogen to break down 100 pounds of crop residue. If you can get that ratio with corn stover and wheat stubble, you can form humus. It really works out to be about 20 parts or less carbon to one part nitrogen. Straight manures are generally less than 10 to 1.

As residues break down, the correct carbon to nitrogen ratio falls to somewhere between 10 to 1 and 20 to 1. In other words, if you have a lot of sawdust that you want to put on your field, you need to determine what the carbon content of the sawdust is. It is probably somewhere between 200 and 400 to 1 in terms of the carbon to nitrogen that is in it. Let's figure it is 200 to 1 because that is easier to calculate. That means you have one part nitrogen for every 200 parts carbon. You would have to use an extra 9 pounds of nitrogen to break down every 200 pounds of sawdust.

An old Albrecht rule of thumb says the microbes eat at the table first. This means they take all the nutrients a plant normally might use and utilize them first or until they no longer need them. If residue decomposition needs the nutrients, then there will be none for the plant. There always has to be enough for the microbes as well as for the crop. Microbes have to convert nitrogen and other nutrients into the right form before the plant gets its requirement.

Since we are talking about organisms, let's look at decomposition of organic residues with release of nutrient element constituents. To me, that is important and it is a natural cycle, but you can speed up that cycle by overusing nitrogen. When you overuse nitrogen and burn out humus, you release nutrient elements tied up in organic residues and eventually the elements that are constituent parts of humus.

Soil organisms are necessary to form humus in the soil, and to improve the physical properties of soils. Organisms help keep that soil friable. It is the same thing if you put mulch over a really hard soil. It loosens it up. Here, microbes do the work on the underside of the mulch.

There is a difference between mulching and working residues into the soil. If you put mulch on top, then you have the bottom of the mulch and the top of the soil where the microbes and the mulch come in contact to break down the mulch. Such an arrangement does not cause all the nitrogen to be confiscated for decomposition purposes. As soon as you work mulch into the soil, you have permitted all kinds of microbial contact, allowing more nutrients to be digested by the microbes as a part of the increased decomposition process. This can cause nitrogen to be short for the growing crop, unless enough extra nitrogen is applied to match the need.

When you apply manures and composts, potassium and phosphate will increase in the soil by more than what is found in the manure. This is a consequence of plant nutrient release from insoluble, inorganic soil minerals—in other words, from the decomposed rock, or past fertilizer nutrients that have been "tied up" in the soil.

Soil mycorrhizae are fungi in the soil. They actually extend the root system of a plant. Mycorrhizae establish and enter the plant, and in turn the plant feeds the mycorrhizae in terms of the nutrients it needs. The mycorrhiza also conveys nutrients to the plant. One of the nutrients is phosphate. In short, mycorrhizae are plant feeders.

In 15-year studies with pines and oaks, researchers found that broadcast application of high amounts of commercial nitrogen to feed the trees will kill all the mycorrhizal fungi in the soil. Pine trees need mycorrhizae. Even if use of commercial nitrogen is ceased, mycorrhizae will not come back until boron has been increased to the toleration point. Once you get boron up where it is supposed to be, then you can bring back mycorrhiza fungi.

In the late 1970s, I had a client in southeast Missouri with whom I had worked for a couple of years. His son graduated from an ag college in another state with a major in plant science and a minor in agronomy. He was there each year when recommendations were given for his dad's farm. Farm prices were low and he wanted to farm, but right now he needed a job. He said to me, "You know, if it would work out, I would like to work with you." I hired him to pull samples and work with me. One day while working the same farm together, we stopped to eat lunch. He said, "You know, Neal, I have worked for you a couple of years. It took me 18 months or so to get my head straightened out. What you were telling me wasn't matching up with what I had been taught in school. I had to start seeing examples and watching and looking at the soils to learn how what you said applied. If someone had said, you need to know about cation exchange capacity and base saturation, I would have replied that I knew about that. Our textbook had a section on exchange capacity, and it had a section on base saturation percentages, but it did not tell us how to use either on the farm. The problem was the professors didn't understand how to teach us to use it either. I never really learned how to use exchange capacity and base

---

Revelations of Species

"Microscopic examination of the small feeding roots of any plant growing on a virgin soil," says S.C. Hood, "will show a network of fungus mycelia over the root surface. The thickness and density of this net will vary with the plant and the soil conditions. On most herbaceous plants it consists of two layers. The outer one is made up of mostly brown or gray septate (sectioned) hyphae spreading over the root surface and sending strands into the surrounding soil. This outer layer is made up of most Basidiomycetes. There are often tangles of mycelia in the surrounding soil, containing small rhizomorphs (root-like bodies) which present different forms and colors, according to the species represented.

"It has been fully demonstrated that this symbiosis is not involved in the process of photosynthesis, since the production of fiber and other carbohydrate materials goes on whether fungi are present or not. It is, therefore, a fair hypothesis that this fungus-plant root symbiosis of mycorrhiza promotes the production of amino acids for building of the protein molecules."

—*William A. Albrecht*
The Albrecht Papers, Volume III *(1989)*

saturation until I started to work with you. I didn't learn it sooner because of all the roadblocks that had been put in my head. But when you go from farm to farm, it gets to the point where you can't deny it anymore. Even though you were taught one way, you just have to realize it wasn't the right way."

It is ingrained in academia that all they need is pH, phosphate and potash. I have conducted training programs about calcium-magnesium use. It usually lasts a half day. I take what University of Wisconsin says about calcium-magnesium, what the University of Iowa says, what the University of Missouri says, and what various universities say, based on what they write up in their research publications. I read it to the farmers in the room because so much of it is exactly opposite of what I am telling them. The universities teach that if the pounds are found in the soil, you are okay because by putting on N, P and K the pounds will release. They don't look at base saturation. Basically, with every university, what they write on calcium-magnesium will tell you that if you have a high magnesium soil, it makes no difference; and second, you can't do anything about it anyway. They will tell you that you can't change a high magnesium soil and get the magnesium out of it.

I have clients who started with me in the late 1970s. They had 65% calcium and 25% magnesium. In five to six years they had 65% calcium and 15% magnesium. You can't get magnesium out of the soil if your calcium is below 60% base saturation. I have seen experimental farms at certain universities in the Midwest that have less than 60% saturation of calcium. They have used nitrogen so long they have driven calcium out. When they put on lime, often they put on high magnesium lime. As a consequence, their calcium levels never reach the Albrecht minimum. In western U.S. soils, when they need lime, they rationalize that keeping the pH down is the key to success, for which reason they go to gypsum (calcium sulfate) instead of calcium carbonate.

In reality calcium sulfate under such conditions will not properly adjust the calcium content in the soil. In medium to

Symbiotic Relationship

It is probable that this symbiotic relation began when the first primitive plant forms left the primordial sea and took to the land. There were primitive forms of fungi and algae, both of which had developed in water. When cast on dry land, as separates, both were helpless. The fungi could not make carbohydrates. The algae could not secure mineral nutrients from the rocks. But united in a partnership, both could survive. The algae made carbohydrates for both, and the fungi extracted from the rocks the mineral elements needed by both of them.

[There is nothing to suggest that this relationship does not persist to the present, especially in the lichens, the first builders of soil. In their development of complicated structures, higher plants kept a part of this early relationship.]

—S.C. Hood
Hood Laboratory Report, private papers,
Acres U.S.A. collection

heavy soils with base saturation below 58% calcium, gypsum will not successfully drive out sodium or magnesium because calcium sulfate will not take calcium levels high enough above the 60% saturation required for this program to properly work. This is further explained in a concise way in the video, *Hands-On Agronomy.* Consultants tell me it has helped them convince one after another of their clients, who took time to watch the video, how important it is to lime calcium deficient soils even if the pH is considered high.

There is a phrase that isn't used very often these days. It is antagonistic action against plant pathogens. This comes very close to saying, with Albrecht, that the anatomy of dealing with bacterial and insect attack is seated in fertility management, and not in buying toxic materials from Dow Chemical or Monsanto.

This makes exchange capacity and base saturation the most important discovery since van Helmont grew trees in a tub to nail down the role of earth minerals and air in plant production. In short, the chemistry has to be right so that the biology in the soil can function. Chemistry provides the physical structure of a soil so that it can provide the correct environment for biology. When soil microorganisms can do their job, the soil itself will in fact fight plant pathogens. Unfortunately, this objective does not mean single factor activity.

Still, it isn't unusual to hear a farmer say, once on the program, that he has less insect, disease and weed problems. One farmer told me, "The year you got me started using copper, I didn't have the problem with wheat rust that I used to have." Copper has a reputation for controlling rust as well as "Take-all" disease in wheat.

The better the organisms in the soil work, the more strength they will confer on the plant. In any case, removal of toxicity from the soil—either the residue of pesticides or over-applications of minerals that rely on homeostatic control—falls within the purview of the microbial function.

The soil is alive and it has to be kept alive in order to deliver top yields and quality.

How can we know whether we have the right environment for the microbes? A good test is the earthworm population. With the right soil environment, not only are microorganisms going to do better, but also the earthworms and macroorganisms will do better as well. Elliott C. Roberts of the Lawn Institute once made an evaluation of live microbes in the soil. He said that there are approximately 900 billion microorganisms per pound of healthy soil. That is why we talk about a microorganism weight equal to an average size cow in every acre of soil. That is why failure to return adequate residues to the soil is tantamount to starving the microbes. This, in turn, will starve the plant in terms of its ability to get what it needs. The microbes have to do the converting. One of the laws of thermodynamics states that life can come only from life. If the soil is dead biologically, nothing is going to grow from it. The soil is the plant's stomach. If we do not have the microorganisms in our stomach to do the job, how are we going to live? Hans Peter Rausch of Germany put it this way. "Bacteria and other microflora in the area of the plant's root system, through which it receives nutrients from the soil, belong to the same group of bacteria and other microbes found in the intestines of humans and animals." The very microbes that are digesting nutrients in the area of plant roots are the same ones that help digest the food we eat.

My wife was bitten by a spider, so they put her on some antibiotics. After she got over the spider bite, she had a terrible, terrible cold. We went to the doctor, albeit not to the same fellow who prescribed the penicillin. He said she should have taken lactobacillus and built her system back up. What she did in the earlier instance was kill off the beneficial microbes in her treatment of the spider bite. Her body wasn't able to provide the materials she needed to fight off the cold germs.

Earthworms are often used as an example of the biological health of the soil. I look for fields where earthworm castings are thick. Frankly, you don't see a lot of corn fields heavy with earthworm castings. However, you will find somewhat more soybean fields with significant amounts of earthworm castings. There are times when I can take a probe of soil and collect castings in abundance from the same area. Just take a three-by-five card and rake the top of the casting pile onto it. I have purposely collected enough earthworm castings for a soil sample in a number of fields, and ordered out audits to see what the difference was between soil and castings. This has been done in several counties in southeast Missouri.

It is often said that when the earthworm emerges from the soil, it actually balances out those castings left behind with a better concentration of nutrients than contained in the soil itself. But instead, our soil analysis shows that if the soil is high in calcium, the castings will be high in calcium. If the soil is low in calcium and high in magnesium, the castings will be low in calcium and high in magnesium. In terms of base saturation per-

Hands-On Agronomy

centages, the percentages have been improved, but not normally enough to solve the excesses or deficiencies. What the worm had there to digest is what you are going to find, except for one thing. The castings contain a higher concentration of micronutrients. The point to be made here is that when you get microbes and earthworms to work in the soil, a new level of micronutrient availability is foreordained. Just be sure you supply the minimum needs for micronutrients until the soil tests show there is a sufficient supply for the crop to be grown.

Perhaps some readers have heard about the college that didn't recognize micronutrients, to which agronomist John Porter answered, "But the plants do, and they didn't go to college." Those castings not only concentrate micronutrients, the earthworms in fact write a meal ticket that enables microorganisms to do better. Eight to ten earthworms per square foot means up to one million earthworms per acre. One report states that a square foot of castings will contain 2.5 times more magnesium than the soil, three times more calcium, five times more nitrogen, seven times more phosphorous or 11 times more potash. Frankly, I have not found double rates of anything until testing the trace elements. I am not saying that earthworms are not valuable. I am saying that whenever you see results such as those mentioned above, you have to ask a few more questions.

Earthworms do help aerate the soil. They provide avenues for air and conduits for water, not just for entry down but also for capillary return.

Most producers have various types of soil with which to work. None can be so remotely located that a "magic fertilizer" salesman can't find them. This American original has a material to put on. He says if the farmer puts it on, he can quit using other fertilizers. There are some products that are types of gypsum with compost in them. There are humates that work wonders. There are heavy clays with a high micronutrient content and an even higher exchange capacity. In terms of buying those things, I tell the client, "Until you get a calcium saturation between 60 and 70%, and magnesium between 10 and 20%, you are really never going to know whether these products measure up or not." When the physical structure is out of whack, or the nutrient balance is off, micronutrient products which generally help to stimulate either microbes or plant growth are not likely to do the best job.

A man and his two sons had me sample their farm. When I returned to deliver the results, I sat down and told them what they should do. When we were finished, the father said, "Well, Neal, I hope this won't make you mad, but we are not going to do any of that." It didn't make me mad, but it sure made me curious. He told me about a company that had a certain product. He intended to start using that product at the recommended rate of 300 pounds per acre for several years, and then he would cut back to 200 pounds per acre. He stopped using any commercial fertilizer except nitrogen. He had harvested some excellent crops based on his past yields. Now he wanted to see what the nutrient levels were in every one of his fields. "They tell me that when I put 300 pounds on," he said, "next year my phosphate and potash and other nutrients will be better than they are this year. All we are going to do is put that 300 pounds of material on and use some nitrogen." He asked if I thought he would get into trouble with this, and I said that he had been growing crops up to now, and with the levels he had, I didn't think he was going to achieve his top yields. If he had told me he was going to use this product in the first place, I could have told him in which fields he could expect to achieve better results, and which ones he wouldn't improve as we discussed each sample. As it was, this was important enough to go back over the samples again for just that purpose.

The next year father and sons had me come back and sample the whole farm again, The father said, "Neal, on every field where you said we would see a difference, we could see it. On every field where you said we wouldn't, we couldn't tell it was worth putting it on there." Where they could see the difference was where the calcium was between 60 and 70% base saturation, and where magnesium was between 10 and 20%.

Hands-On Agronomy

I learned that from a fellow up in Wisconsin who was selling a humate fertilizer while there to help put on a soil fertility seminar. During an exchange, he said, "I can't understand it. I sell humates to farmers and some of them come out to meet me and pat me on the back and say that this is the greatest stuff ever. I go right down the road to another farm, and this guy is ready to run me off with a shotgun because 'all I did was take his money.' Now maybe you could say that one farmer paid attention, and the other one didn't. But I'll have a farmer who will say that the humates worked just great over here but over there on that field it looks like he threw his money away." The key was the nutrient balance. He went back to the farms where there were fields that worked, and some that didn't. He told them that for the humate to work well, the calcium had to be up above 60%, and the magnesium had to be in the 10 to 20% range, and proved it by using a detailed soil analysis.

The humate is a material that generally delivers response via its micronutrients. These nutrients are seldom limiting factors until calcium and magnesium are available in proper supply. Inputs such as humates stimulate the microbial activity because they contain a lot of nutrients we do not know how to measure. We seldom have the soils the way we need them. What we really do is get them in the minimum basic shape, and then we start applying what I call a broad spectrum micronutrient rich material. At that point we enter the twilight zone of not knowing how to measure.

Those broad-spectrum micronutrient, mineral-rich fertilizers support higher microbial populations in the soil. So far commercial agriculture makes little use of these materials because they are "too expensive." Most of the time only people who work with microbial inoculants and stimulants invoke the use of these materials, but the gap between knowledge and field application is closing.

It may be that we take the numbers game too seriously at times. We see this when we leave the time honored plains of university agronomy and climb to the frontier uplands of biologicals. Using a biological stimulant calls for having the basics in place, albeit with room enough for new parameters. In terms of phosphorus, for instance, if the numbers reach 236 or 238, I won't tell a farmer operating on a minimum fertilization-type program that he needs phosphorus when using a biological stimulant in his program. It now becomes the function of microbial activity to release enough phosphorus, which in any case is plentiful as warehoused in the soil. Then the perceived deficiency will not materialize. Yet if the so-called commercial fertilizer is to stand alone, the numbers should go up to 300. Our objective is to take care of major deficiencies, after which the microbes help to take care of the rest. We keep on monitoring the situation, of course. If it somehow starts to go backwards, there has to be a reason. I cannot think of a thing that will cause the phosphate level to go backwards by using a biological or microbial stimulant, but there is one thing that can cause a biological stimulant not to work well, namely an over-supply of undigested residues. Without a proper decay system, there will not be an adequate release of the phosphates held in escrow by those residues. But once a minimum desired value is achieved— as long as you use a reliable biological stimulant—maximum buildup is no longer indicated as a great requirement. In fact, a good microbial program may eliminate phosphate application on soils initially showing an adequate level for a matter of four or five years, but always based on adequate levels being there, as shown on a reliable soil analysis.

Trade laboratories are now starting to measure the microbial content of soils. The cost can be high, but considered in terms of one sample of good soil and one bad soil, the bite out of a fertilizer budget is not astronomical.

Bi-o-log-ic / bī-e-'läj-ik / *n* [G *biologie,* fr. *bi-* + *-logie* -logy] 1 a biological product used in medicine 2 a biological product used in agriculture and/or animal husbandry 3 special products that rely on life to lend an assist to crop production chiefly via nutrient release, nitrogen fixation and several leaf feeding and inoculation processes 4 products based on growth hormone principles, namely gibberellins, auxins and cytokinins 5 in general, life products that impact on the energy exchange of chromosomes and nucleotides

16

An Environment for Microbes

I HAVE WORKED WITH FARMERS who use all types of materials. One product out of Utah is called Azomite. Another out of Mississippi has the trade name Flora-Stim. A humate out of New Mexico was called Clodbuster. Colorado furnishes material with the trade name Planters II. There are Leonardite products out of North Dakota, sea kelps out of Norway and the east and west coast, and algae out of Klamath Falls, Oregon. I could mention perhaps many other products—each with a purpose, each of value if used as directed under the right conditions. The pages of *Acres U.S.A.* advertise many products which have validity if used properly. But if used on a soil that is not balanced with the proper levels of soil nutrients, one may be hard pressed to see a profitable response. Much the same is true of the biological stimulants. If you don't have the right conditions for biologicals to work, they are not going to do a good job. A product will work great in one field and not at all in the next because the minimum condition has not been met. But if the soil is right, biologicals are easy to work with and the easiest to make the recommendations for. The late Jim McHale, a former Secretary of Agriculture in Pennsylvania, was among the first to prescribe biological products based on achieving maximum balance for major and secondary nutrients as a prelude. Before further comment, perhaps what is meant by the term biological stimulant would be helpful. These are products designed to stimulate the microbial population that are already present in a given soil.

I had a client who grew sweet corn. He decided to use a biological seed treatment on his crop. The directions read, mix ten parts water with one part biological and mist on the seed. He "didn't have time" to mist the seed, so he just soaked it in that stuff and planted it. In the rows with those seeds, the sweet corn didn't come up to a stand at all. He just overdid it in terms of that inoculant. The company will tell you if you soak it, you will get a worse response, not a better response. If you don't know for sure, just follow the instructions. Just because a little is good does not mean that more will be better.

I planted green peas in my garden, using the same biological. One row was a control. I soaked the seeds with the 10 to 1 mixture for the second row. And I planted the peas in the third row after spraying the material over the row where they would be planted. The peas were planted in cold soil. A biological inoculant should cause those to emerge faster if the material is used properly. One morning the row that I sprayed over the top was up from one end to the other. The other two rows were barely popping through. The next day it was still uneven as to how they came up. By the third day, they were all up. The treated ones were a day and a half to two days ahead in terms of growth.

There are other advantages to biologicals besides getting the plants up faster. I believe there are some health advantages just because we stimulate the microbes, and there are some advantages to getting the root down deeper and faster. After all, the plant is going to send its roots down before it pushes growth out the top. If you stimulate faster root growth, you can get the plant to come up faster.

A lot of the companies that sell biologicals want to do all the work with the farmer themselves. As a result, there are a number of these materials that I have never worked with and probably a lot more of them that I have never heard of. The ones I am most familiar with are hydrogen oxide chelated trace minerals and specific plant extracts. In other words, the fabricators take minerals, plant extracts and hydrogen oxide and put them together in certain combinations. All have their own formulas. One product many clients use makes use of four different seaweed extracts, two fish extracts and one extract from corn. All the extracts supply basically a kinin response. Growers can view it much as they would a cytokinin effect. Cytokinin is a growth regulator that governs the germination of a seed.

I have observed biologicals from almost every point of view including that of the farmer, the formulator and the consultant. Several companies have hired me to help solve their field problems.

If you have a soil that has the right amount of minerals specific to available calcium and phosphorus, and you have four to five inches of crumbly soil with few residues that have to be broken down, you can use a biological inoculant both in fall and spring and not have to use a heavy amount of commercial nitrogen. In some cases I have had a nitrate test run and found that there is enough nitrate nitrogen, so that no extra nitrogen is required for the nitrogen replacement product to work.

I have worked with clients who began using biologicals in 1975 and raised corn every year, and never used a commercial nitrogen at all to do it. When they started they were not organic or natural farmers in any sense of the word. They were simply commercial farmers. There were not thousands of them. There were not even hundreds. There were just a few of them out there. Needless to say, it is hard to find university documentation on these materials. In 1978, I met a microbiologist named

Dr. Dwayne Vance at North Texas State University. One of the companies hired me to join him on a trip to Europe. We were to make presentations to the various organizations and administrations that had say-so over sales in Europe.

I was hired because of my consulting experience with biologicals right in the fields and he as the laboratory expert. He had taken some of the biologicals and run a sealed vacuum test. A sealed vacuum test involves putting soil in a growth chamber. The only thing that gets in is whatever is pumped in. They start with the soil and pump argon into the chamber. When you pump argon in, it drives all the nitrogen out. Then they inoculate the soil with a biological. No nitrogen increase shows up in that soil at all. The argon is then pumped out, and air is pumped back into the chamber. At this point they start to see a nitrogen increase in the soil. No commercial nitrogen is added. Only the activity between the biological, the soil and the air is involved.

They can also start by having air in the chamber. The microbial stimulant is added. It starts to work immediately, and nitrogen levels start to increase. What that means, and what Vance was saying, is that there is some mechanism that enables the plant to get the nitrogen it needs from the soil, with the nitrogen coming directly from the air and not from a commercial source.

Dr. Vance visited the Sloan-Kettering Institute about a month before we went to Europe. He said that Sloan-Kettering had already developed a material for soil application that would take nitrogen directly from the air, into the soil and into the plant. They reported that the only problem was the energy source. It was so expensive that commercial nitrogen was lower priced.

I also had the chance to work with Dr. Robert Fischer from Virginia Commonwealth University. He is a microbiologist, perhaps one of the best in the United States on the workings of these products in the soil. DuPont also hired him to consult on various microbial development programs. He became interested in biological products because he found that if used at the proper rate, he could calibrate in hours how much faster radish

Hands-On Agronomy

Growth Hormones

There are three groups of growth hormones, each of which can interact to affect plant changes and growth patterns. There are the *gibberellins*. Unfortunately, these degrade rapidly and lack functional stability. They can easily be produced by plants if nutrition is ample and proper. There are the *auxins*. These are very complex compounds related directly to environment and character of nutrition. They decompose or can be degenerated rapidly in each type of environment. . . . Most herbicide compounds are auxin-like, albeit without nature's finely tuned governing capacity or application apparatus.

Last, there are *cytokinins*. These are produced in culture systems under laboratory control. They are stable, natural, and exchangeable to the biological energy field of soil and plant systems. They are basically cell dividers. That is to say, they stimulate cell division and enlargement. They cause differentiation of plant tissues and bud formation. They regenerate shoots from root segments, increase rate of germination, and induce flowering. They reverse the effect of plant inhibitors such as excess cold or heat, or improper light conditions. They offset coumarins that prevent germination and eliminate the need for infrared stimulus or magnetic effects on seed germination.

Cytokinins used in all areas of life systems can increase the capacity of those systems to utilize fertilizers 20 to 30% better. Cytokinins stabilize and enhance chlorophyll efficiency and tend to improve protein synthesis and function in leaves of plants. Thus they increase photosynthesis capacity. In relying on this fact the farmer must make certain that the soil's nutritional capacity is equal to the task of filling the increased demand for leaf production. Cytokinins mobilize plant nutrients and tend to draw elemen-

> tal nutrients to the areas of application, either on seeds, transplants, or leaves. Finally, the cytokinin input from any good eco-farming product has the effect of delaying senescence or early die-back of plants because now the plant can overcome and correct nutritional deficiencies.
> —*Charles Walters & C.J. Fenzau*
> Eco-Farm: An Acres U.S.A. Primer *(1975)*

seeds would sprout which he called the cytokinin response. His cotyledon studies, published in *Acres U.S.A.*, are classics. His work on lettuce seed sprouting is also a matter of record. But when he tried to take his findings into the field, he really got discouraged. We sat up one night until 5:00 a.m. talking about what had happened with biologicals.

From the initial work in 1975-78, I thought that by 1985 every farmer in the United States would be familiar with biologicals. Unfortunately, many roadblocks surfaced to sour the situation. In one meeting, Vance told of the many legal and commercial barriers invoked to keep biologicals out of the mainstream. He saw the educational system as the main drawback. By the mid-1980s, it had become a case of the school of sciences versus the school of agriculture.

"There is a real rift between us," one professor told me. "When you enter course study in preparation for microbiology, chemistry comes first. But the students who are going to major in agronomy are treated differently. They get to take an easier chemistry course for their second unit. Those in the school of science have to take a harder course. Everybody ought to take the hard course because they would come out and understand the same things we do. As it is, they really didn't get the basics down in terms of all the required chemistry. So what really happens is that there is a gulf between the microbiology department and the agronomy department. That is why you are never going to find very many agronomists who understand and accept how biologicals work."

One major state university had three different experimental farms. They were going to test two of the biological products I am talking about. They had to provide all the information about how they ran the tests. When I went there to see it, the control plot was better than where they had used either of the biological inoculants. I had never seen that before. They had a control, a gallon per ten acres of each biological, quarter-rate fertilizer, half-rate fertilizer and full-rate fertilizer. They ran soil tests before they started, and it was pH, phosphate and potash all the way. It was in the contract that the company could also run soil tests. Dr. Fischer went down and took the samples. They told him they already had soil tests, and they didn't want him to take any more. He said that it was in the contract, and he was going to take soil samples out of each and every plot, which he did. The fellow in charge got angry and upset. He got angry because you could see exactly what those fellows could do. The control had a better exchange capacity and a better humus content than any one of the plots on which the biological had been used. The plot that received the biologicals had the lowest organic matter and the lowest exchange capacity on all three farms, and this replicated over several different plots.

They had a field day at another major eastern ag school. One part of an area that was not on the tour was used for biological tests which looked as good as those with commercial fertilizers. There was another part where all the tours came together. Everything was clearly marked. The plots where they had used biologicals were worse than the controls, much as in the prior example. The school officials kept insisting that they could not show what had been used on those plots in the past until finally a court case forced the issue. In the court case they produced research material that revealed what they had done in the past. On the very plots that they "randomly selected" for application of biologicals, they had used a program some three years earlier that left toxic cadmium levels. The biologicals were used on these exact plots. For these several reasons, what I have to say about biologicals is not based on university research.

In the area of Gibson City, Sibley and Melvin, Illinois, a dealer who sold one of the popular bio-stimulants had a good reputation. He farmed about 500 acres and he also sold seed corn. He decided to try a biological "on ten or 20 acres." He had other growers "trying it on ten or 20 acres" of corn and soybeans. Applications were made by helicopter. They sprayed 1,400 acres and then had to move to another area to spray 600 more acres. Where they sprayed the 1,400 acres, they could see a difference in the corn within a week. But on the last 600 acres, they didn't see any difference in the corn where they had sprayed. It was the same product, the same guy spraying it, too. They forgot about the water source. When they moved, they changed from one town's water to another town's water. The water they changed to had fluorine and chlorine in it. When they found that out, they switched and redid the whole 600 acres and got the results.

There are seemingly enough case reports to paper the farm country from one end to the next. Consider the experience of a farmer who used commercial nitrogen on one side of a field. The other side got no commercial nitrogen, though all of the land got hog manure. On the one side, he had 154 pounds of actual nitrogen plus hog manure. On the other side, he had hog manure and one gallon per ten acres of a bio-stimulant applied one time. This non-irrigated land had yields all the way from 170 down to 100 bushels per acre. That particular year it was somewhat dry, and the yield was 128.63 bushels per acre with 28% nitrogen. The biologically treated soil in the same field made 137.03 bushel per acre (and he didn't spend money on commercial nitrogen).

Another farmer had 1,000 acres. A dealer came to see him about using a biological on 20 acres, and the farmer made a mistake. He talked to me, and I advised him not to do it. I told him to try it on a little bit, but he used it on every acre of corn, and he didn't leave a check. It is always a mistake not to leave a check. When I was in the area in July, the corn looked great.

That fall I saw the farmer and asked him how his corn checked out. He said it actually didn't do very well. He made about 40 bushels less corn per acre than neighboring farmers. He grew corn on corn. He used the biological without any other nitrogen source whatsoever. And he only had a half inch of crumbly soil.

It comes right back to what has been said all along. When you use biologicals, remember that first of all they utilize the microbes in the soil. There might not be any microbes in the product, but they utilize microbes in the soil to do the job. The next thing to be considered is that if you don't have enough aeration, the microbes are not going to be able to work the way they must to get nitrogen out of the air. The air must be inhaled into the soil. It has to be in contact with the work site. With such products, if you don't have four or five inches of crumbly soil, or do something to achieve it, you are going to have to rely on commercial nitrogen or lose a part of your corn crop. The farmer in question told me that his leaves started turning yellow in August. I asked him how many leaves turned, and he said about four. He called the dealer and the area supervisor, but a lot of the guys selling biologicals then knew too little about nitrogen in agriculture. The supervisor said not to worry about it. Unfortunately, a non-worry disclaimer won't compensate for the loss of 40 bushels of corn per acre.

Still, there are things you can do even late in the season to avoid this situation. Even after you find four yellow leaves, if the corn is in the silking stage or before, put on 40 pounds of actual nitrogen in the form of ammonium nitrate (120 pounds of the product as sold), and you won't lose a bushel of corn. Once you get past that four-leaf stage there will be some loss. If three leaves show nitrogen deficiency, put on 30 pounds of nitrogen. If four leaves show nitrogen deficiency, put on 40 pounds of nitrogen, and if five leaves show nitrogen deficiency, the maximum amount to use is still 40 pounds of nitrogen. If you are going to fly it on, use ammonium nitrate. If you have a high-boy with drops on it, and you can get across the corn, you can use 32% liquid. The 32% can burn the corn leaves unless you get it down, and unless you get at least one-half inch of water from irrigation or rainfall, it will not be as effective as the straight ammonia nitrate due to the urea content.

The best thing to do when using a biological is to get a nitrate and ammonia analysis before the corn tassels. Be sure that you have one pound of nitrogen per 100 pounds of residues in addition to a biological. If you have 40 pounds of nitrate nitrogen in a soil and you are going to use a biological, you do not have to worry about using additional nitrogen except to decompose any corn stalks you have left. If you are certified organic and don't know what the nitrate nitrogen level is, and you are going to use a biological, then put on 40+ pounds of actual nitrogen from an organic source if you are going to raise any high nitrogen requirement crop.

In terms of legumes, soybeans, alfalfa, dry beans, you don't have to worry about four inches of crumbly soil if the biological approach is to be used. First, you don't get the big response as is the case with a high nitrogen crop. Take soybeans. Farmers who have used the biological approach can go out and put it on at planting time, one application. With adequate lime and phosphate, they will harvest about five or six bushels more beans per acre. Expect to get a better protein content in soybeans and alfalfa with these microbial or biological stimulants.

In alfalfa, if you want to know how your potassium is being taken up, take a knife and cut the alfalfa plant off at the ground. Take the top and bend it down to the tip and see if you have leaves setting on the bottom half. The better your leaves set, the better utilization of potassium you are getting. If you get up to the middle of the stem and don't have any leaves you are not getting enough potassium into that alfalfa. If that is the case for you, just try a good bio-stimulant.

Cotton is a woody type plant. While it is a high nitrogen requiring plant, it doesn't require the amount of nitrogen that corn does. It also works very well with the biologicals, with or without additional nitrogen.

A working equation for crop production runs as follows: where 200 pounds of nitrogen on corn is indicated, a maximum

Hands-On Agronomy

of 100 pounds of nitrogen on cotton is the norm. You can often find poor aeration and the magnesium levels at 20% or higher in a cotton field. Just pull up the stalk and look at the roots. You should have one tap root that goes straight down. But when that magnesium level gets up to 18 or 19%, that tap root will split in two and fork. Where farmers have applied a gallon per ten acres of an effective bio-stimulant at planting time, the tap roots will go straight down in that tight soil. Something happens that enables that plant to push the root straight on through.

Take a knife and cut through a corn stalk with a biological and another with only nitrogen. The thinnest rind will be the one with commercial nitrogen. Now if you have 2.5 inches of crumbly soil or less, the commercial nitrogen will beat the biological if you use it by itself. But if you use the biological and apply nitrogen by tassel time on such a soil, you won't lose out to the commercial nitrogen. If you have four or five inches of crumbly soil and you start out with 40 parts per million nitrate and enough added nitrogen to break down residues, you are not going to have a problem. If you probe between the rows and find that you have four or five inches of crumbly soil, don't worry. If you don't have it, and the corn is short enough, you can come through with an anhydrous applicator without any anhydrous in the tank. With the applicator's points deep—6 or 7 inches if possible—you can get some air into the soil and won't have to come with 30 or 40 pounds of additional nitrogen.

When I first started working with biologicals, I told a client, Joe Walters, M.D., in California that I was going to send him a pint of this material to use in his garden. He got excited and said, "You mean you have a material that will do that! Don't send me a pint, send me a gallon." I sent it, and then the telephone rang a few days later. It was one of his patients, the TV and movie personality, Eddie Albert. He got interested because his doctor was interested, and because he was a proponent of natural agriculture. That was in 1976. In 1978, a big company in Hawaii decided it would use the biological on corn. This was decided via contact with Eddie Albert. I tripped to Hawaii and met both the client and Eddie Albert, and together we went to look at the fields.

Up to that point, this was the hardest soil that I had ever seen. It tested 45% calcium and 40% magnesium. It needed 12 tons of lime to the acre, and they didn't have any lime. They raised 180 bushel corn in the summer, 165 bushel corn in the winter, and they took three crops of silage corn per acre off this land every year. They left check plots. They sold silage down the road to Meadow Gold Dairy and received a premium because it was fresh.

How did they get corn to grow on that soil? They used 160 pounds of nitrogen, and they also used four tons of chicken litter for each of the three crops of silage. Even so, this soil was so tough they would get a big John Deere ripper and go in and rip it out. It would come out in chunks like paving stone. Then they would water the chunks and run over them with a big disc to break them up. When the clods were reduced in size suitably, they would plant again. That is where I came in—to run a test before using a biological. Here was the scene. They had a half-inch or less of crumbly soil. It was tight and heavy with an exchange capacity between 40 and 50. There was a calcium deficiency and a magnesium excess. They put four tons of chicken litter on the entire field. They used 160 pounds of nitrogen on the so-called commercial side. They used no nitrogen and just a gallon per ten acres of the biological on the other side. They made seven bushels more corn per acre where they used the biological over where they used the commercial nitrogen.

How could they come in there and do that on such a tight soil when I am telling you all these other things? Number one is that they ripped the soil deep three times a year. Number two, the manure was put on at four tons per acre before each of the three crops of corn silage which got the microbial population working and kept the top loose enough to allow air to enter. They also aerated the soil by cultivation.

You can have all these adverse conditions and still make a biological work if you keep in mind the things related up to now.

They didn't use 40 pounds of nitrogen, but they didn't need to because they had four tons of poultry litter.

If I were to summarize these few lessons in a whiplash line or two, I would say leave a check plot, walk your fields, and see what you look at. If you farm with a certain viewpoint for 50 years, you are going to be making a mistake if you don't leave a check plot. One of my clients in Illinois farmed about 500 acres. He decided that biological stimulants worked, so he used it on every acre. One year he told me he got to wondering whether or not he would be doing better if he had kept on using commercial nitrogen. He said he didn't have any place to compare it so he just went to his neighbor and got some liquid nitrogen and put it on a field near his house. He made two rounds on a relatively even field. He harvested 12 bushels more corn where he didn't use that nitrogen. But if he had kept a test plot, all doubts could be handled year to year.

Directions for use are important. It always amazes and amuses me when a farmer decides to substitute his judgment for years of experiments most suppliers have invested in their products. I have in mind a product used in cotton production. The company would tell growers it lasts about six months. They also say for best results, put it on in spring and fall. In one case, a farmer didn't discover until he got from one end of his field to the other that he had failed to turn the sprayer on. You could see right where the application had been made and where he skipped it on that one pass through the field. Growers who take photographs can point to the stops and starts of the sprayer. Results are often that dramatic. It might not show up as much in soybeans, but it will in high nitrogen requiring crops such as wheat, cotton and corn.

I was up in Illinois one day with Eddie Albert and a group of farmers looking at soybeans. The grower had taken a field and split it into three parts. He was intending to grow soybeans on it the following year. He treated ten acres in fall, and in spring he treated the same ten acres again. Another ten acres of the same field were also treated that spring. The last ten acres received no treatment. In that part of Illinois it was standard practice to omit fertilization on soybeans. We dug up some soybeans. On the basis of nodulation alone you could tell where two applications had been made compared to none. There was triple the nodulation. It was double the nodulation where the application had been made only in the spring. Yet looking out over the field, you couldn't see a visual difference in the size or appearance of the beans at about 12 inches in height. Many a farmer has said, "No difference," even in the hopper, until he weighed the areas separately at harvest.

The results do not seem to respect geography. I have assembled records from corn plots in Virginia to tomatoes in Ohio. Each entry has its related story. Campbell's ran a test with biologicals one year, and it was "all systems go." They ran a test the second year and spent a large sum of money to have the experimental acreage hand weeded so as not to possibly flaw the test. The people who sold it to them and set it up didn't go back to counsel with them. After they got word there was a problem, the company asked me to go there. They had water standing in the fields. The plot with the gallon per ten acres was not better than the control. When I put the probe into the soil, I could see they had no aeration at all. If they had just come earlier and run something down the middles, they could have taken care of that problem.

Wheat was the first crop to receive this venturesome type of fertility assist in Illinois. Wheat harvest in the area is generally in June. A portion of a field had a fall and a spring application at a gallon per ten acres. The treatment made about ten bushels more wheat per acre than where the traditional 100 pounds of actual nitrogen had been used. If a good biological is used on wheat and a low spot presents a tell-tale yellow before the crop has headed out, think "aerial application." Fly on 40 pounds of nitrogen. It will result in an extra ten bushels of wheat per acre.

In any country, the farmer seems to expect miracles. No wonder he is sometimes a victim of foo-foo dust salesmen and so partial to snake oil. And yet the way many farmers use perfectly

Hands-On Agronomy

The Physiological Approach to Livestock Nutrition Problems

While broken bones, depraved appetite and other gross physical symptoms first called our attention to the needs of animals for minerals, bones and blood studies and balance techniques have been the tools by which quantitative needs for all-round nutrition have been established. There is ample evidence of the urgent need for many more of these physiological studies to fill in the gaps of our knowledge of the mineral nutrition of livestock. We were all amazed by the identification of a lack of *cobalt* as the cause of the losses among grazing animals in Australia, New Zealand and elsewhere, and of the minute amount of the element required to prevent the troubles. Recently, areas of cobalt deficiency have been located in the United States, (Baltzer et. al., 1941). Recently, also, large areas where *copper* deficiency is a practical problem have been discovered, apparently involving other physiological functions besides blood regeneration. Additional instances of *iron* deficiency are being uncovered, and *manganese* and even *magnesium* can no longer be neglected in certain feeding situations.

These recent discoveries regarding mineral elements teach us several things. In the first place, we cannot rest on the assumption that, aside from salt, calcium, phosphorus, and iodine in special situations, commonly fed rations will always meet mineral needs. We know of too many cases where this is not true, and we have learned that the same feed may vary widely in mineral content. More important, these recently discovered cases of mineral deficiency in practice were uncovered where the shortage was bad enough to develop acute physical symptoms which demanded attention. Are there much more widespread cases of deficiencies too mild to be detected by gross

> observations? Here we should learn a lesson from vitamin research—that the subacute troubles recognizable only by physiological tests, may be the more numerous and the more important.
>
> —*L.A. Maynard*
> *paper delivered before the American Society*
> *of Animal Production, 1941*

valid products would make anything like a secret formula whispered by a dying monk to a titled traveler pure hokum. But as Paul Harvey says, there is the rest of the story.

I recall a German baron who decided that he would use a biological stimulant. The U.S. company guaranteed him that should he experience a loss, they would make up the difference. He turned in a bill, and they sent me over there to check it out. The bill was based on a loss because the rye crop was not making heads. When I got there, I had to sludge through water halfway up my boots while in the fields. It was April, and they had an unusual amount of rain. Obviously, a biological is not going to work in such a situation because there is no air. I doubt that you are going to get anything else to work either under such conditions. Huge piles of stubble from the last crop were also in evidence. With residue that hadn't broken down and with a nitrogen shortfall, there wasn't enough nitrogen to feed the crop and break down the residue at the same time, thus the lack of grain heads.

The reports are endless. One farmer collected soybeans from the side on which he had used a biological and kept some in a box. When he harvested the other side of the field, he also kept some in a box. He marked the boxes and said, "You can blindfold me, and I can figure out which one is which." He would put some of each in a cup and take a ruler and level them off, put the beans on a postage scale and weigh them. He concluded that the beans that got the biological would weigh heavier, and indeed they did.

I recall a Texas ryegrass pasture. The grower used ammonium sulfate on most of the pasture, holding back about ten acres in each pasture where he used a biological. The root system with ammonium sulfate and the root system with the biological made a significant contrast. There was no other nitrogen source used on the side receiving the biological. He had not used commercial nitrogen in the past. Basically, the idea was to see if a biological inoculant versus ammonium sulfate would deliver a difference. And there was a difference, in favor of the biological in this case.

Biologicals and related products have their place; just don't count them as miracle products that will solve all the fertility problems of agriculture. But for farmers interested in natural systems, count these products as valuable and worthwhile tools to learn about—and use!

Hands-on / 'han(d)- zän / *adj, oft attrib* [ME, fr. OE; akin to OHG *hant* hand; akin to OHG *ana* on] 1 the act of learning by doing, as in agronomy—the primacy of practical knowledge over subjective textbook fare [*subjective,* in turn, must be defined as a product of the mind without reference to outside reality 2 a colloquial term used in agriculture for agronomists who take scientific knowledge into the field 3 manual skills in trades and farming based on physical ability mixed with practical intellectual skills

17

How Accurate
is the Soil Analysis?

TIME AFTER TIME a farmer or grower has asked, "Based on the type of soil testing you do, what would be recommended for making the highest crop yield possible on my field?"

First of all, take the needed soil tests far enough ahead to assure there is sufficient time to get the results, locate the required materials, and apply them in a timely manner. For liming materials and trace elements such as iron, manganese or copper, the best response should be expected when applied using a time frame such as applying them in the autumn prior to planting in the spring. Before the crop begins rapid growth in the spring is generally considered the proper time to sample in order to see soil fertility levels at their best. (Provided the soil is not drought stressed or large amounts of sulfur have not been applied in the last two to six months. And provided sampling can be done in order to avoid areas where nitrogen has been knifed in, or recently broadcast in large amounts over the past thirty days. This is because any of these situations could significantly lower the soil pH and make it appear that lime or potassium is needed when such is not the case.) Otherwise, if you want to consider your soil needs at the time they will be greatest and the three cautions above do not apply, sample as soon after harvest as possible.

We count on each sample received as having been taken to correctly represent the area being tested. (To assure this is correctly achieved, note and follow the instructions on taking soil samples provided in this chapter. These instructions are also available on our website at www.kinseyag.com or anyone interested can contact us and request a free copy.) Correct representation being the case, the more completely you inform us about the crop you will be raising or any factors such as compost or manure applications with an exact analysis, the better we can advise concerning needed soil amendments and fertilizers.

If the crop is to be newly planted or has been there for years, *especially if it is trees or vines*, that needs to be noted. Yields can vary widely due to climate, especially moisture availability, so we have to rely on those sending the tests to give the proper yield information, especially in areas where we don't already have a base of clients who grow that particular crop. In some areas all crops are irrigated, in others they are not. We need to know if the land is irrigated and the method of irrigation because it can influence the amount of nitrogen, sulfur and boron recommended. And it can strongly influence how and when to properly take the samples.

Also be sure to state as clearly as possible what type of crop you intend to grow. For example, when a sample lists the crop as "corn," unless stated otherwise, it is taken to be the most commonly sampled type—corn for grain—not silage corn, sweet corn, seed corn, or popcorn, which could require quite different recommendations. The same is true for other types of crops too. If this information is not correctly provided, there can be no real-

Hands-On Agronomy

istic values established for making nitrogen recommendations. It even matters whether you will be raising 90-day or 110-120 day corn. 90-day corn needs the bulk of its nitrogen early in the season. But for 110-120 day corn, it needs to be assured that there is adequate nitrogen and sulfur over a longer period of time

Be sure to list the fertilizers that are available for use in the area. Most certainly nitrogen materials will be available, but which types are easiest to obtain? The grower needs to tell us. The same goes for phosphate and potassium. This way a form that is readily available will be selected helping to avoid unnecessary delays and the additional time and expense to make corrections. But if you do not know or list the sources, we will choose what should be best for your soil.

Finally, the type of fertility program the grower wants to pursue should be stated. Most growers choose the excellent program. But unless your crop is already producing top yields, when growers calculate the costs to provide excellent yields and quality, most find the costs involve spending more for fertilizer than they are sure the present crop is worth. In the end, it will generally be worth far more than any other program you could use, but prove out the expense versus the income on a small acreage first. For the standard row crop and small grain farms, better to begin with a building program or maintenance program and stick with it for at least three years.

Perhaps this will help explain why it is important to know more than just the fact that a particular crop will be planted on the areas where soil tests have been taken and fertilizer recommendations requested. Just keep in mind, the information provided along with a soil sample is a key factor in determining the best fertilizer program for achieving the best response whether quality and/or yield is the goal you are seeking.

An accurate soil analysis is vital for properly understanding and fertilizing any soil for consistently growing the best crops and maintaining top soil fertility. Any recommendations that are made are based on the soil test and can be no better than the sample that is taken and sent for analysis. The aim is to identify and correct any problems in order to raise the overall soil fertility and improve or maintain yields and/or crop quality.

Samples are received and analyzed for recommending fertilizer and soil amendments from farmers and growers on every continent except Antarctica. It would be far easier and cost less for most of them to send their soil samples to a lab nearby rather than here for an analysis, but the accuracy of the soil analysis and resulting recommendations are what one after another will admit makes it worth the effort and cost.

By way of introduction for those not familiar with the soil analysis, perhaps an explanation of what information is measured and supplied should be provided as background before going any further. A complete report for each sample has two parts—the soil analysis and the recommendations.

The basic soil analysis will normally include:
  Total Exchange Capacity (T.E.C.)
  Soil pH
  Organic Matter (Humus) in percent
  Nitrogen (ENR from colloidal humus)
  Sulfate (as S) in ppm
  Phosphates (as P_2O_5)
  Olsen test or P value (included at no charge if pH is
    above 7.5)

Percent Base Saturation of:
  Calcium in lbs./acre
  Magnesium in lbs./acre

Potassium in lbs./acre
Sodium in lbs./acre
Other Bases
Exchangeable Hydrogen

Trace elements:
  Boron in ppm
  Iron in ppm
  Manganese in ppm
  Copper in ppm
  Zinc in ppm

Additional tests can be run (all optional):
  Cobalt in ppm (We encourage this for each sample that
      you send to us for the first time if it will involve
      growing food or even feed for livestock.)
  Molybdenum in ppm
  Chlorides/Salt Concentration
  Aluminum
  Limestone Analysis
  Manure Analysis (N-P-K only)
  Manure Analysis (includes S, Ca and Mg plus B, Fe,
      Mn, Cu, & Zn)
  Compost Analysis

Recommendations for specific fertilizer amendments are tailored to the grower's expressed short or long term goals, and take into account the previous history of crops and fertilizers for that location, farming conditions in the area, the type of operation (for instance organic or conventional), fertilizer preferences, and any other pertinent information as supplied by the grower in addition to the condition of the soil.

Each soil is tested in more detail than is customarily requested by farmers or other growers and provided as well with its own specific set of recommendations. Some needed materials may not always be stocked by local dealers. This tends to be especially true for clients that are certified organic. Recommendations are not designed to sell specific fertilizers or fertilizer programs. Fertilizers or soil amendments are not sold as a part of this program. To the extent possible farmers and growers are encouraged to work with local dealers to obtain the needed fertilizer materials.

Taking a good soil sample is too often relegated to the least important job on the farm. And just about any way that can be imagined has been used to hurry up and get it all done. The way the soil samples are taken is extremely important, as the recommendations you receive from soil tests will only be as good as the samples you send for analysis. Following the instructions below will assure that the samples you send are taken in the way required for a proper analysis.

When is the best time to take a soil sample? Soil samples may be collected any time of the year. Late spring and early summer sampling avoids the rush, shows the soil's fertility at its best and gives time to plan a fertility program which can begin directly following harvest if necessary. However, if no samples have been taken within the last two years, the best time to sample is as soon as circumstances permit. *Caution:* we recommend that if possible, no soil samples be taken when the topsoil is so extremely dry that plants like grasses, etc., will not grow there. Also if nitrogen has been applied in the last 30 days, or sulfur in the last 6 months, soil tests should not be taken from those fields until the above-mentioned waiting periods have been completely met.

It is recommended that sampling should be done every year if fertility is high and/or trace elements are being used to achieve top yields.

Prepare a soil map of the areas being tested. A good map assures that sampling is repeatable from year to year and will be useful at the time of fertilization. Designate a number, or some other identification, even a name—up to 8 characters—for each field. Use permanent lines such as roads, ditches and fences for boundary lines. Divide the field map into areas that have the same color, slope, texture, and drainage and past history of erosion. Each area should have the same cropping history, fertilizer and manure treatments and the same intended crop for all the ground within that area. Assign each of the areas sampled a specific number or letter (or a combination of both) so you can correctly identify it. For example, Field #2 could have three areas: A—the high ground, B—the sloping ground, and C—the low, level ground. The numbers written on the sample bag would be 2A, 2B, and 2C.

Sample Map

It is recommended that sampled areas represent no more than 20 acres (8-9 hectares) the first year this testing program is used, even if soils are uniform in texture and relief. Areas with taller or shorter plants, different weed or grass patterns, higher or lower yields, etc., should be avoided, or sampled separately if large enough to fertilize properly. The next time samples are taken, combine areas that by analysis have been shown to be alike. In addition some may decide to combine very small areas that have all the same characteristics into one composite sample.

When samples are being taken if any of the rules given below or the guidelines given elsewhere in this chapter are ignored it is likely a waste of time and money to have that soil analyzed.

Sample at least 300 feet away from gravel or crushed limestone roads and stay at least 20 feet away from fencerows or the edge of a field.

Avoid, or sample separately, the following:

Eroded hillsides or low spots

Terraces, ditch banks, old roadbeds or fencerows

Animal droppings, urine spots, burn piles, old manure, straw or hay stacks

Areas around sheds, barns and / or where buildings have formerly stood

Lime, fertilizer, or chemical spill areas and fertilizer bands

Dead and back furrows

There are also some specific guidelines for use when collecting a soil sample. For the soil sample bag use a new plastic bag, soil-sample container, or plastic container. Zip-loc bags are fine—as long as they have never been used—but put Scotch tape over the writing or attach masking tape to write on because all types of marking ink can rub off of the bag during shipment. Do not use paper sacks from the grocery store, bread wrappers, or such items, due to possible contamination. Avoid using a plastic bucket that has been used for other purposes. Even repeated washings of a bucket used to mix salt and minerals for feed can still result in contamination of the sample.

Label the sample bags with your name, the farm name if any, field number and sample area. Make sure the labeling on the bag matches the number of the field and area on our map. Labeling the bags to match the areas before taking the sample helps.

A SOIL PROBE is recommended for easiest and best sampling results. Using a soil probe or shovel, sample down to a depth of 6½ - 7 inches (4 inches for no-till crops, orchards, vineyards, pastures, hay meadows, lawns, etc., where soils will not be worked), or take additional cores as subsoil samples, using 6 - 7 inch increments to the depth the soil will be thoroughly mixed when worked if that will be deeper than 6½ - 7 inches.

Put the soil, using several probes from like areas to make up the sample, into the sample bag. Removal of obvious debris (roots, leaves, etc.) is fine but unnecessary, as it will not adversely affect the sample. If you do remove debris from the sample, be careful that none of the actual soil is removed with it.

Probe the soil every 50 to 100 paces, always taking a minimum of 5 probes per composite sample for smaller areas, and one probe for every 1 (one) to 2 (two) acres from larger areas. Only a small amount of soil is necessary for analysis. A cupful of soil is more than enough. Just be sure your sample represents the entire soil profile, if mixed, in order to send only a small portion.

Please remember: this will be a very detailed analysis, which will only be as accurate as the sample you send. The *Hands-On Agronomy Workshop* DVD has a section on taking soil samples properly, and provides a visual look at how to sample. If samples from the very same area have previously been sent for analysis and recommendations, they should be properly identified as such, so that each one can be taken into account before new recommendations are made.

Pack all samples as tightly as possible, especially if sent via U.S. Mail. For larger packages (more than 2 or 3 samples), we recommend UPS (United Parcels Service), Federal Express or a reputable shipper of that type. Soils may be sent wet or dry (use a Zip-loc or plastic lined bag for wet samples). Samples can be dried at home by spreading them on waxed paper and air-drying. DO NOT DRY THE SAMPLES IN AN OVEN. It is okay to leave samples to dry in the sun.

Fill out and enclose a worksheet with your samples. The requested information to be sent along with the samples is extremely important. We have soil worksheets available for your convenience. You can request copies of the soil worksheet via phone: 573 683-3880: Fax: 573 683-6227: E-mail: office@kinseyag. com; or download a copy from our web site at www.kinseyag.com.

When sending samples, recommendations can only be at their best if the sample is correctly taken and the worksheet is completely filled out. It is especially important to know if you are organic. Also tell us what forms of nitrogen you have available and other fertilizers as well if you prefer to use them. And be sure to state whether liming has been done, and if so, the approximate month or season, the year, or years (up to 3 years ago) and the amount applied.

Mark which program level you desire (excellent, building, maintenance, or minimum input) and fill in your name, address, phone number and email if applicable. If shipping inside the United States mainland, include a copy of the worksheet in the envelope with payment in your box of samples. Call for specific instructions before shipping from Hawaii or from outside the U.S.

Samples can be sent for analysis without a worksheet, but it will usually slow down the testing of the samples because the information needed to process them is not as readily available. Additional changes after the recommendations have already been sent will result in additional charges. When you do not have a copy of our worksheet to use please give:

your name

address and telephone number

any limestone applied in the last 3 years—including amount, type, month (or season) and year of application

last year's crop and yield

the crop to be grown next and the top yield this particular field has achieved for the intended crop (if known)

actual fertilizer materials available

whether you are an organic or conventional operation

any special goals

If the soil samples originate outside the U.S.A., please check with the office to make the proper arrangements first. For soils shipped from other countries you will need to make special arrangements with us concerning payment, a specific address to be used to properly clear U.S. Customs, and for exemption stickers which are always needed due to USDA regulations.

If you will need samples back by a specific time, always call to see if that deadline can be met before sending samples for analysis.

Deep Nutrient Sampling and Necessary Fertilizer Applications

When considering how to build up soil fertility, the most important zone to consider is the aerobic zone—the top 6 to 7 inches (as deep as a fence post rots). This is the part of the soil that contains the microorganisms that can only operate properly when adequate oxygen is present.

The greatest exception to sampling the aerobic zone—roughly considered as 6 3/4 inches because an acre of soil down to this depth will generally weigh about 2 million pounds—is when all materials must be placed on top of the soil and will not be worked into the top 2 inches or more. Take the topsoil sample as only the top 4 inches for such cases in order to avoid over-saturation of any required nutrient in the top few inches. This is necessary and extremely important to consider because too much of one nutrient added to the soil will cause a deficiency of some other needed nutrient. For example, too much phosphate will tie up zinc, too much potassium ties up boron, too much nitrogen ties up copper, and too much of any one of the various liming materials will tie up at least a portion of just about all the elements we can measure with a soil test, with phosphate usually being the exception. Thus, borderline levels now become deficiencies for the plants intended to be grown there.

Because of such serious possibilities, think of the aerobic zone as the most important consideration for soil testing. Even more, track this area separately because, given the choice, every plant will feed in the aerobic zone. It is the area where nutrients are most available because the microbial activity there is at its greatest. The soil is the plant's stomach!

The depth to which soil sampling should be done after considering the aerobic zone depends on the circumstances and the way you intend to use the information gained. If a ripper will be pulled through at 5 feet deep, it may be of interest to see what is down there. But once you know what is lacking, how can you affect fertility levels at that depth? Essentially checking that deep, you have what you have to work with and not much chance of immediately affecting the fertility level at that depth. About the best that could be hoped for would be to break up any hardpan and allow roots and moisture to penetrate more easily to better utilize whatever fertility is already there.

A major key to effective fertilization in terms of cost is the use of sampling to measure what you have as deeply as the roots may have a tendency to penetrate. But then, continue to utilize testing at the deeper levels to prove or disprove what changes are possible there based on the type and amount of fertilizers that have been applied.

Next determine how deep you have the ability to work the soil and the efficiency of the equipment used to mix the applied materials with that soil. The key is to achieve a homogenous mix. Consider the rule of thumb that adequate mixing of the nutrients applied is only satisfactory to half the depth the equipment is able to thoroughly mix the soil.

Keep in mind that thorough mixing is of utmost importance. Where the material is applied in clumps, if it is something the plant requires, roots will concentrate there, and we again have to consider the "law of the maximum". Phosphorous ties up zinc, etc. But also would the contents of the clump in terms of fertilizer excess cause toxicity problems for roots that would normally penetrate that area. Better to be safe than sorry.

When the depth to which fertilizer can be thoroughly mixed is determined, figure the needs in 6-7 inch increments once you drop below the aerobic zone. For example, if it is determined that implements can work the soil to a depth of 30 inches and will adequately mix to 15 inches, back off and sample to 12 inches and apply the materials calculated for that depth. If 18-20 inches, figure to the 18-inch depth, etc.

The question that matters most to this point is how well the fertilizer, lime, compost, etc., will be mixed with the soil. When it comes to fertilization, it is a good rule to follow that in the long run too little is always better than too much.

For soils where an increase in subsoil fertility is desired, the following comments are of particular importance, still keeping in mind the points made above.

If a soil can be thoroughly mixed and it would not provide an excess of nitrogen, applying 250 lbs./acre of 11-52-0 (monoammonium phosphate) for each six inches of depth would not be too much phosphate. Furthermore, the nitrogen will be gone in no more than 8 months, likely far sooner. However, better to thoroughly mix 250 lbs./acre in the top 6-7 inches just before planting than do a poor job to a greater depth. In addition, the deeper you place the phosphate, the less efficient it will tend to be at remaining in an available form over time. But from what we have seen, if it is correctly applied and mixed, it will increase P levels in the form the plant needs, to the depth it is applied, even though availability is not as great the deeper it is placed.

Sulfur will tend to move downward through the soil. Placing it extremely deep is not an efficient use of sulfur unless there are nutrient excesses that could be affected properly by its use. Many sampled areas would not benefit from sulfur placed in the 12-24 inch levels, but others which have adequate calcium could when there is a very high or excessive sodium level.

Concerning the application of lime and/or gypsum to the soil, if the topsoil and subsoil need the same amounts, consider the complete depth as receiving all that is required. But if the subsoil needs more than the topsoil, the question is, how well would the amount needed deeper down ever be kept from the top portion? For this reason, only apply liming materials according to what the subsoil needs when it is equivalent or less than the topsoil and when it can be completely mixed as required. So long as it can be mixed correctly, supplying desired potassium from 0-0-50 would benefit when recommended and applied to the complete depth needed.

Boron should only be applied to the aerobic zone. If there is ever a hardpan, the boron moving from the top could accumulate to toxic levels somewhere in the root zone. The more that is applied at once, the greater the chance that damage can happen. Since boron will leach out anyway, or move downward from the top, it is best to apply it on top and only where shown to be required.

Iron sulfate (in the proper form—white or blue green in color) can benefit the crop if truly needed. However if the aerobic zone is deficient and the immediate subsoil exceeds 40 ppm and the ppm of manganese is adequate, but below iron, deep rooting crops can compensate and will likely receive an adequate amount to supply the need. However, if liming materials are placed in the subsoil and iron is barely adequate or deficient, this will only make the problem worse for future root and top growth. Even more, the extent of the problem for most farmers will not be determined until the end of the third year after the lime has been mixed in. On specific samples that have the need, applying the recommended lime should not be a problem. However where calcium is too high, iron availability may be just as much a problem at greater depths. Iron applied then will only benefit to the extent it can be worked in at all depths. Even if the iron were thoroughly mixed and was twice the amount needed in the top 12 inches, it would only serve to benefit in the long run, so long as it can be kept in an available form or converted to an available form by sulfur acidulation.

Manganese tends to tie up in the soil the deeper it is placed or even naturally as you continue to check it at lower depths in the soil. An application to the aerobic zone is likely the only time manganese will have a lasting benefit for the amount of material required and the subsequent cost.

Copper tends to release slowly and remain available, but good microbial activity in the aerobic zone seems to help provide a more even distribution. Without further information, the expense of building copper in the subsoil may not be cost effective because of the lack of microorganisms to help. Another consideration is whether it can be thoroughly mixed so as not to cause a problem. In general, no problems have been experienced with topsoil applications of copper sulfate up to 35 lbs./acre when broadcast and well mixed.

Although zinc tends to decrease in availability with depth, the greatest problem would be if clumps or high concentrations would accumulate in specific areas and cause phosphate tie up. It is likely that an even distribution, even at deeper levels, would pay dividends in years to come.

Compost can only be properly evaluated with a representative analysis in order to determine what it can do for individual soils. Depending on the levels present and the amounts available for application per acre, some or all of the phosphate and potassium may be supplied. The big question is, can it be mixed and will sufficient, but not inordinate, amounts remain available at the lower depths.

If there is any doubt, it is recommended that fertilizer materials be applied and worked in to the minimum depth of homogenous mixing as a certainty. We can always continue to treat from the top and make better progress by correcting more easily and economically even if specific excesses are already present.

There are those who say that using the Albrecht system of soil testing to feed the soil and let the soil feed the plant has not proven to be effective in this way or that, and they may even feel it has actually caused problems for soils they have worked with in one way or another. Consequently, from time to time we are asked, "If the program really works as well as you say, how could something such as this happen?"

There is no pat answer to such a question, but there are several possibilities which come to mind when statements such as this are reportedly made by a consultant, or perhaps even a farmer or grower who has suffered a loss while trying what he was told is the Albrecht method of soil fertility management.

First consider the question of the validity of the soil test itself. Anyone can say they are using the Albrecht system of soil testing. There are many tests that make such claims simply because they use cation exchange capacity and base saturation percentages on the test they have determined to use for making fertility recommendations. But as has been shown over years of working with farmers and growers, the measured calcium, magnesium, potassium and sodium figures from one test to another can be quite different.

Calcium is perhaps the prime example. On the test we use, a medium to heavy soil should have around a 68% base saturation of calcium for maximum benefit. But when the figure on the test we use is 68%, other laboratories' soil tests have shown closer to 60%, others 75%, and some even 80% for exactly the same soil. Which one is right? The answer would be all of them, if you or the one using the soil test truly knows how the number corresponds with the correct calcium level in the soil and what that means in terms of any additional needs. But as the percent calcium goes up or down, it will also change the percentages of the other elements like potassium, sodium or magnesium on the test as well. This is where the truth of what the different soil tests show suddenly becomes more difficult to determine.

In measuring magnesium, when the ideal of 12% shows on our test, other labs whose calcium tests higher can drop to as low as 8% magnesium on the same soil, while still calling for 10 - 20% magnesium as the proper range on their test. On a medium to heavy soil, when magnesium rises above 12% it is already causing the soil fertility requirements and, depending on the crop, also the yield to suffer. If the magnesium is of no consequence at these levels, as many who are considered to be authorities claim, then it makes no difference. But from our experience, it certainly does matter; in fact it is a critical factor for achieving the highest yield for the most economical fertilizer cost. For example, if you are growing corn, and the magnesium is at 12%

on the specific test we have run, with calcium at 68% as stated above, it requires 1.0 lb. of nitrogen to grow each bushel of corn. But if the magnesium is raised by just 2%, it now requires 1.25 lbs. of nitrogen to grow each bushel of corn. So on the other test mentioned above, which was being used by another consultant claiming to follow the Albrecht system, if the farmer raises the magnesium to the recommended minimum of 10% as reflected on that test, he is actually pushing it too high for maximum nitrogen efficiency because anything over 8% on that test is like being over 12% on the test we use. This would also reduce the yield of soybeans or alfalfa on that soil, and it is likely to be the case for whatever crop that is intended to be grown there.

Next consider whether the person doing the recommendations understands what the soil test actually is showing needs to be done. Can the consultant consistently determine the good from the bad just by looking at the soil test results? If not, how could he really understand how to properly use the Albrecht system correctly in the field? Sometimes the soil test can be correctly done, but the person doing the interpretation does not really understand what the tests actually show needs to be done. Making incorrect fertilizer recommendations can cause even the best fertility program to look bad. Again how do you know what is right? One good way to find out who can truly help is to first determine what the numbers are supposed to be on the soil test for best results. Then sample an area that consistently produces well, and one that consistently does poorly, and ask the one who claims to understand the test to choose which is which, and explain why and then recommend what should be done to bring the poor area up closer to the good area in terms of yield.

Another possibility that could give poor results is when someone just partially follows the program, and as a result, it makes the program look bad to those who are observing from a distance. Even when the Albrecht system is correctly employed, it can require as much as three years of following the program to begin to see the greatest benefits. To prove the program out for yourself, choose a uniform area large enough to justify buying and spreading the fertilizer and soil amendments needed, but small enough to follow through on all the soil test shows to be needed for three full years. After three years on the program (which means choosing a uniform area, soil testing it each year, and applying exactly what the test shows to be needed for top fertility based on the tests for that year and the crop to be grown), it will be clear whether the time and expense is worth your effort.

Therefore, if someone tries to tell you that the Albrecht system does not work, first find out if they are judging it based on only one year of results. If a soil has not been receiving the determined needs for several years, how likely is one year to make a big difference? It may happen, but after three years of properly following the program on a soil that needs the fertility levels to be rebuilt, it will do even better.

And finally consider the soil test numbers themselves. But keep in mind, the numbers do not have to match everyone else's numbers. The big test is whether the consultant knows what the numbers mean well enough to get the best results in the field.

We find the greatest challenge to the use of the Albrecht system is that of helping the farmer or grower determine that all the nutrients shown to be missing, when provided correctly, will result in the best yields and quality. It is not our goal to get people to send us soil tests, but to convince them to begin in a fashion that will allow at least a test of three years duration. Once that is done it will be evident that this system only fails when someone fails to understand or use it correctly. It is not necessary to take our word or the word of anyone else when you have proven it for yourself right on your own soils.

Acknowledgments

In addition to those named in the dedication, I wish to acknowledge my debt to the following: to Bill Shriver, Bill Swirbul and Brookside Laboratories and to those who tolerated my leanings toward natural systems. I want to particularly thank Bob Boehle, Lou Flohr, Jan Zweip, Bob Perry and Andy Skapura for their help and inspiration during my Brookside years. And finally, a special thanks to the late Dr. J.F.L. Childs, who continued to give support over the years, and was the first to begin a persistent encouragement concerning getting the material I use down in book form. Without these people and many others, what is printed here would not be possible.

Readers will note the use of boxed materials to support— much like a condiment—the digestibility of the general text. All credit for this goes to Charles Walters whose vast knowledge and resources pertaining to soil fertility made it possible.

Thanks are due the following for permission to use copyrighted materials in those boxed presentations. The other boxes are amply credited in the presentation itself.

Page 5. "Remember That You are Dust," from *Soil, Grass & Cancer*, 1959, pp. l, 4.

Page 13. "Weeds-Guardians of the Soil," from *Weeds, Guardians of the Soil*, Devin-Adair, 1950, pp. 11-12.

Page 25. "The Land," from *Earth Foods*, Follett Publishing Co., 1972, pp. 53-54.

Page 42. "The Importance of Calcium for Large Yields," from *More Food from Soil Science*, Growers Chemical Corp., 1965, p. 72.

Page 67. "Silica," from *Silica: The Forgotten Nutrient*, Alive Books, 1990, pp 27-28, 74.

Page 114. "Application of Fertilizer," from *Natural Food & Farming*, Natural Food Associates, 1961.

Page 125. "Quality Produce Demands Proper Composting," from Natural Food Associates Convention speech, 1961.

Page 177. "Calcium and Phosphorus," from *Health from the Sea and Soil*, Exposition Banner Book, 1962, p. 152.

Page 217. "Comparisons of Manures," from *Humus & The Farmer*, Rodale Press, 1949, p. 120.

Page 257. "Only Small Quantities of Minerals are Needed," from *Food Power from the Sea*, Acres U.S.A., 2005, pp. 185-186.

Page 328. "Versatility and Industry in the Soil," from Magnificent Microbes, Atheneum Press, 1976, pp. 11-12.

Index

acid rain, 21
acid salts, 82
acid soil, 68, 81
acidity, 215
actinomycetes, 210, 330-331
adsorbs, 34, 61
aerobic bacteria, 331
aerobic microorganisms, 128
aerobic organisms, 209
aerobic zone, 373, 376
aggregates, 118
Agricultural Testament, An, 205
agronomist, 15
Ahlson, Charles B., 177
air, 96, 324
Albert, Eddie, 355-356, 357
Albrecht method, 4
Albrecht model, 187
Albrecht Papers, Volume I, The, 141, 153
Albrecht Papers, Volume III, The, 7, 334
Albrecht system, 44, 187, 377-379
Albrecht, William A., 2, 3, 7, 10-11, 16, 44, 61, 141, 153, 164, 176, 184, 221, 227, 334
alfalfa, 10, 58, 65, 68, 78, 112-114, 158, 187, 213, 216, 222, 224, 233, 252, 258, 310, 329, 354, 379
alfalfa weevil, 117, 120
algae, 327, 331, 336
alkali spots, 244
alkaline soil, 81-82
almonds, 309

aluminum, 319
aluminum toxicity, 74, 174
American Society of Animal
    Production, 360
ammonia, 112, 144, 154
ammonium hydroxide, 145
ammonium nitrate, 129, 132, 140, 142-144, 153, 231, 233, 295
ammonium sulfate, 117, 127, 134, 138-139, 143, 144, 147, 153, 231, 233, 295
ammonium thiosulfate, 129, 139
anaerobic bacteria, 331
anaerobic conditions, 128
anaerobic microorganisms, 128
anhydrous ammonia, 116, 134, 143, 144, 145, 147, 150-151, 154
animal nutrition, 260, 359
anion, 27, 30, 33, 242
anion, defined, 28
apples, 241, 309
aragonite, 76
atomic absorption, 31
auxins, 349
available calcium, 206
available nutrients, 203
azaleas, 68

bacteria, 50, 68, 69, 145, 330, 331, 338
balance, 68, 97, 162, 226, 251, 341
barley, 10, 241, 245
base exchange, 42

Hands-On Agronomy

sodium, excess, 236, 240-241, 242-243, 259, 375
sodium molybdate, 255, 258
sodium nitrate, 246
sodium saturations, 242
sodium tetraborate, 265
soft rock phosphate, 164, 167, 174-176
soil, 37, 57, 254, 338, 373
soil acidity, 74-75, 148, 152, 215
soil air, 96, 324
soil analysis, 236, 341, 366
soil audit, 47-49, 60, 182
soil balance, 53, 99, 167, 226
soil biology, 324, 326, 337
soil colloid, 30, 33, 120, 154, 269
soil compaction tester, 98
soil conditioner, 58, 97, 104-106, 244, 245, 246, 326
soil feeders, 5, 159, 167
soil fertility, 4, 7, 19, 199, 262, 363
soil food, 113
Soil, Grass & Cancer, 18
soil map, 47-49, 368-369
soil microorganisms, 328
soil model, 83
soil pH, 65, 70, 76-78, 162, 208, 255, 268-269, 364
soil probe, 46, 145, 370-371
soil probe test, 98
soil sample, 11, 31, 45-49, 367-371
soil solution, 80, 185
soil, stability, 118-119
soil structure, 57-58
soil system, xv, xviii
soil test, 35, 83, 182-183, 205, 207, 252, 254, 316, 363
soil texture, 25, 76
soil water, 96
soil worksheets, 371-372
Soils and Men, 219
soils and rocks, 22, 25
solubility, 141
Solubor, 265
sorghum, 191, 230
soybeans, 3-4, 79, 120, 158, 162, 163, 190, 191, 192, 230, 233, 253, 267, 282, 290, 291, 292, 310, 328-329, 357-358, 360

soybeans, nitrogen and, 120
stalk strength, 147, 192, 296
starter fertilizer, 167
steely wool, 281
straw, 213
strawberries, 310
streptomycetes, 210
subsoil samples, 370
sugar beet lime, 77
sugar beets, 241, 245
sulfate, 154, 222, 223, 225, 289
sulfur, 73, 93, 95, 122, 144, 153-154, 161, 216, 222-223, 228, 241, 243, 254, 269, 284, 286, 291, 318, 329, 375
sulfur, deficiency, 231
sulfur, defined, 220
sulfur levels, 225, 232
sulfur, minimum amount of, 225
Sulphur Institute, 226, 228
Sul-Po-Mag, 182, 190, 232
sum of cations, 243
superphosphate, 159, 163-164, 165, 170, 230, 232
sweet clover, 58
Sykes, Friend, 217

"Take-all" disease, 337
TEC, 32-33, 243-244
Tennessee Valley Authority, 164, 166
test plot, 357
Tiedjens, V.A., 42
tillage, 58, 64, 97, 98, 246
tilth, 61
timber, 228
tissue test, 80, 128, 130, 233
tomatoes, 241, 258, 278-279, 291, 293
tomatoes nutrient chart, 297
top yields, 368
total exchange capacity (TEC), 32-33, 243-244
total nutrient analysis, 206
total nutrient tests, 187, 188
total nutrients, 203
toxicity, 74
trace element deficiency, 252
trace element tests, 41
trace elements, 8, 150, 197, 226, 246, 252, 257, 260, 269, 367

trace minerals, 280
tree crops, 46
tricalcium phosphate, 159, 165, 169
triple superphosphate, 159, 163, 166, 169, 230
Trouse, Dr. Al, 103, 106
turkey litter, 213, 299

University of Illinois, 11
University of Missouri, 2, 3, 11
urea, 129, 142-143, 144, 154
urine, 215
USDA Yearbook of Agriculture 1938, 219

vacuum test, 348
Vance, Dr. Dwayne, 347-348
vegetables, 230, 296
vines, 228
Voisin, André, 18, 53
volcanic ash, 325
von Liebig, Justus, 53, 204

Wallace, T., 257
walnuts, 291
Walters, Charles, 33, 49, 147, 350, 381
Walters, M.D., Joe, 355
water, 110, 325-326, 352
water penetration, 246
water pH, 268
water pH tests, 41
water retention, 60
water-logged soils, 287

watermelons, 66, 231
weak stalk, 80
Webb, Cohn, 281
weed killer, 262
weeds, 194, 213
Weeds, Guardians of the Soil, 13
wet conditions, 102-103
wet soils, 63-64
wheat, 12, 139-140, 142, 158, 192, 222, 230, 259, 285, 289, 290, 291, 300, 302, 304, 358
winegrapes, 44, 223, 225, 230, 234, 235, 241
Wischusen, J.F., 261
Wittwer, Sylvan H., 8, 9
woody-type plants, 228
worms, in sheep, 280

yellow plants, 150
yield, 73, 75

zinc, 46, 147, 162, 208, 253, 277, 301-302, 318, 377
zinc deficiency, 147, 224
zinc, defined, 276
zinc excess, 62
zinc, pH range, 255
zinc, pounds of, 253-254
zinc sulfate, 303

Agriculture in Transition

BY DONALD L. SCHRIEFER

 Now you can tap the source of many of agriculture's most popular progressive farming tools. Ideas now commonplace in the industry, such as "crop and soil weatherproofing," the "row support system," and the "tillage commandments," exemplify the practicality of the soil/root maintenance program that serves as the foundation for Schriefer's highly-successful "systems approach" farming. A veteran teacher, lecturer and writer, Schriefer's ideas are clear, straightforward, and practical. Softcover, 238 pages. ISBN 0-911311-61-0

From the Soil Up

BY DONALD L. SCHRIEFER

 The farmer's role is to conduct the symphony of plants and soil. In this book, learn how to coax the most out of your plants by providing the best soil and re-moving all yield-limiting factors. Schriefer is best known for his "systems" approach to tillage and soil fertility, which is detailed here. Managing soil aeration, water, and residue decay are covered, as well as ridge planting systems, guidelines for culti-vating row crops, and managing soil fertility. Develop your own soil fertility system for long-term productivity. Softcover, 274 pages. ISBN 0-911311-63-7

Science in Agriculture

BY ARDEN B. ANDERSEN, PH.D., D.O.

 By ignoring the truth, ag-chemical enthusiasts are able to claim that pesticides and herbicides are necessary to feed the world. But science points out that low-to-mediocre crop production, weed, disease, and insect pressures are all symptoms of nutritional imbalances and inadequacies in the soil. The progressive farmer who knows this can grow bountiful, disease-and pest-free commodities without the use of toxic chemicals. A concise recap of the main schools of thought that make up eco-agriculture — all clearly explained. Both farmer and professional consultant will benefit from this important work. Softcover, 376 pages. ISBN 0-911311-35-1

The Non-Toxic Farming Handbook

BY PHILIP A. WHEELER, PH.D. & RONALD B. WARD

 In this readable, easy-to-understand handbook the authors success-fully integrate the diverse techniques and technologies of classical organ-ic farming, Albrecht-style soil fertility balancing, Reams-method soil and plant testing and analysis, and other alternative technologies applicable to commercial-scale agriculture. By understanding all of the available non-toxic tools and when they are effective, you will be able to react to your specific situation and growing conditions. Covers fertility inputs, in-the-field testing, foliar feeding, and more. The result of a lifetime of eco-consulting. Softcover, 236 pages. ISBN 0-911311-56-4

To order call 1-800-355-5313 or order online at www.acresusa.com

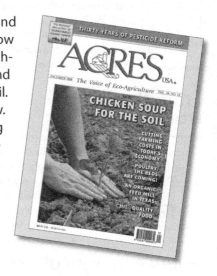

Made in the USA
Monee, IL
28 May 2024

59051940R00233